The Open University

Environment: Sharing a Dynamic Planet

# Introduction, Life, Water

Environment: Sharing a Dynamic Planet

# Introduction, Life, Water

Edited by David Humphreys, Nigel Clark, Sandy Smith, Petr Jehlička and Nick Bingham

This publication forms part of the Open University module DST206 Environment: sharing a dynamic planet. Details of this and other Open University modules can be obtained from the Student Registration and Enquiry Service, The Open University, PO Box 197, Milton Keynes MK7 6BJ, United Kingdom (tel. +44 (0)845 300 60 90; email general-enquiries@open.ac.uk).

Alternatively, you may visit the Open University website at www.open.ac.uk where you can learn more about the wide range of modules and packs offered at all levels by The Open University.

To purchase a selection of Open University materials visit www.ouw.co.uk, or contact Open University Worldwide, Walton Hall, Milton Keynes MK7 6AA, United Kingdom for a catalogue (tel. +44 (0)1908 858785; fax +44 (0)1908 858787; email ouw-customer-services@open.ac.uk).

The Open University, Walton Hall, Milton Keynes, MK7 6AA

First published 2013.

Edited and designed by The Open University

Typeset by the Open University

Printed in the United Kingdom by Page Bros, Norwich.

ISBN 9 781 7800 7326 2

1.1

# Contents

# DST206 module team

Claire Appleby, Consultant

Roshni Amin, Media Developer (Sound and Vision)

Mustafa Bektik, Media Developer

Dr Nick Bingham, Co-chair and Block 6 Leader

Prof. Andrew Blowers, Advisor

Avinash Boroowa, Media Project Manager

Dr Mark Brandon, Advisor

Clare Butler, Proofreader (freelance)

Wendy Chalmers, Learning and Teaching Librarian

Prof. Nigel Clark (Lancaster University), Block 1 Leader

Heather Clarke, Cartoonist

Matt Compton, Media Developer (Sound and Vision)

Prof. James Connelly (University of Hull), External Assessor

Sian Contell, Sound and Vision Assistant

Howard Davies, Media Developer (Interactive Media)

Ben Duncan-Jones, Production and Presentation Administrator

Jeff Edwards, Graphic Artist (freelance)

Dr Susan Fawssett, Consultant

Pam Furniss, Block 3 Leader

Richard Golden, Production and Presentation Administrator

Owen Horn, Media Developer (Sound and Vision)

Dr David Humphreys, Co-chair and Block 4 Leader

Jason Jarratt, Media Developer (Interactive Media)

Dr David King, Module team member

Dr Maggie King, Module team member

Dr Nick James, Consultant

Dr Petr Jehlička, Interim Co-chair and Block 5 Leader

Dr Victoria Johnson, Consultant

Jo Mack, Sound and Vision Producer

Dr Wendy Maples, Module team member

Isobel McLean, Indexer (freelance)

Margaret McManus, Rights Consultant (freelance)

Katie Meade, Rights Executive

Dr Dick Morris, Consultant

Lucy Morris, Curriculum Manager

Dr David Morse, Consultant

Dr Pat Murphy, Consultant

Greg Muttitt, Consultant

Dr Donal O'Donnell, Module team member

Celeste O'Neill, Media Developer (Editor)

Dr Philip O'Sullivan, Block 2 Leader

Mark Overton, Curriculum Manager

Neil Paterson, Media Assistant

Dr Stephen Peake, Consultant

Dr Parvati Raghuram, Academic coordinator (AV)

Will Rawes, Media Developer (Interactive Media)

Matthew Rigby-Burr, Media Developer (Graphic Designer)

Dr Jane Roberts, Learning Outcomes and Assessment Group Lead

Amber Ross, Media Developer (Editor)

Mat Schencks, Media Project Manager

Dr Joe Smith, Module team member

Dr Sandy Smith, Module team member

Prof. Robert Spicer, Adviser

Howie Twiner, Media Developer (Graphic Artist)

Dr James Warren, Consultant

Kelly Weekes, Curriculum Assistant

Chris Wooldridge, Editor (freelance)

# Block 1  Introduction

# Chapter 1   Living on a dynamic planet

Nigel Clark

# Contents

# 1 Introduction

On 21 December 1968 humans broke free of the gravitational pull of the Earth and ventured into space for the first time. As astronauts Frank Borman, Jim Lovell and William Anders left Earth orbit and set out for the Moon on the Apollo 8 spacecraft they did what no humans had done before: captured an image of planet Earth in a single photographic frame. The images of the 'whole Earth' taken from space by astronauts on the Apollo missions have become an inspiration and focus for thinking about the Earth as a home, a place that humans share with each other and with other forms of life (Figure 1.1). During the voyage Anders observed, 'We came all this way to explore the Moon, and the most important thing is that we discovered the Earth' (quoted in Chaikin, 1994, p. 119).

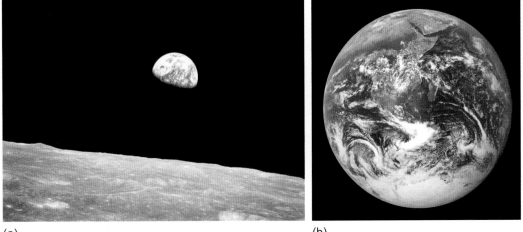

(a)                                        (b)

Figure 1.1   (a) The famous 'Earthrise' photo taken as the Earth appeared over the horizon as Apollo 8 orbited the Moon; (b) A whole Earth photograph taken from Apollo 8

By the end of 1972, 12 men had walked on the Moon. The images they sent back accentuated the stark contrast between the blue-green 'liveliness' of the Earth and the dark, lifeless void of outer space. There were no political borders; no colour-coded differentiation of countries or empires (Figure 1.2). The photographs prompted many people to share a vision that many scientists already subscribed to: that the Earth functioned as a single, integrated system. Perhaps more than any other human achievement the Apollo space programme illustrated a common planetary home that we share with other people and with other species.

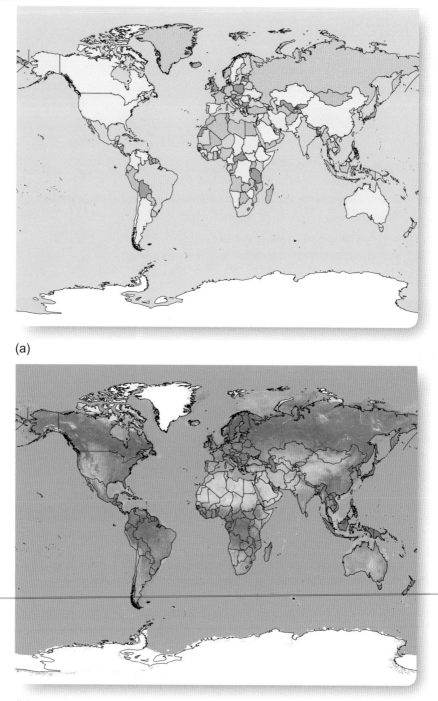

(a)

(b)

Figure 1.2   Maps simplify some information and data, but omit others. They help clarify certain types and levels of detail but are inevitably incomplete: (a) A political map of the world; (b) A geographical map of the world

But the images were, quite literally, snapshots. They offered static views of our planet at moments in time some 4.6 billion years since the formation of the Earth. During that time our planet has continually changed. Over the course of a year there are seasonal changes of vegetation and rainfall and the annual advance and retreat of polar ice caps. Over longer time horizons – thousands and millions of years – swathes of green grasslands and forests have expanded before drying out and turning brown, deserts have turned green before once again becoming desert, the world's land area has contracted and expanded as sea levels rose and fell, thick ice caps have advanced and retreated across continents, different species have been born, thrived and become extinct. And over an even longer timescale – tens of millions of years – whole continents have been pulled apart or moved together, land masses have migrated slowly across the surface of the planet, new oceans have opened up and old ones have disappeared (Macdougall, 2006). We can be sure that similar changes will happen in the future.

We live on a dynamic planet. The environment that human beings inherit and pass on to future generations is continually changing. It is from a sense of the variable, dynamic character of the living and non-living Earth that we set out on this module to explore some of the major environmental issues of our time. Many of these issues converge on the question of how we share the planet, not only with billions of other human beings, but with other living things as well.

In order to introduce the block question *What are the causes of environmental change?*, we now move from the long-distance view of our planet from deep space to one particular place on its surface: a place where land, sea and the atmosphere meet.

# 2   Where the land meets the sea

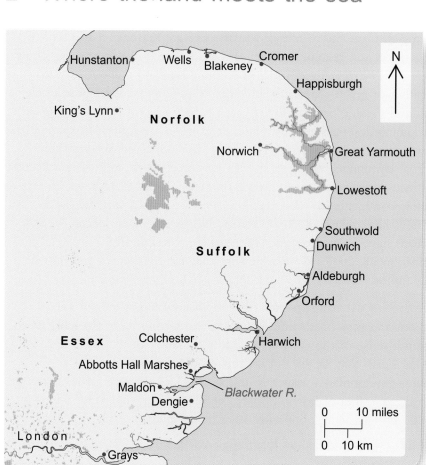

Figure 1.3   Map of East Anglia

Our focus is on the East Anglian coastline of the United Kingdom. Here the coast is continually shifting, and this has troubling consequences for many of the people who live there (Figure 1.3). Embracing the counties of Essex, Suffolk and Norfolk, this coastline provides us with a sense of the dynamism and variability of our planet at one particular place. The East Anglian coast is a place where people live and work, a place they value in various ways. It is a stretch of coastline that has seen many invasions. There are military installations from as recently as the Second World War, some of which are now succumbing to erosion. But another type of invasion is taking place. In places the coast itself is crumbling and yielding to the sea, in some places by several metres a year. And with this focus on a more intimate scale come clear signs that this lively part of the planet is also a place where people live, and that environmental change can bring with it fear and uncertainty. The changing relationship between land and sea poses challenges to people in this particular part of the world. Similar challenges are shared by others, in many other places, and these challenges look set to intensify in the foreseeable future.

One reason for this is climate change. There is now compelling scientific evidence that human activity is warming the Earth's surface through the release of greenhouse gases that warm the planet. (You will explore the causes and science of climate change in Book 2, Chapters 1–4.) For example, fossil fuel burning releases carbon dioxide, the world's most important greenhouse gas. The increased atmospheric concentration of greenhouse gases leads to the Earth retaining more solar radiation than would otherwise be the case. This warming causes the sea level to rise for two reasons:

- Glaciers and terrestrial ice sheets start to melt, with the melt-water running into the oceans.
- The water in the oceans increases in volume as it warms due to a process known as **thermal expansion**.

Even if greenhouse gas emissions could be stabilised at present levels, the atmospheric temperature would continue to increase for a number of years, so the oceans would continue to warm and expand. Water also has a higher **thermal inertia** than air: that is, it takes longer to warm or cool than air. So even if the atmospheric temperature is finally stabilised, there will be a period of at least several decades when the oceans will continue to absorb heat from the atmosphere (Hansen et al., 2005). In short, the planet is committed to some sea level rise in the future irrespective of any actions humans take to address climate change. This illustrates that human actions do not just have consequences today. The consequences of what we do can stretch over time into the future.

However, there is some scientific uncertainty about the degree to which sea levels will rise. Estimates by the scientists who work for the Intergovernmental Panel on Climate Change (IPCC) have indicated a range from 18 to 59 cm over the course of the twenty-first century (IPCC, 2007). The rise by the end of the century could be as much as one metre. While the exact rate of sea level rise is not known, it is clear that the sea will advance, across beaches, marshes, estuaries, river deltas

**Thermal expansion**
An increase in the volume of a liquid or matter in response to an increase in temperature.

**Thermal inertia**
A measure of the rate of change at which a material approaches the temperature of its surroundings.

and sand dunes. As the twenty-first century unfolds, places where the land and sea meet will be transformed.

Coasts are, of course, only one of many sites at which climate change will have significant impacts. Climate change is likely to lead to expanding deserts, the migration of species, an increase in deforestation and more severe storms. But coastlines have a special significance. Reefs and shallows off the coasts are fertile zones of marine life. Plants, animals and other organisms form rich communities along tidal zones and coastal hinterlands. Humans have gathered at these life-rich boundaries for hundreds of thousands of years, and human settlements have proliferated on coasts and deltas. Today over 630 million people live within 30 feet (9.14 metres) of sea level, and this is where two-thirds of the world's cities with populations over 5 million are sited (McGranahan et al., 2007).

The East Anglian coastline offers an indication of the challenges coastal communities will face. As environmental writer Jules Pretty puts it, 'the coast strongly defines this region. Beach, salting, sea wall and marshland. Fishing and smuggling, farming and sailing. Birds watched and birds shot. Created communities, deserted resorts, eroded cliffs, villages underwater, caravan parks and whole new invented places' (Pretty, 2011, p. 14). His book *This Luminous Coast* recounts a walk and occasional boat ride along this length of coast that took a year. But his travels are also our opening to another trip of much greater proportions, a journey in time that will take us back as far as the earliest human settlers in north-western Europe, and on to the present day and the possibilities of the foreseeable future.

# 3    Defending places on the coast

'This is a coast about to be lost. Not yet, but it will happen soon', writes Pretty (2011, p. 13) of the East Anglian coastline, with regard to the long-term threat of rising sea levels. But, as Pretty recounts, this is not a new predicament. Much of the ancient Norfolk fishing village of Eccles was swept away by a violent storm in 1604. A few miles to the south, the old parish of Whimpwell now lies under the North Sea (although the name lives on in nearby Whimpwell Green near Happisburgh). Further south again, the once bustling port of Dunwich lies submerged off the Suffolk coast. A storm-driven sea surge took some of the town in 1286. More buildings succumbed to a fierce storm in 1328, and by the mid seventeenth century a church and a few houses were all that remained of old Dunwich (Pretty, 2011). Local legend has it that at certain tides the bells of sunken churches toll beneath the waves. Other medieval buildings from old Dunwich have since fallen into disrepair (Figure 1.4).

Figure 1.4   Some ruins from the lost city of Dunwich

Such stories have added a haunting appeal to the East Anglia coastline for generations of tourists and holidaymakers. But coastal erosion continues to threaten coastal settlements, making this a contemporary problem about ways of life and places to live. Continuing erosion raises pressing questions about how today's human inhabitants of the region might best respond to the force of the sea. These are not just questions for local people. They are of such importance that they are being addressed at a national level.

Since the mid 1990s, the UK government's Department for the Environment, Food and Rural Affairs (DEFRA) has been producing Shoreline Management Plans (SMPs). The entire coastline of England and Wales has now been divided into different 'cells', each with a plan for managing the interface between land and sea. Each plan attempts to provide a comprehensive assessment of the risks associated with coastal processes, taking into account tidal patterns, wave dynamics and the composition of beach and seabed. The plans take into account the human use of the land and those components of the built environment that might be vulnerable to environmental change. The intention of the plans is to pass on the coastlines to future generations who can enjoy them and live and work there.

**Intergenerational equity**
The principle of fairness between generations.

**Sustainable development**
Development that does not leave a degraded environment for future generations.

The notion of responsibility for future generations provides the kernel of the principle known as **intergenerational equity**. This encompasses fairness or justice between different generations and holds that no generation can assume a privileged position for itself by acting in a way that results in a degraded environment being passed on to future generations. Intergenerational equity is central to the concept of **sustainable development**, an idea that was endorsed at the United Nations Conference on Environment and Development at Rio de Janeiro in 1992 and which has since become the philosophical basis of much environmental policy making. The most commonly cited formulation of sustainable development is 'development that meets the needs of the present without compromising the ability of future generations to meet their own needs' (World Commission on Environment and Development, 1987, p. 43). The definition combines the need for people to interact with and use the environment in a way that is sustainable over the long term with economic development that satisfies basic needs for all people and their aspirations for a better life. There is a recognition that environmental change, now and in the future, will have different impacts on different places and populations, and the way sustainable development is implemented will vary from place to place. Sustainable development is the aim of the UK government's SMPs.

Those responsible for SMPs do not assume that every valued feature of the coast can or should be protected. Decisions about investment in coastal defences are based on both environmental and economic assessments. The risks to humans and other species are thoroughly assessed, as are the opportunities for human land use. Three possible strategies may be pursued. The first is to defend an area of coastline (known as hold the line). The second is to pursue a strategy of managed retreat, allowing coastal erosion but seeking to manage the pace at which it takes place. The third is to pursue no active intervention and to let natural forces dictate the pace of erosion.

## Activity 1.1   Shoreline Management Plans and sustainable development

Imagine you live or work along a stretch of coastline in East Anglia. What features might you be looking for in a Shoreline Management Plan? Include the concept of sustainable development in your answer.

### Comment

Much will depend on the relative weighting that you would like to see given to environmental conservation and development in your locality. Your answer will depend on how highly you value the coastline in environmental and economic terms. The higher you value the existing coastline, the more likely it is that you may favour a policy of hold the line for the coastline. For policy makers, decisions such as these depend on the weighing up of the various costs and benefits. The benefits of sea defences should outweigh the costs of constructing and maintaining these defences.

Unsurprisingly, SMPs have proved contentious (Zsamboky et al., 2011). This is clear when we consider the case of Happisburgh (pronounced Haze-burra) in North Norfolk, where local people have formed a Coastal Concern Action Group. Just south of the vanished Whimpwell Green, Happisburgh has been losing land to the sea at varying rates for centuries. Both lives and properties were lost in the town in the severe storm flooding of the east coast of England in 1953, and since the 1970s accelerating encroachment by the sea has eroded farmland and taken a number of homes. Numerous dwellings continue to be threatened. As the local Shoreline Management Plan notes, as well as exposure to waves coming onshore from the North Sea, there is a strong north to south current running along the coast (Hiscock, 1998). This means that when erosion takes place, there is a net southerly drift of sedimentary material (Figures 1.5 and 1.6).

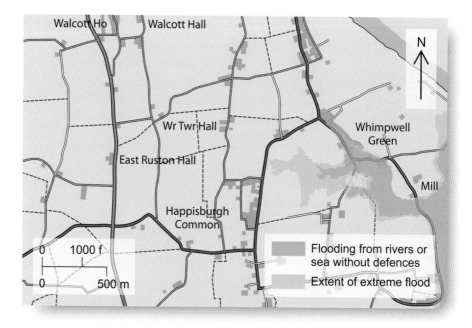

Figure 1.5   Map of Happisburgh showing properties at risk of flooding

In keeping with the idea of 'working with nature' that underpins DEFRA's management of coasts and waterways, the official policy since 2003 has been to 'allow retreat through no active intervention' (North Norfolk District Council, 2003). But as the Happisburgh Coastal Concern Action Group (CCAG) views it, this strategy has unfortunate consequences:

In North Norfolk, the SMP made it clear that places such as Happisburgh (and others) must be left to erode to provide sediment to the long shore drift thus providing better beaches for down drift communities. So communities such as Happisburgh etc. are expected to become voluntary losers to create winners down drift.

(CCAG, 2009, p. 3)

Figure 1.6   Coastal erosion at Happisburgh

The Group is also concerned by the way that policy changes over time. Happisburgh residents who bought houses when the local coast was designated worthy of protection later found that the policy had changed. The impact on house prices of a decision not to 'hold the line' against the encroaching sea can be substantial: in a now infamous incident, one Happisburgh homeowner who tried to raise a loan on her home found that it was currently valued at one pound sterling (*Eastern Daily Press*, 2008). The Coastal Concern Action Group has also suggested that other species are valued more than human livelihoods (CCAG, 2009). So what should be valued in the environment, and what do we mean by value? Should all species be valued? If so, should some be valued more than others? And should humans sometimes be valued more, or less, than other species?

One way we might view the efforts of the Coastal Concern Action Group is as an expression of Nimbyism. The acronym NIMBY – 'Not in My Back Yard' – has been in use for several decades to refer to environmental campaigning in which the protagonists value their local environment more highly than more distant environments. The term **Nimby** denotes pejoratively that local environmental protestors are rarely concerned about the environment on principled grounds and care primarily about their local environment. For example, the charge of Nimbyism has often been applied to the locating in North America of

**Nimby**
The term 'Nimby' refers to someone who values the local environment more than more distant environments.

polluting industries and waste dumps away from white, middle-class suburbs and closer to poorer marginalised communities (Figure 1.7).

Figure 1.7   Robert Bullard

The environmental sociologist Robert Bullard (Figure 1.7) has argued that the cumulative result of successful Nimby campaigns by more politically influential, white, middle-class communities in the USA has been the location of environmentally risky economic activities in poorer, often mainly black, neighbourhoods. On this view, where environmental risks are located, and which communities bear these risks and suffer the consequences, is an expression of power (Figure 1.8). Wealthier communities are better able to resist environmental risks than their poorer counterparts (Bullard, 2005).

## Activity 1.2   Political power and coastal defences

Bullard specialises in environmental politics in North America. But what might his arguments suggest about decisions that are taken on coastal defences in East Anglia, and Happisburgh in particular?

## Comment

One possibility is that the economically more powerful communities are better able to secure a policy of 'hold the line' than less economically powerful communities. On this view, policy makers may be willing to allow coastal erosion at the small and relatively powerless community of Happisburgh, preferring instead to defend more populous urban areas.

Figure 1.8  The locations of highly polluting factories, and those communities that bear the risks of such activities, are often an expression of political power

Many community activists at Happisburgh would resist the Nimby label, saying they are working not just to defend their own immediate environments. They point out that some sites on the coast are of strategic importance. If they are breached and the sea enters it could flood across the Norfolk Broads up to the urban centres of Norwich and Great Yarmouth. Indeed, there is a precedent for this: the 1953 floods, in which thousands of houses were flooded in Great Yarmouth (Figure 1.9). Local groups are aware of these strategically important but physically vulnerable points and how they may fall between the jurisdictions of different coastal management agencies (Pretty, 2011).

Figure 1.9   The 1953 flooding in Great Yarmouth

What begins as a localised engagement with environmental change may grow into organised solidarity with other communities. What is learnt from protecting one's own environment may be shared with other communities bearing similar risks. The Happisburgh Coastal Concern Action Group has become a rallying point for other organisations in the United Kingdom struggling against coastal erosion.

The people in these organisations, and other groups seeking to address environmental degradation, may have different reasons for acting. The presence of deep, heartfelt desires to defend one's own home, community and environment is often an emotional issue involving values such as quality of life and the cultural significance of what is being defended. But rational calculations, such as assessing the costs and benefits of different options, are also important. People will consider issues such as the current market valuation of their home and the cost of moving to a new place. What this suggests is that understanding environmental issues requires an appreciation of both the emotional and the rational values that help spark collective action.

People may be galvanised to act by a sense of injustice and disempowerment when decisions with consequences for local people are being made elsewhere. Again, an understanding of both rational and emotional reasoning is necessary to understand questions of justice and injustice. Justice is a subject that environmental philosophers analyse rationally and logically, and injustice is also something that people feel and which engenders a sense of grievance. The concept of **intragenerational equity** relates to fairness between different groups of people. The Happisburgh Coastal Concern Action Group has voiced frustration with the way that decision making in London is based on inadequate participation, thus failing to take account of local interests and values. By protesting locally and reaching out to forge relations of solidarity with other communities, Happisburgh activists are attempting to empower themselves, not simply against the forces of the sea and tide but in relation to the power of policy makers and coastal management agencies which they see as treating them unjustly.

**Intragenerational equity**
The principle of fairness between different groups of people.

We can summarise some of the main points of our discussion so far:

• Environments are never static but are dynamic, driven by interacting physical and social responses.

• Humans seek to shape their environments, and they respond to environmental change in different ways. In this respect we are like other species, which also seek to shape their environments (e.g. by building nests) and which respond to environmental change (e.g. by seeking different foodstuffs or by migrating).

• Environments are open to different interpretations, meanings and values that sometimes lead to disagreements with other groups.

In the next section we consider some environmental changes of the past, returning once again to Happisburgh in East Anglia.

# 4   Changes in geological time and space

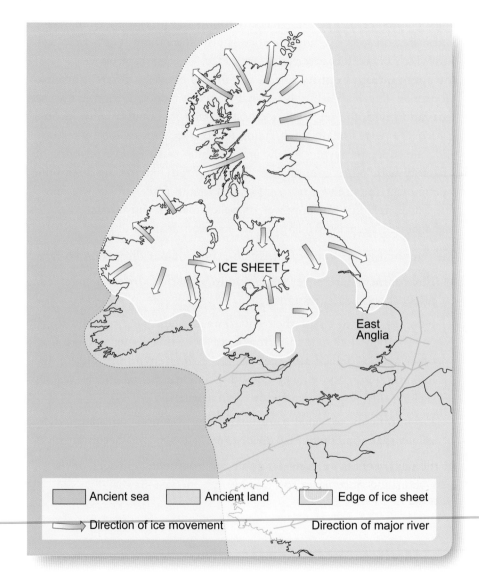

Figure 1.10   A palaeography (geographical features at a past time) of the British Isles, 18,000 years ago (Source: Lucy, 1999)

During the last glacial period (called a 'glacial stage'; see Box 1.1), thick ice sheets covered much of North America, Asia and northern Europe, including the northerly British Isles (Figure 1.9). These ice sheets depressed the Earth's surface, and even though they retreated around 11,500 years ago, the land is still rising due to a process known as **isostatic rebound**. Since the ice retreated, land in the north of the British Isles, which was covered by thick ice sheets, has gradually continued to rise, while that in the south, which had no ice cover, has been tilting down, causing a relative rise in sea level in this area at a rate of about 0.15 of a metre per century. This is the main reason for the long-term encroachment of the sea along the East Anglian coastline. Coastal erosion in East Anglia is thus determined by events of the past that have consequences in the present and for the future.

**Isostatic rebound**
The rise of land masses that were depressed by ice sheets in the past.

What would the landscape have looked like in East Anglia while the ice sheets were at their maximum? 18,000 years ago an ice sheet up to 1000 metres thick reached as far south as North Norfolk, approximately where Happisburgh is today. But had you stood there you would have seen no coastline. Because so much water was locked up in ice sheets, sea levels were about 120 metres lower than today and the British Isles were joined by land to continental Europe. These transformations of the landscape are related to natural climatic change that is still taking place. It is only in geologically very recent times that human beings have been a significant driving force in changing the climate.

---

### Box 1.1  Ice ages

Ice ages are long-term colder periods in the Earth's history. At the moment we are in an ice age called the Quaternary Ice Age, which has lasted for about 2.6 million years. Ice ages are characterised by many fluctuations in temperature. We are currently in one of the warmer periods of this ice age known as an 'interglacial stage'. The cooler periods are called 'glacial stages'. The present interglacial stage has lasted for about 11,500 years and is a geological epoch known as the Holocene. The 'Little Optimum' and 'Little Ice Age' were minor temperature fluctuations that occurred during the present interglacial stage (Figure 1.11).

---

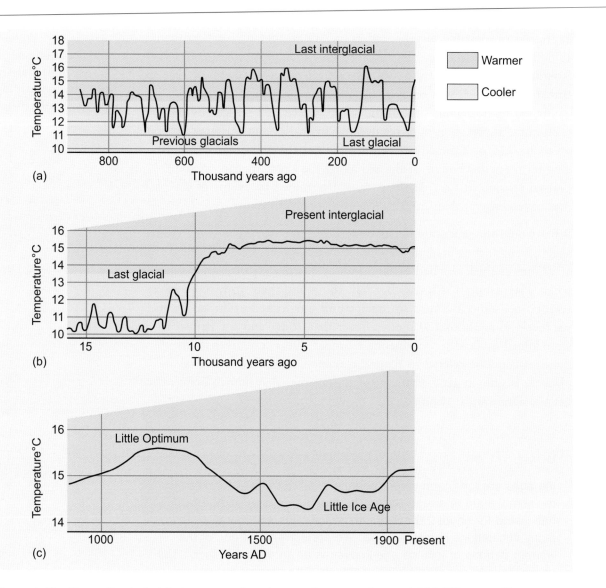

Figure 1.11   The estimated global mean surface temperature over the past 800,000 years (Source: adapted from Houghton et al., 1990)

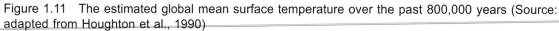

### Activity 1.3   Temperatures of the Earth over geological time

Consider Figure 1.11:

1   What is the general temperature change between a glacial stage minimum temperature and an interglacial stage maximum temperature?

2   How often do glacial and interglacial stages occur?

Comment

1   The glacial stage minimum (global mean surface temperature) is about 11 °C, and the interglacial stage maximum is about 16 °C, so the temperature change is about 5 °C.

2   There have been about four glacial and interglacial stages in the last 400,000 years, which suggests they occur about every 100,000 years.

What would conditions have been like even further back in the past, through multiple glacial and interglacial stages and their wildly vacillating transitional phases? Until recently, the earliest evidence of human occupation of north-western Europe was around 700,000 years ago (Roberts and Grün, 2010). However, while the coastal erosion of Happisburgh has had deleterious impacts, it has also had the fortunate effect of revealing previously undiscovered traces of human habitation.

## 4.1   The first Happisburghers

In 2000 a local man walking his dog spotted a flint handaxe on the beach, exposed by crumbling cliffs. Subsequent archaeological fieldwork uncovered a cache of some 70 flint tools and flakes, together with bone fragments. Dating techniques suggest these artefacts were deposited some 780,000 years ago (Parfitt et al., 2005). Analysis of ancient vegetation and pollen found alongside the stone artefacts indicates that the climate was in an interglacial stage, although cooling towards a glacial stage. From their analysis of plant and animal remains, researchers have been able to piece together a picture of the environment which these early humans would have inhabited:

> Beetle and plant macrofossil remains indicate a large, slow-flowing river fringed by riparian habitats that included reed-swamp, alder carr, marsh and pools, with forest close by. A large river is also indicated by Acipenser sturio (sturgeon), and proximity to the estuary and salt marsh is indicated by marine molluscs, barnacles and foraminifera.

> (Parfitt et al., 2010, p. 232)

The large river that archaeologist Simon Parfitt and his colleagues refer to would have been a confluence of the ancient Thames and the now extinct Bytham rivers, while the estuary would have opened out into the North Sea, as the Blackwater Estuary does today further south in Essex. The flint artefacts and plant and animal remains suggest that the early 'Happisburghers' were hunter-gatherers. The combination of forest, grassland, river, swamp, estuary and sea coast suggests this would have been a resource-rich environment that humans shared with southern mammoths, equids (horse family), voles, elk and red deer (Roberts and Grün, 2010). Also present were hyenas and possibly sabre-toothed tigers. Temperature ranges indicated by beetles and other fossil remains suggest that Happisburgh's summers 780,000 years ago were similar to today, while winters were probably at least 3 °C cooler (Parfitt et al., 2010). This would have been an extremely challenging environment for early humans (Figure 1.12).

Figure 1.12 Artist's reconstruction showing activity of early humans at Happisburgh, c.800,000 years ago

**Boreal zone**
The boreal zone relates to the coniferous forests of the north of the northern hemisphere, including much of Canada, Scandinavia and Russia.

Until this evidence was unearthed, it was not known that humans this far back could endure the conditions of a northern winter and the stresses of a highly variable climate. This is the only site on the Eurasian land mass north of 45 degrees latitude where there is evidence of human occupation at this time (Figure 1.13). Early humans were thought to be best adapted to Mediterranean and African climates, and most researchers believed that northern Europe – where the temperate zone meets the colder **boreal zone** – was beyond their limit of tolerance (Parfitt et al., 2010). As Parfitt and his multidisciplinary team of researchers conclude: 'This has significant implications for our understanding of early human behaviour, adaptation and survival, as well as the tempo and mode of colonization after their first dispersal out of Africa' (Parfitt et al., 2010, p. 229). It is still uncertain exactly how early humans coped with the winter temperatures of northern latitudes: whether this required physical adaptation, seasonal migration, or technological developments such as simple clothing, shelter and fire (Parfitt et al., 2010).

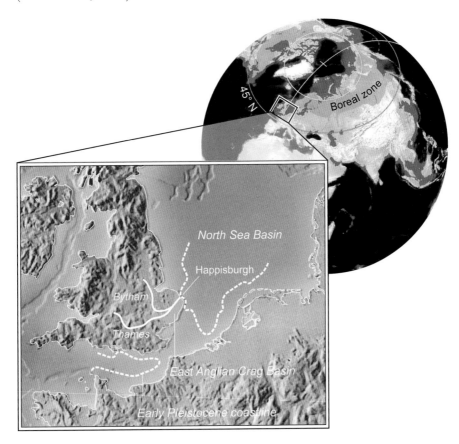

Figure 1.13   Map of northern Eurasia with 45 degrees latitude line (Source: based on Parfitt et al., 2010, p. 229, Figure 1)

The emphasis so far in this chapter has been on environmental changes over time. We have seen that climate and other aspects of the natural environment have rhythms and cycles at many different scales, from the daily ebb and flow of tides and the succession of night and day, through to the fluctuations between glacial and interglacial stages over tens of thousands of years and movements in and out of ice ages over millions of years. But a sense of the magnitude of climatic and environmental changes over time has important implications for understanding the movement of human beings – and other living things – across the spaces of the Earth. Here the use of the word 'space' is very different from the use of the term at the beginning of this chapter: the outer space through which Earth travels around the Sun. The concept of geographical space is three-dimensional and covers the entire surface of the Earth, and the expanse from the molten core of the Earth to the Earth's surface, and from the ocean depths to the edge of the atmosphere. Often, however, the term space is used to refer to movements across the surface of the Earth.

Climate change has had multiple impacts on human dispersal through and across space over hundreds of thousands of years, providing both new opportunities and threats (Figure 1.14). The falling sea levels which accompany glacial stages opened new routes for migration, while the warmer and damper climates of interglacial stages encouraged the spread of dense and, for early humans, often impenetrable forest. One important cause of human migration has been the periodic greening of the Earth's largest desert – the Sahara of North Africa – leading, during episodes of high rainfall, to a more fertile Sahara, followed by the drying out of the desert during periods of drought. Populations of flora (plant life) and fauna (animal life) have been 'sucked in' to the Sahara during rainfall episodes before migrating out from the Sahara when the rains failed (Fagan, 1990). This is the Saharan pump theory and it has been used to explain several waves of human dispersal, including that of an earlier species of human, *Homo erectus*, who, according to one theory, left Africa around 2 million years ago and dispersed gradually across Europe and Asia. Human remains have yet to be found at the Happisburgh site; there is speculation that the uncovered artefacts may have been crafted by *Homo antecessor*, a descendant of *Homo erectus*.

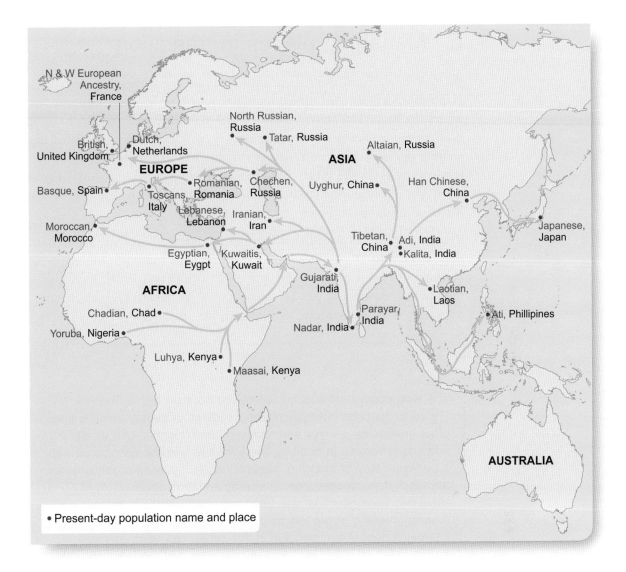

Figure 1.14   Map showing early human migrations out of Africa (Source: Braun, 2011)

This section has focused on environmental change by putting contemporary changes into a long-term historical and geological context. By going back in time we have sampled the Earth's potential for variability and change. And we have seen how today's challenges of living on a dynamic planet are nothing new.

# 5   Managing places in transition

We now move from the ancient estuary where the earliest known Happisburghers dwelled, down the coast to the present-day estuary where the River Blackwater opens out to the North Sea. The Blackwater Estuary is a site with a history of human management of the shifting interface between land and sea that has had important consequences for the plants and animals which live here (Figure 1.15). As at Happisburgh, the landscape looks very different today from how it looked in the past (Figure 1.16).

The sea here teems with fish and other marine life, including the oysters that are famous from this part of the world. The mudflats, too, support abundant life, and many of the species of worms and snails, including the *Hydrobia ulvae* snail, can be found only in estuaries. The salt marsh forms a coastal **ecosystem**, vibrant with life (Box 1.2).

---

### Box 1.2   Ecosystems

The term ecosystem was coined by the botanist Arthur Tansley (1935) to describe interdependent groupings of plants, animals and other organisms, as well as inanimate components (such as water and soil minerals). In ecology, the term has become associated with a particular way of studying interactions among living organisms, an approach that concentrates on energy and material exchanges. However, 'ecosystem' is also used more colloquially to refer to any area or grouping of organisms that can be regarded as functionally interdependent. An ecosystem in this sense can be of any size, from a clump of mossy vegetation on a rock, to the layer around the world where life is to be found, the *biosphere*. The biosphere includes land, the atmosphere, oceans and other bodies of water, such as rivers and lakes.

---

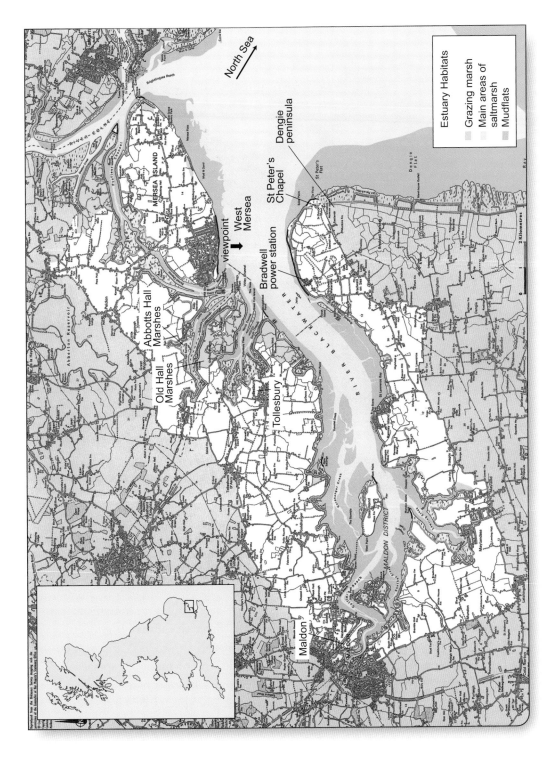

Figure 1.15  The Blackwater Estuary

(a)

(b)

Figure 1.16    (a) A recent view over the Blackwater Estuary towards the Dengie peninsula; (b) A reconstructed view, from the same point, as it would have appeared 18,000 years ago during the summer. An ice sheet lay just to the north, so people would have needed warm clothing. The Blackwater (in the background) was a river not an estuary, flowing in summer although frozen in winter. The land extended across to the European continent. The North Sea did not exist and the Blackwater flowed to the nearest sea to the south-west of England

Around the Blackwater Estuary, a few square miles of marshland can contain over 200 plant species, such as the rare saltmarsh goosefoot (*Chenopodium chenopodioides*), sea barley (*Hordeum marinum*) and golden samphire (*Inulacrithmoides*), along with dozens of mammal species and over 1000 species of invertebrates. Above all, these marshes provide breeding and feeding grounds for some 240 species of birds, especially wildfowl such as wigeon and teal, and waders such as redshank, golden plover, dunlin and lapwing. They are a crossroads for bird migrations that link the local ecosystems to habitats thousands of miles away. For a number of species this is a stopover on an important migratory highway – the so-called East Atlantic Flyway which connects the northern polar regions with Africa. Other bird species, including the dark-bellied brent geese that breed in the Taimyr Peninsula in the Arctic tundra of Siberia, spend the winter here (Figure 1.17).

The UK is a signatory to the European Union's Habitats Directive, which stipulates that coastal management should involve no net loss of intertidal habitats. This is a considerable challenge. Since medieval times, some 40,000 hectares of Essex salt marsh have been converted to agricultural use, leaving only 4400 hectares, which is 10 per cent of the UK's total. As an intertidal ecosystem, salt marsh would naturally migrate inland as the sea encroaches.

## Activity 1.4   The ecological effects of coastal sea defences

What might be the consequences of a policy of 'hold the line' for salt marsh habitat?

### Comment

The salt marsh's gradual migration inland is blocked by the construction of sea walls to maintain the existing shape of the coastline. These sea walls prevent this movement. The marsh is caught between the walls and the rising water, a process termed 'coastal squeeze' (Figure 1.18). However, if conserving the surviving salt marsh is imperative this could be achieved through a policy of managed retreat or no active intervention. So a policy aimed at environmental conservation might run counter to one that aims to conserve coastal dwellings.

One example of managed retreat, managed by the Essex Wildlife Trust, is at Abbotts Hall Farm, an area of farmland on the north side of the Blackwater Estuary. Here, a three-kilometre sea wall has been deliberately breached at five points, allowing the sea to flow in. This enables the low-lying meadows to be gradually transformed back into salt marsh, which is then able to migrate inland as sea levels rise.

But, and as you saw with respect to Happisburgh, managed retreat is not always a favoured option for those whose livelihoods are threatened by the encroaching sea. However, governments have offered financial incentives for farmers willing to manage their land in ways which enhance its value for conservation. Although managed retreat has been successful in some places, it remains an inexact practice, with uncertain and unpredictable impacts.

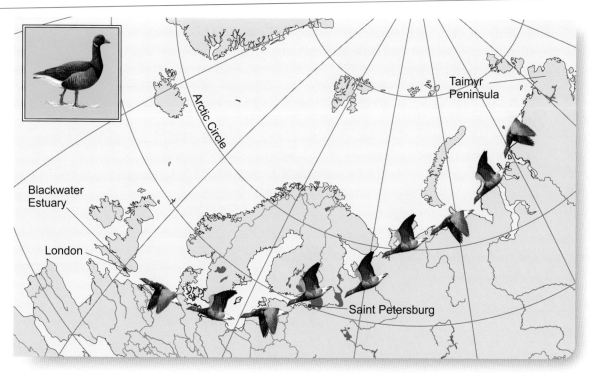

(a)

(b)

Figure 1.17 Brent geese: (a) Their migration route to the over-wintering site in the Blackwater; (b) In flight over the Blackwater Estuary

**Coastal 'squeeze'**

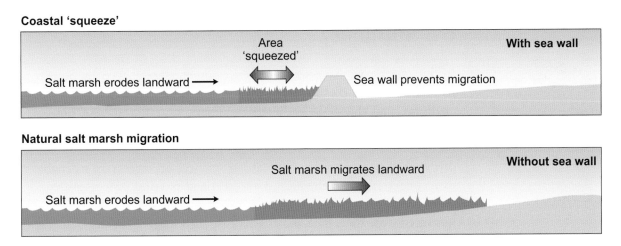

**Natural salt marsh migration**

Figure 1.18  'Coastal squeeze' occurs when salt marsh is prevented from migrating inland away from the rising sea level

Salt marsh serves as a first line of defence against wave action and rising seas in a similar fashion to the way mangrove forests offer a buffer against storm surges and tsunamis in warmer latitudes. In the Blackwater Estuary, coastal managers are attempting to mitigate a situation in which erosion has been exceeding the creation of salt marsh. But ultimately, if local sea level rise continues, nothing can prevent the inundation of the Essex marshlands. Climate change will accelerate this process and could also lead to more extreme events, such as more frequent and more intense storms which would add to the risk of flooding caused by sea level rise.

# 6   Summary

In this chapter we have seen how environments are shaped by both natural and social forces. This points to the need to study environmental change in an 'interdisciplinary' way. Throughout this module insights from the natural sciences and the social sciences are brought together so that we can begin to grasp the scale and complexity of the challenges we face. The natural sciences are necessary to enable us to understand the chemical, biological and physical processes that lead to environmental change, and how it can be identified and measured over time. The social sciences, such as geography, politics and economics, guide us in our understanding of the social, cultural and economic processes that impact on the natural world. They also point us to the differences between social **actors** and help us make sense of the range of ways in which humans engage with each other and with the world around them.

**Actor**
A term used to denote a variety of individuals, social groups and institutions, such as a government, community group, business or international organisation.

Although contemporary environmental change should be imagined as something in which humans play an important role, we should bear in mind that we occupy a tiny moment, a fragment of time in the history of the Earth (Box 1.3). But while human interference in the environment is a very recent phenomenon, the changes now occurring as a result of our activities, especially greenhouse gas emissions, could have devastating consequences within one or two generations.

---

### Box 1.3   Humans on Earth

The Earth was formed some 4.6 billion years ago. However, modern humans (*Homo sapiens sapiens*) only evolved 150,000 years ago. To put this into perspective, if we imagine the history of the Earth as one calendar year, with the Earth forming on 1 January, modern humans would not appear until the last day, 31 December, and then only 17 minutes before the end of the year.

---

In this chapter you have encountered a range of concepts that are used in the sciences and social sciences. Here we focus on two concepts that have arisen several times in the chapter. They are *time* and *space*. Together they constitute the first of three groups of key analytical concepts that you will work with on this module. You will be introduced to the other two in the next two chapters.

We have seen how episodes in the past may continue to shape our environment today and far into the future. The rising sea levels along the coast of East Anglia are the result of isostatic adjustment due to the retreat of ice sheets that covered much of the British Isles thousands of years ago and of global climate change caused by human-induced emissions of greenhouse gases over the last three centuries. The environments of these coasts are thus shaped by dynamic natural and social processes that play out over very different timescales.

Time may be imagined as a *linear* concept, with one moment following another in a continuous and unbroken succession in perpetuity. But time may also be conceived in terms of *rhythms*. Some rhythms are repetitive and predictable, such as the movements of the Earth around the Sun, the tides and the seasons. Others are less predictable, such as the timing of ice ages and changes in sea level.

We have also seen that environmental change varies over space as well as time. The Blackwater Estuary, for example, is one example of an ecological space with its own defining features, such as organised agriculture and salt marshes, that give it a unique identity. Although bounded it is connected to other places. The river links the estuary upstream, the coast links it to the oceans. The estuary is connected to Siberia by migrating geese, and to other spaces by the transport and movement of people. We may conceive of space in a variety of ways: in terms of scale (between the local and the global); and as boundaries (natural boundaries, such as rivers and valleys; human constructions, such as sea walls; and political and administrative boundaries). Space may also be *transboundary* as when environmental processes cross natural boundaries, such as mountain ranges or deserts, or political boundaries, for example between two countries. The concept of distance is essential to how we define space. Distance can separate spaces, although social and economic processes such as migration, transport, trade, money transfers and telecommunications can connect distant places.

However, economic processes can themselves often be volatile and unpredictable. The global economic downturn that began around 2008 has led to less money being available for environmental protection, with policy makers preferring to concentrate public spending on more pressing economic or financial concerns. Spaces and people can find themselves exposed, not only to the dynamics of the physical world but also to the shifting, changing forces of the social world.

# References

Braun, D. (2011) 'Modern humans wandered out of Africa via Arabia', *National Geographic*, 7 November [online], newswatch.nationalgeographic.com/2011/11/03/modern-humans-wandered-out-of-africa-via-arabia/ (Accessed 20 June 2012).

Bullard, R. D. (2005) 'Environmental justice in the twenty-first century', in Bullard, R. D. (ed.) *The Quest for Environmental Justice: Human Rights and the Politics of Pollution*, Berkeley, CA, University of California Press.

Chaikin, A. (1994) *A Man on the Moon: The Voyages of the Apollo Astronauts*, London, Michael Joseph.

Coastal Concern Action Group (CCAG) (2009) *Response to Consultation on Coastal Change Policy*, 20 September [online], http://www.happisburgh.org.uk/content (Accessed 18 June 2012).

Eastern Daily Press (2008) 'House worth less than a loaf', 7 July [online], http://www.edp24.co.uk/news/house_worth_less_than_a_loaf_1_165200?ot=archant.PrintFriendlyPageLayout.ot (Accessed 20 June 2012).

Fagan, B. (1990) *Journey from Eden: The Peopling of our World*, London, Thames and Hudson.

Hansen, J., Nazarenko, L., Ruedy, R., Sato, M., Willis, J., Del Genio, A., Koch, D., Lacis, A., Lo, K., Menon, S., Novakov, T., Perlwitz, J., Russell, G., Schmidt, G. A. and Tausnev, N. (2005) 'Earth's energy imbalance: confirmation and implications', *Science*, vol. 308, no. 5727, pp. 1431–5.

Hiscock, K. (ed.) (1998) *Marine Nature Conservation Review: Benthic Marine Ecosystems of Great Britain and the North-east Atlantic*, Peterborough, Joint Nature Conservation Committee.

Houghton, J. T., Jenkins, G. J. and Ephraume, J. J. (eds) (1990) *Climate Change: The IPCC Scientific Assessment*, Cambridge, Cambridge University Press.

Intergovernmental Panel on Climate Change (IPCC) (2007) *Climate Change 2007 – The Physical Science Basis: Contribution of Working Group I to the Fourth Assessment Report of the IPCC*, Cambridge, Cambridge University Press.

Lucy, G. (1999) *Essex Rock: A Look Beneath the Essex Landscape*, Saffron Walden, The Essex Rock and Mineral Society.

Macdougall, D. (2006) *Frozen Earth: The Once and Future Story of Ice Ages*, Berkeley, CA, University of California Press.

McGranahan, G., Balk, D. and Anderson, B. (2007) 'The rising tide: assessing the risks of climate change and human settlements in low elevation coastal zones', *Environment and Urbanization*, vol. 19, no. 1, pp. 17–37.

North Norfolk District Council (2003) *Kelling to Lowestoft Ness Shoreline Management Plan* [online], http://www.northnorfolk.org/files/PU3b12a_Happisburgh_N.pdf (Accessed 20 June 2012).

Parfitt, S. A., Barendregt, R. W., Breda, M., Candy, I., Collins, M. J., Coope, G. R., Durbidge, P., Field, M. H., Lee, J. R., Lister, A. M., Mutch, R., Penkman, K. E. H., Preece, R. C., Rose, J., Stringer, C. B., Symmons, R., Whittaker, J. E., Wymer, J. J. and Stuart, A. J. (2005) 'The earliest record of human activity in northern Europe', *Nature*, vol. 438, no. 7070, 15 December, pp. 1008–12 [online], doi: 10.1038/nature04227 (Accessed 16 June 2012).

Parfitt, S., Ashton, M., Lewis, S., Abel, R., Coope, G., Field, M., Gale, R., Hoare, P., Larkin, N., Lewis, M., Karloukovski, V., Maher, B., Peglar, S., Preece, R., Whittaker, J. and Stringer, C. (2010) 'Early Pleistocene human occupation at the edge of the boreal zone in northwest Europe', *Nature*, vol. 466, no. 7303, 8 July, pp. 229–33 [online], doi: 10.1038/nature09117 (Accessed 16 June 2012).

Pretty, J. (2011) *This Luminous Coast*, Woodbridge, Full Circle Editions.

Roberts, A. and Grün, R. (2010) 'Early human northerners', *Nature*, vol. 466, no. 7303, pp. 189–90.

Tansley, A. G. (1935) 'The use and abuse of vegetational concepts and terms', *Ecology*, vol. 16, pp. 284–307.

World Commission on Environment and Development (1987) *Our Common Future*, Oxford, Oxford University Press.

Zsamboky, M., Fernández-Bilbao, A., Smith, D., Knight, J. and Allan, J. (2011) *Impacts of Climate Change on Disadvantaged UK Coastal Communities*, York, Joseph Rowntree Foundation.

# Chapter 2   Our place, your place

Nigel Clark

# Contents

# 1   Introduction

The town of Saint-Louis, Senegal, on the Atlantic coast of West Africa, is highly vulnerable to some of the predicted effects of global climate change. In this chapter we examine this town to see how places are made through their spatial connections to other places and their temporal connections to past times. Our primary concern is not with deep-seated movements of the Earth itself but with movements across the Earth's surface. Humans not only travel from place to place. They also set things in motion, by extracting minerals and natural resources from the Earth and manufacturing and trading goods. These human-induced movements cause changes in the environment which, like the dynamics of the Earth itself, are a source of risk and uncertainty, as well as opportunity, for people and communities.

Other species also undertake journeys both locally and over great distances. In order to arrive at Senegal we set out once again from East Anglia along a flight path that arcs across the east Atlantic, a route taken by millions of migratory birds.

# 2   Transglobal migration

While anthropologists and archaeologists have been able to reconstruct the likely migratory routes taken by the early humans who left Africa (Figure 1.14), some of whom ended up living around the estuaries of East Anglia some 780,000 years ago, it is not clear how fast the migrations happened. The journeys involved may have taken tens or even hundreds of thousands of years. When the first humans finally arrived at Happisburgh they found themselves sharing their estuary with birds making a journey of similar magnitude every year (Figure 2.1).

Figure 2.1   Blackwater Estuary waterfowl

Like the now extinct estuary of the ancient Thames–Bytham river confluence, today's Blackwater Estuary offers a range of habitats for migratory waterfowl. For many of these birds, the East Anglian marshlands are stopping-off points on an annual migration between the polar and boreal regions of the northern hemisphere and sub-Saharan Africa: the route known as the East Atlantic Flyway. New technologies such as satellite tracking have greatly improved the understanding of bird and animal migration and their geographical ranges and stopovers. In the case of birds, this builds on over a century of accumulated knowledge from tracking individuals using metal bands (Boere and Stroud, 2006).

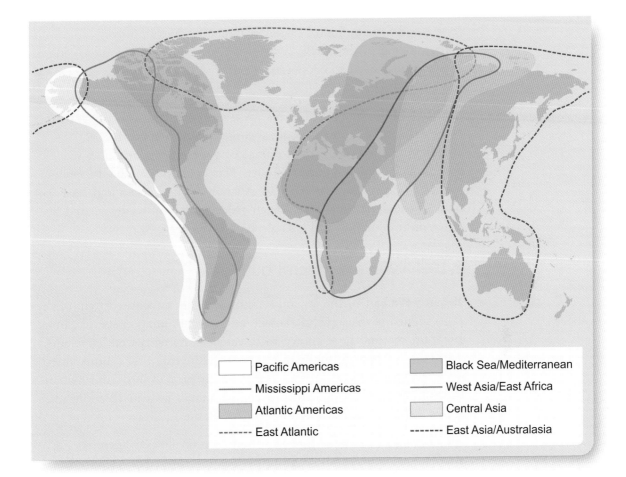

Figure 2.2   The eight flyways of waders/shorebirds (Source: based on Boere and Stroud, 2006, p. 42, Figure 4)

Waterbirds are some of the animal kingdom's great migrators, embarking annually on intercontinental circuits of the planet. Migration, as avian experts put it, 'connects many bird populations in time and space, either at common breeding areas, during migration, or at shared nonbreeding areas' (Olsen et al., 2006, p. 384). These trips involve numerous resting and feeding stops, and many waterbird species revisit the same sites, one of the reasons why the protection of habitats like the Blackwater Estuary marshlands is so important. Over the course of the twentieth century, the mapping of entire migratory routes – or 'flyways' – has taken place. A **flyway** is the entire range of a migratory bird species (or groups of related species, or distinct populations of a single species) through which it moves annually from breeding grounds to non-breeding areas, including intermediate resting and feeding places

**Flyway**
The range of a migratory bird through which it moves annually.

(Boere and Stroud, 2006). Flyway mapping enables improved understanding of the challenges that a bird may encounter and of the countries that need to cooperate in order to maintain a safe passage for it.

Although bird migration patterns are more complex than the idea of flyways can fully capture, the idea works well in practice for coordinating the conservation efforts of governments and non-governmental organisations (NGOs). This applies especially to multi-species flyways – such as the East Atlantic, Central Asian and East Asian/Australasian flyways – which group migration routes shared by different bird species into a single system (Figure 2.2).

## 2.1   Flyways and viral outbreaks

Towards the end of the last millennium a highly infectious strain of the avian influenza virus H5N1 (known as 'bird flu') jumped species. In 1997, for the first time known to researchers, humans were infected with H5N1. Through the first decade of the twenty-first century there were several outbreaks in both commercially farmed birds and humans. By 2011, avian flu had claimed over 300 human lives in 12 countries across Asia, Africa and the Middle East (Reuters, 2011).

**Hazard**

An event or happening that poses a threat to humans or to the environment.

**Risk**

The product of the probability (or likelihood) that a particular hazard will occur and the severity of the potential harm.

Although most of the outbreaks to date are small scale, there is international concern about avian flu as a human health hazard. A **hazard** may be defined as an event or happening that poses a threat to humans or to the environment. A **risk** may be defined as the product of the probability (or likelihood) that a particular hazard will occur and the severity of the potential harm. Risk may be expressed numerically:

Risk = Probability that a hazard will occur × severity of the hazard

So, the greater the probability and the more severe the hazard the higher the risk. Similarly, a low probability of a weak hazard poses a low risk. There are intermediate categories of risk. Figure 2.3 shows one way that risk may be categorised: the darker the shading, the higher the risk. Note that a severe hazard does not necessarily indicate a high risk. If a large asteroid were to collide with the Earth the hazard would be cataclysmic, but the probability of such an event is low, and most experts consider such a scenario to be low risk. Similarly, a high probability does not necessarily denote a high risk. There is a high probability that humans will catch the common cold at least once a year, but the hazard this poses to human health is low. So catching a cold is low risk.

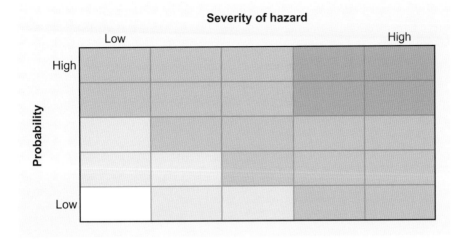

Figure 2.3   A categorisation of risk

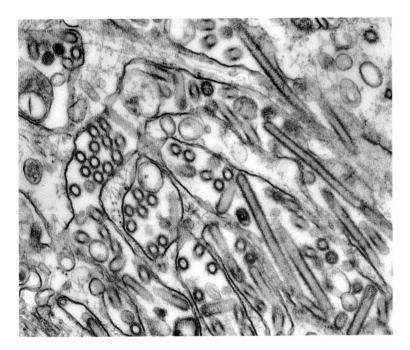

Figure 2.4   Magnified view of the H5N1 virus

In contrast to the common cold, avian flu is a greater hazard, although so far the probability of humans catching it is very low. There has so far been no widespread outbreak of the H5N1 virus (Figure 2.4). But epidemiologists fear that the virus will continue mutating, and a strain will eventually develop that can be transmitted more easily to humans. As the chief veterinary officer of the Food and Agriculture Organization of the United Nations (FAO) put it in late 2011, 'Preparedness and surveillance remain essential … no one can let their guard down with H5N1' (Lubroth, quoted in Reuters, 2011). A mutation would increase the probability of large numbers of people becoming affected and thus increase the risk to humans, possibly leading to a global influenza epidemic on the scale of the 1918 outbreak (so-called Spanish flu) in which some 50–100 million people died worldwide (Taubenberger and Morens, 2006).

Figure 2.5   Bar-headed goose

In 2005 there was evidence that the virus could be mutating when an outbreak of highly pathogenic avian influenza infected the wild bird populations of Qinghai Lake nature reserve in central China. Up to 6000 migratory birds were killed, including up to 10 per cent of the total world population of bar-headed geese (*Anser indicus*) (Figure 2.5) (FAO, 2008; Normile, 2005). Local commercially farmed poultry was also infected. The World Health Organization (WHO) stated that wild birds should be seen as a reservoir for the pathogenic strain of H5N1 which could be passed on to domestic birds (Bingham and Hinchliffe, 2008). Because of the way that migrations connect many different bird populations in time and space, and because multi-species flyways bring multiple populations of birds together in the same staging grounds, wild bird migrations came to be seen as potential vectors of a global influenza pandemic. US Department of Agriculture virologist David Saurez commented at the time that if wild birds are carrying H5N1, 'it will be difficult or impossible to control the spread from country to country' (quoted in Normile, 2005, p. 426).

Concerns that migratory birds were spreading H5N1 grew when avian influenza was detected in Africa, far away from East Asia, the originating site of H5N1 (Figure 2.6).

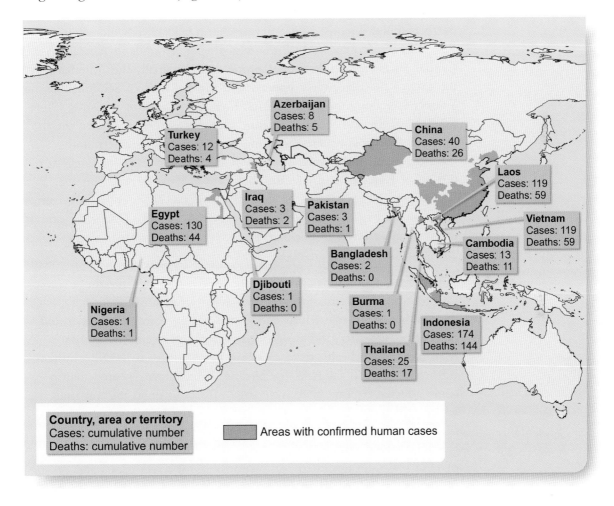

Figure 2.6   Map showing outbreaks of avian influenza between 12 and 18 October 2009

Activity 2.1   Bird migration and the H5N1 virus

Look at Figures 2.2 and 2.6. Can you explain why there might be anxiety over the role of migratory birds with regard to the transmission of H5N1 from birds to humans? It helps to know that there is evidence that the virus can survive extended periods in the chilly lakes and wetlands of the polar regions. Where might the Blackwater Estuary and the wetlands of Senegal fit into such accounts?

As Figure 2.2 shows, major flyways meet or overlap, especially in the northern polar regions. These flyways bring wild birds which frequent East Asia into contact with birds with staging grounds in Africa, Central Asia, the Middle East, Europe and potentially the Americas. In the case of the Blackwater Estuary and the wetlands of Senegal, there is a direct link along the East Atlantic Flyway: the area of wetlands where the Senegal River meets the Atlantic Ocean was seen as one of the potential 'hotspots' where migrating birds from the northern and southern hemispheres mix. Epidemiologists noted: 'Potential areas for mixing of Eurasian and African ducks are in West Africa, near the Senegal and Niger Rivers, the floodplains of the Niger River in Nigeria and Mali, and Lake Chad' (Olsen et al., 2006, p. 385). Ducks are one of the families of birds at risk of H5N1 transmission between domestic and wild fowl.

Much of the globe thus appears to be woven together into an interconnected transmission zone for avian viruses. Multi-species flyways, which for many bird enthusiasts are an object of wonder and fascination, are also a form of global spatial interconnectivity that transmits human health risks. But human responses to H5N1 outbreaks further heightened the risks for birdlife. It has been reported that in some affected regions there have been efforts to drain the wetlands where wild birds thought to be at risk from the H5N1 virus gathered, to cull these birds and displace them from breeding and roosting grounds (Birdlife International, 2007). The FAO claimed that the risks of H5N1 were exaggerated and responsible for overanxious and drastic responses to the spread of avian flu (FAO, 2008). The FAO's view that risks were being exaggerated indicates that risk is not just something that experts can judge and quantify. It is also a matter of perception (Box 2.1).

## Box 2.1  Risk perception

Risk perception is the subjective judgement that an individual makes about a risk. A hazard may have a very low risk, yet if people perceive the risk as being high this will affect their attitudes and the actions they take. For example, the evidence suggests that the risk of being bitten by a poisonous snake when walking in the heathlands of Scotland is extremely low. But someone who is concerned with the potential severity of the hazard rather than the statistical probability of the hazard occurring might perceive the risk as high, and refuse to enter heathland environments (Figure 2.7). Similarly, people may believe that the risks of a hazard are low and as a result expose themselves to hazards unnecessarily. An example would be entering a nuclear power plant without wearing the recommended protective clothing.

Figure 2.7  Walking in the Scottish heathlands: a low-risk activity?

## Activity 2.2   The global spread of avian flu: reviewing the evidence

So far, it has been suggested that the migration of wild birds was responsible for the global spread of the H5N1 virus. But might there be other explanations?

Research later suggested that it was not wild birds that had infected the domesticated fowl in the vicinity of Qinghai Lake, but vice versa. There are several intensive poultry farms near Qinghai Lake and it is common practice to use poultry manure (a known vector for H5N1 transmission) as feed in fish farms around the lake. The evidence now suggests the source of the outbreak was commercially farmed birds (Bingham and Hinchliffe, 2008; FAO, 2008). Outbreaks of H5N1 around the world were occurring primarily in large-scale poultry operations and their timing did not correlate with the movements of migratory birds. There is now evidence that infection patterns are correlated with the movements of commercially farmed poultry. The routes of transmission can be traced along the railways, roads, border posts and factory farms through which the vast international trade of poultry flowed, much of it illegal and unregulated. For some critical commentators at least, the global mass movement of poultry and poultry products appears to be a far greater source of health risk and uncertainty than the migration of wild birds (Bingham and Hinchliffe, 2008; Birdlife International, 2007).

This discussion illustrates that at any given time the scientific knowledge base for a risk may be incomplete and uncertain. Uncertainty is a condition that arises when something cannot be precisely measured and understood. Early explanations that the spread of H5N1 was caused by wild birds did not stand up to scrutiny. Later research revealed that the spread of the virus did not correlate with wild bird flyways whereas it correlated closely with the transport of poultry (Box 2.2).

## Box 2.2   Correlation and cause

Correlation is a statistical measurement of the relationship between two variables demonstrating that when one changes so too does the other. A commonly used expression in the sciences and social sciences alike is that correlation does not imply causation. In distinction to correlation, causation is when a change in one variable causes, directly or indirectly, a change in another variable.

To illustrate: let us suppose a factory has been releasing poisonous chemicals into a river and at the same time there is an unusually high death rate of local aquatic life. Here there is correlation. Scientists would not accept this correlation as evidence of cause without further investigation. If they found evidence of abnormally high levels of the poisonous chemical in dead fish in the vicinity of the factory and if they were also able to rule out other possible explanations for the death of aquatic life, then they would conclude that the factory's release of the chemicals was killing the fish.

Let us also suppose that during the period when the chemicals were released the factory's football team enjoyed a good spell of results. Here there is clear correlation, but no plausible causation.

So if B changes when A changes, this does not necessarily mean that A has caused B to change. It could mean that B causes A to change. Or there could be another variable – X – that causes both A and B to change. Or the correlation between changes of A and B could be pure coincidence.

It is necessary to bear in mind the distinction between correlation and cause when examining environmental change, the causes of which are often a complex mix of natural and social processes.

## 2.2   Protecting the East Atlantic Flyway

The realisation that there was a low correlation between outbreaks of avian flu and wild bird flyways but a high correlation between the outbreaks and poultry transportation routes prompted a rethinking on the causes of the outbreak. This in turn has led to a renewed appreciation of the importance of protecting the habitats of migratory birds. Avian experts argued that if the natural wetlands favoured by migrating birds are reduced or degraded, these birds are more likely to be displaced to sites shared by domestic birds, thus increasing the risk of viral transmission between different bird species. The United Nations Environment Programme (UNEP) (2006) reported, 'Restoring tens of thousands of lost and degraded wetlands could go a long way towards reducing the threat of avian flu pandemics'.

Two international agreements relevant to the conservation of migratory bird habitats are the Convention on the Conservation of Migratory Species of Wild Animals (CMS) of 1979 and the African-Eurasian Water Bird Agreement (AEWA) of 1995. The latter agreement brings together agencies seeking to protect the birdlife of the East Anglian coastline and those working to conserve the wetlands of Senegal. In seeking to preserve ecosystems along the entire flight path of migratory birds and in weaving together into a single system distant spaces such as the Blackwater Estuary conservation areas and Senegal's Djoudj National Bird Sanctuary, the AEWA represents a more holistic approach to managing the risks to migratory bird species.

Figure 2.8   Djoudj National Bird Sanctuary in the Senegal River Basin, a wetland that is home to a wide range of bird species

The origins of the AEWA derived from a small agreement in 1985 aimed at protecting the waterbirds of the northern European Arctic. It soon became apparent that as the birds in question wintered in Africa, a more expansive agreement including African countries was needed. The AEWA is now the world's largest flyway agreement, covering several multi-species flyways that link Africa with the eastern Eurasian land mass and the northern polar regions. Providing a transcontinental platform for research, monitoring and conservation activities, the AEWA seeks to protect the habitats of some 170 species of migratory waterbirds across its 28 signatory nations under the slogan 'no park is an island'. It works to ensure that protected areas in different places are linked up and that conservation activities within wildlife reserves retain strong connections with the social worlds around them (Beintema and van Vessem, 1999).

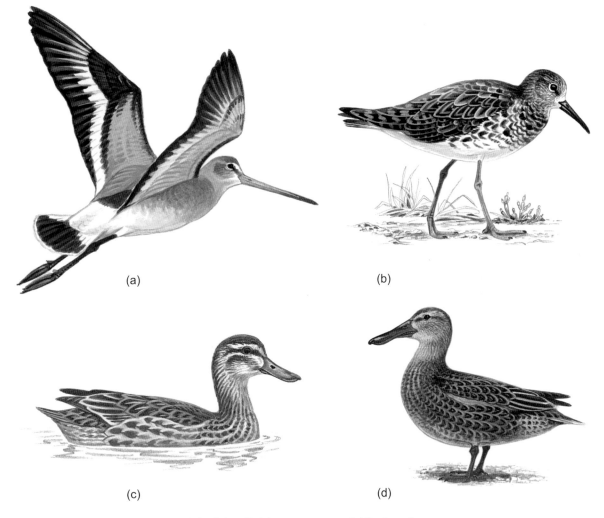

Figure 2.9   (a) black-tailed godwit, (b) ruff, (c) garganey and (d) shoveler

This idea of sustaining associations with local communities has been especially important in the Djoudj National Bird Sanctuary (Figure 2.8). Located some 60 miles north-east of the city of Saint-Louis on the bank of the Senegal River, the park is the third largest bird sanctuary in the world. Created in 1971, it was awarded World Heritage Site status a decade later by the United Nations Educational, Scientific and Cultural Organization (UNESCO). Djoudj's special significance is that it is the first major freshwater source that migrating waterbirds reach after crossing the Sahara desert. Sharing the waterland habitat with thousands of pelicans, flamingos and other charismatic African avifauna, an estimated three million migratory waterbirds pass through the park between September and April, including aquatic warbler, garganey, shoveler, ruff, pintail and black-tailed godwit (Figure 2.9).

Like the Blackwater Estuary, with its ageing sea walls and reclaimed pastures, the park has a long history of human habitation and modification. Local people lived in the Senegal River delta area well before the park was established. In the early years of the park a strict protection regime was enforced, resulting in the forcible exclusion of communities who had formerly lived and worked within the bounds of the bird sanctuary. This led to conflicts and cases where local people were accused of 'poaching' park resources. However, since 1990 a change of policy has led to the integration of local people and their livelihoods with the management of the park. Local participation has had positive effects. Now, many villagers are employed as volunteer park wardens and with a return to traditional livelihoods has come a new local involvement in ecotourist ventures (Diouf, 2002).

## 2.3   Globalisation

**Globalisation**
The geographical extensification and intensification of social networks on a global scale.

**Action at a distance**
Where an action in one geographical space influences events in another space.

We have begun to see how local places are linked to other places. The concept of **globalisation** highlights the way that individual places are increasingly interconnected to other places by many different kinds of transactions. To British sociologist Anthony Giddens, globalisation is the geographical extensification and intensification of social networks on a global scale (Giddens, 1990). A concept related to globalisation is what French sociologist Bruno Latour has termed **action at a distance**, whereby an action in one geographical space can influence events some distance away in another space (Latour, 1987). Under globalisation, social transactions take place over greater distances and with greater frequency. Globalisation is commonly used by social scientists to refer to economic interconnectivity (such as international trade and money markets), political interconnectivity (such as the creation and functioning of international organisations) and social interconnectivity (such as travel and social networking sites).

---

## Activity 2.3  Globalisation

What examples of globalisation have we considered in this chapter?

### Comment

The international trade of poultry is one example. The advent of modern forms of transport means that food now travels longer distances before it is consumed compared with 50 years ago. (You will examine the production and transport of food in Book 2, chapters 5–8.) Another example is increasing cooperation between different continents, nations and places. The African-Eurasian Water Bird Agreement is an example of international cooperation that involves sharing information, techniques and 'best practice'.

---

Globalisation can make places more similar; for example, with the emergence of global brands and the development of similar practices in work, economic production and leisure. Indeed, around the globe poultry farmers are now moving towards similar intensive factory methods for poultry farming. But while globalisation may cause places to become more similar it can also promote social and environmental diversity. For example, in Senegal's Djoudj National Bird Sanctuary we have seen local people with experience of sharing ecosystems with wildlife becoming active participants in the management of conservation areas. This is an example of the way that global connections – in the form of new agreements and cooperative ventures – can actively support and strengthen the very characteristics that make places distinctive.

Globalisation is usually used to refer to social processes that involve the exercise of human agency. It is less common to refer to ecological processes as globalisation. But as we have seen, other species such as birds were mobile on a global scale, making regular journeys between the Blackwater Estuary and Djoudj National Bird Sanctuary long before humans were. Processes such as animal and bird migrations and the transmission of pollen and seeds on winds are forms of interconnectivity that should be seen as globalisation in their own right.

And human activities can profoundly influence these global ecological processes.

Globalisation, therefore, continues to be a complex and challenging process. Over recent years, surveys have shown that the populations of numerous species of migratory birds that arrive in the UK from Africa are in sharp decline. It is now understood that cyclical changes in the local climate in Africa make a big difference to bird numbers: in drought years birds are less able to build up the reserves they need to fly across the Sahara. Human-induced loss of habitat in some parts of Africa is a contributory factor. Global climate change is also impacting on local climatic conditions (Eccleston, 2008; Gray, 2010). This suggests that to understand environmental change we need an expanded notion of globalisation that encompasses both natural and social processes.

In the following section, we look more closely at the Atlantic coast of Senegal. We examine the various ways in which global connections can make local places, and also generate opportunities and risks for the people who live there.

# 3 Saint-Louis, Senegal: a city at risk

Saint-Louis is the nearest city to the Djoudj National Bird Sanctuary. Founded in the 1650s by French traders, the city is famous for its colonial architecture. It was granted UNESCO World Heritage City status in 2000 (Figure 2.10). The old colonial city is located on a narrow island (just over 2 km long and about 400 m wide) near the mouth of the Senegal River. At this point the river is separated from the Atlantic Ocean to the west by a narrow sand spit, about 300 m wide, which has also been urbanised. Another part of the city lies on the eastern mainland. Much of the city lies very close to sea level.

For several centuries, Saint-Louis – or Ndar in the local Wolof language – was the capital of French West Africa, a hub of the slave trade and a centre for the export of gold, ivory, animal hides and gum arabic (sap from the acacia tree used in printing, cosmetics and glue). These transactions – the complicated and often troubling movement of goods and people associated with a period of European world expansion – helped shape the city. At the same time, a class of local, female entrepreneurs – often of mixed African and European descent – played a key role in the cultural, economic and political life of Saint-Louis. Both local and global processes have thus created and shaped a city to which its inhabitants have come to feel a deep attachment.

(a)

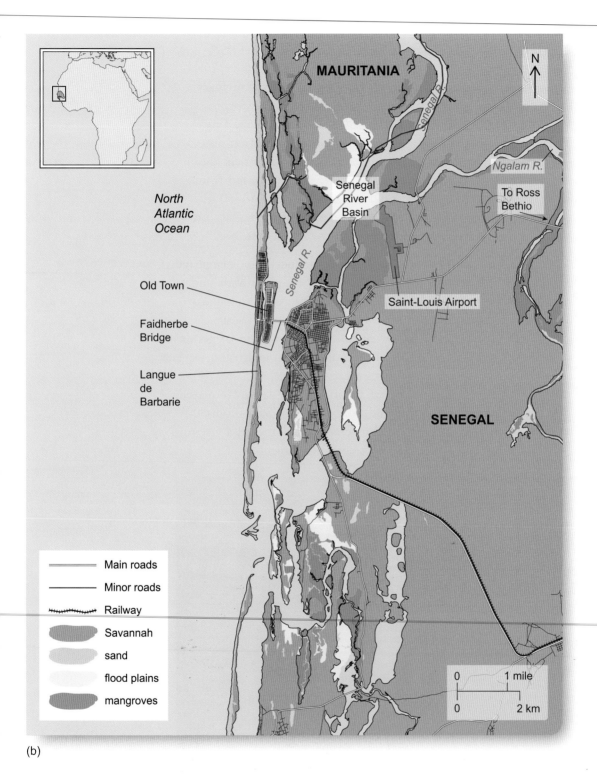

MAURITANIA

N

North
Atlantic
Ocean

Senegal R.

Ngalam R.

Senegal
River
Basin

To Ross
Bethio

Old Town

Saint-Louis Airport

Faidherbe
Bridge

Langue
de
Barbarie

SENEGAL

Main roads

Minor roads

Railway

Savannah

sand

flood plains

mangroves

0            1 mile

0            2 km

(b)

Figure 2.10   (a) Saint-Louis, Senegal; (b) A map of Saint-Louis in the north-west of Senegal

To understand the environmental risks that the people of Saint-Louis face requires an awareness of, first, those natural processes that generate natural hazards and, second, the natural and social factors that lead people to inhabit areas at risk of potentially dangerous physical changes. Like the settlements along the East Anglian coast, Saint-Louis is under threat from water. In 2008, the UN organisation Habitat named Saint-Louis as the African city most at risk of rising sea levels due to climate change. The city is also at risk from coastal erosion and river flooding. Since the late 1990s, there have been several episodes of severe flooding, inundating large sections of the city and triggering health problems, especially among children.

The Senegal River is one of the larger African rivers, flowing through four countries: Guinea, Mali, Mauritania and Senegal. The slope of the land is so gentle on the lower river basin above Saint-Louis that, at times of low tide, seawater would naturally flow about 200 km upriver. The Senegal River has a length of 1641 km. The river flow is seasonal, depending on rainfall in the river basin, with an intense rainy season from June to October (Table 2.1).

Table 2.1    Mean monthly rainfall in Saint-Louis

| Month | Jan | Feb | Mar | Apr | May | Jun | July | Aug | Sept | Oct | Nov | Dec |
|---|---|---|---|---|---|---|---|---|---|---|---|---|
| Rainfall (mm) | 1.5 | 1.9 | 0.2 | 0.0 | 0.1 | 6.8 | 40.2 | 94.3 | 92.3 | 23.0 | 0.3 | 0.7 |

Source: Climate-Charts.com (2010)

With high river flow and seasonal rainfall, the Senegal River carries large amounts of sediment that is deposited where the river slows down, particularly where it flows into the Atlantic Ocean. As the ocean cannot remove the sediment quickly, over time a river delta has built up at the mouth of the river. The delta is under the influence of coastal processes: winds, waves and tides, including the offshore southerly-flowing Canaries Current and Trade Winds blowing from the north-east. These give the Senegal River a wave-dominated delta in which wave erosion and a southerly-flowing longshore current have formed a long, low spit, which extends about 16 km to the river's mouth. The low-lying island on which the colonial city of Saint-Louis sits was formed from sediment deposits within the Senegal River.

Attempts have already been made to solve Saint-Louis's flooding problem. In 2003, abnormally strong rains fell and the Senegal River rose to dangerous levels. Hydrologists warned that if nothing was done the river flow would breach the dykes protecting the city. The Senegal government decided to dig an outlet canal to allow the river to join the Atlantic Ocean earlier, 20 km before its existing exit. Within 48 hours the water level of the river began to fall, and after ten days the water level was approximately one metre lower. The canal's inauguration was televised and the government praised. However, in the following weeks and months, the force of the redirected river flow caused the breach to widen dramatically from its original 4 m. By 2006 it had reached a width of 1500 m, although it has since stabilised. To the south, the deposition of sediment has caused the original river mouth to close up because there was insufficient water flow to maintain the opening. This has changed the character of the former river channel because it no longer has fresh water flowing through it and is now a lagoon without flowing water rather than an estuary with a fluctuating mix of fresh and sea water. The relocation of the river mouth has also led to erosion of the bank opposite the new opening. Overall, the breach has achieved its intended purpose of reducing flood risk from river water for Saint-Louis but it has not diminished the risk from rising sea levels.

Given the risks the city faces, why do people choose to live there? The combined coastal and riverside location of Saint-Louis offers many opportunities. As with a number of East Anglian towns, Saint-Louis's geography provides the physical wherewithal for port facilities and thus openings for trading, fishing and, more recently, tourism. The city has recently grown dramatically, with an increase from a population of 115,000 in 1998 to 200,000 by 2002 (Diagne, 2007). Like many nations with large rural populations dependent on agricultural production, there has been significant rural to urban migration over recent decades as people seek employment. But this is not only a matter of economic opportunity. The cyclical patterns of drought in the Sahel region (Figure 2.11) that affect migratory birds also impact on agricultural animals and plants and the people who rely on them for their livelihoods, prompting people to move to the cities. Large numbers of people settled in dried-out riverbeds and other low-lying areas. With the return of the rains, these settlements were vulnerable to rising floodwaters (Diagne, 2007). Some of the least resourced people in the city responded as best they could, building impromptu flood barriers out of materials at hand, including rubbish. One unintended side effect of this improvisation was that waste matter clogged drainage systems, further contributing to flood and health risks.

A change in the pattern of rainfall and dryness is a natural part of the climate variability of the Sahel region that has occurred over geological timescales. Now, however, it is necessary to consider the additional effect of human-induced climate change.

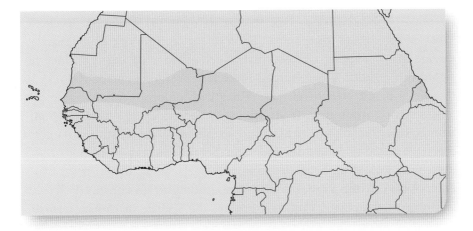

Figure 2.11   The Sahel is the semi-arid geographical zone of transition between the Sahara desert to the north and savannah grasslands to the south. Up to 1000 km wide in places, the Sahel stretches from the Atlantic Ocean to the Red Sea

# 4  Climate change: a tragedy of the commons?

As we saw in the last chapter, human activity is causing an overall warming of the Earth's surface leading to a gradual rise in sea levels. Most climatologists trace human-induced (or 'anthropogenic') climate change to the burning of fossil fuels (such as oil, coal and gas) since the eighteenth century. When burned these hydrocarbons emit carbon dioxide, a major greenhouse gas. Along with other greenhouse gases, atmospheric carbon dioxide absorbs some of the energy from the Sun, namely solar radiation that has been absorbed by the Earth's surface, then re-emitted as long-wave radiation. So the burning of matter previously locked up beneath the Earth's surface has altered the composition of the Earth's atmosphere, leading to an enhanced warming of the planet. (You will explore the science of climate change in more depth in Book 2, chapters 1–4.)

Over time, greenhouse gases can be removed from the atmosphere by natural processes. For example, carbon dioxide can be removed by photosynthesis and stored in what are known as 'carbon sinks', principally forests and oceans. If carbon dioxide and other greenhouse gases are emitted at a faster rate than they can naturally be removed from the atmosphere by sinks, then climate change will intensify. That is the situation we face at this moment in the Earth's history, and it is leading to a cumulative build-up of the atmospheric concentration of greenhouse gases. Carbon dioxide emissions from the past continue to warm the planet, and the emissions we make today will impact on the climate of the future. Because the atmosphere is a single, integrated system, the heat trapped by all atmospheric greenhouse gases combines to transform the global climate in its entirety. Greenhouse gas emissions from any place on the planet thus have consequences for every other place.

One model that is used to explain anthropogenic climate change is the tragedy of the commons. A **common resource** is one that a community of people enjoy, but which no one owns. The atmosphere may be seen as a global common, a shared resource from which all people and countries benefit but over which no one can claim jurisdiction. Climate change is often referred to as a tragedy of the commons. This argument draws on a model developed by ecologist Garrett Hardin (Hardin, 1968). A **model** is a simplified representation

**Common resource**
A resource that a community of people enjoy, but which no one owns.

**Model**
A simplified representation of reality used by social and natural scientists to represent a complex phenomenon.

of reality used by social and natural scientists to represent a complex phenomenon. Models allow scientists to 'filter out' detail and complexity in order to identify the basic workings of a phenomenon. They can be applied to different situations. The value of a model depends on its explanatory power; that is, how well it explains past events and can predict future events.

## Activity 2.4   Models

Can you recall any other examples of models from this chapter?

### Comment

Multi-species flyways are models. They are simplified representations of reality that do not capture the full complexity of bird migrations. Avian scientists are aware of the limitations of modelling flyways, but nonetheless find them useful for explaining and predicting complex patterns of bird movements in a range of different real-world contexts.

Hardin argued that the tragedy of the commons is that each individual user of a common has a short-term interest in over-exploiting the resource. He used as an example not the global commons of the atmosphere but local grazing land held in common by a community and which local herdsmen use for grazing their cattle. Hardin used the concept of carrying capacity when developing his model. **Carrying capacity** may be defined as the population of a given species that can be supported indefinitely in a given area without permanently damaging the ecosystem on which it depends. In Hardin's model the carrying capacity is the maximum amount of grazing the common can support before the land starts to degrade. Providing each herdsman takes only his 'fair share' the common will be conserved. The tragedy arises because each herdsman has an individual incentive to allow his cattle to overgraze. If all herdsmen think the same, then the carrying capacity of the land will be exceeded and the common will suffer the tragedy of long-term degradation. Individual herdsmen will reap individual short-term benefits but the community at large will suffer a long-term loss. In short, what is economically rational for individual actors damages the environment for all. The tragedy thus lies in the mismatch between the individualism of economic rationality, and the common or shared interests of the wider community (Figure 2.12).

**Carrying capacity**
The population of a species that can be supported without permanently damaging the ecosystem on which it depends.

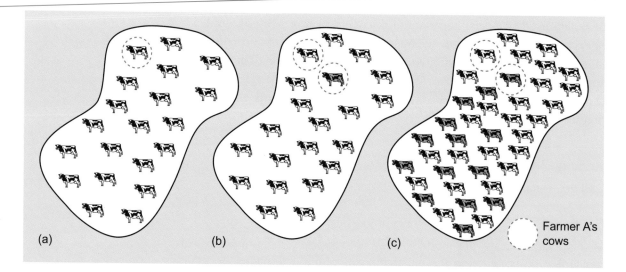

Figure 2.12   The tragedy of the commons. (a) Each farmer begins with one cow; (b) However, if we take the perspective of an individual farmer – say farmer A – it is rational to immediately add an extra cow; (c) If only farmer A adds an extra cow there is no problem, but in practice it is rational for every farmer to add a cow, thus doubling the herd and leading to overgrazing and economic ruin for all

Hardin's model has been used to explain climate change in the following terms. The global atmosphere has a carrying capacity. Atmospheric carrying capacity is defined in different terms from the carrying capacity of land. The carrying capacity of the atmosphere may be defined as the quantity of anthropogenic greenhouse gas emissions that can be naturally removed from the atmosphere by sinks so that no climate change takes place. There is some disagreement on what this carrying capacity is, but it is clear that humans are exceeding it, leading to climate change. There is no incentive for individual countries to stop using the atmosphere as a 'dump' for greenhouse gas emissions. On the contrary, actors release greenhouse gases into the atmosphere because they benefit economically from doing so. It is thus economically rational for individual actors to continue to emit these gases beyond the carrying capacity of the atmosphere, even though it is ultimately environmentally destructive. The tragedy of the commons model thus works at several scales to help explain human-induced climate change: at the level of individual human actors, companies, governments and other actors.

According to the tragedy of the commons model, a significant environmental risk is that individual actors are concerned only with their self-interest rather than the common good. However, Hardin's model was criticised. Hardin assumed that within a local common, access to the resource was open to all, whereas use rights are in fact often agreed and enforced communally. Hardin, therefore, was not writing about a genuine local common, where all members of the community respect the rules for use of the common and cooperate to monitor the access to the resource from outsiders. He was writing about an open access regime, where anyone can enter and use the resource, and there are no rules for shared use. Hardin has since acknowledged these points and agreed that effective and well-managed commons can ensure the conservation of the resource. He later revised his model when writing of 'the tragedy of the unmanaged commons' (Hardin, 1994).

---

## Activity 2.5   How can we prevent the tragedy of the atmospheric commons?

Based on the various arguments you have read on the tragedy of the commons, how would you propose humans address the problem of climate change?

### Comment

The main point that emerges from the debate on Hardin's model is that commons suffer degradation when there are no agreed and enforced rules on use. One possible solution is for all states to negotiate legally binding and enforceable greenhouse gas emission limits. The total of the emissions from all states should be agreed at a level that does not result in anthropogenic climate change. Indeed, states do meet regularly to try to forge agreement on climate change, although so far progress has been very limited for two reasons. First, managing the atmospheric commons is beset with scientific uncertainties. Agreeing scientifically the precise carrying capacity of the atmosphere is problematic. There would also be problems with accurately measuring all greenhouse gas emissions around the world. Second, there is disagreement on the basis for agreeing emissions cuts. For example, which states should be responsible for the deepest cuts, and what should be the target date for emissions cuts? Also, how should emission cuts be monitored, and what actions should be taken against states that exceed their quotas? These have so far proved politically intractable questions.

---

**Precautionary principle**
The principle that scientific uncertainty should not be used as a reason for postponing measures to protect the environment.

One international legal principle that is often invoked in debates on scientific uncertainty is the **precautionary principle**. This principle holds that where there is a risk of environmental damage, scientific uncertainty shall not be used as a reason for postponing measures to prevent such damage. The principle has been incorporated into various international environment conventions and declarations including the 1992 Rio Declaration on Environment and Development (UNEP, 1992). The precautionary principle offers a basis for action when science is unable to give a clear answer.

Human responses to environmental change may be conceived in terms of reducing risk. As we have seen, risk implies the probability of change, and a prediction of the hazard that is likely to occur. A problem with international efforts to reduce climate change is that the sharing of the risks is by no means equal. Some places are more at risk than others. As we have seen, Saint-Louis is at risk from sea level rise, a predicament it shares with other low-lying places around the world, such as small islands, atolls and delta regions.

The Sahel region of Senegal faces different environmental risks. In a 2007 study on the predicted effects of climate change on agricultural productivity, economist William Cline identified both winners and losers. According to his projections, by the 2080s the agricultural capacity of much of Africa looks set to decline by up to 30 per cent, with the Sahel belt particularly badly affected (Cline, 2007; Erickson et al., 2011). However, for the wealthier temperate regions of the planet, a warmer planet looks likely to deliver an anticipated 8 per cent rise in agricultural productivity.

A further political complication to dealing with climate change is that some countries have contributed to the problem more than others. The contributions of different countries to overall greenhouse emissions have been deeply uneven. For example, the average annual amount of carbon dioxide emitted per person in Senegal each year is around 0.46 tonnes, while in the UK it is 8.97, and in the USA, 19.74 (United Nations Statistics Division, 2007). Many of the people who bear the risks of climate change have enjoyed few of the economic benefits of fossil fuel use.

Some 60 per cent of the population of Senegal relies on agriculture for their livelihood. Only a very small proportion of them rely on fossil fuels for agriculture, unlike the heavy fossil-fuel subsidy of agriculture in the industrialised world. These are the people whose livelihoods are likely to become increasingly precarious as a result of greenhouse gas emissions made by wealthier people in distant places. In this way, the far-reaching and pervasive globalisation that characterises global climate change is a source of deep division. As social scientists Timmons Roberts and Bradley Parks put it: 'Climate change is fundamentally an issue of inequality' (Roberts and Parks, 2007, p. 23). Or to put it another way, we might say that this is the tragedy of a world that is not shared in common.

# 5   Summary

Two concepts have featured prominently in the analysis in this chapter. They are *risk* and *uncertainty.* Together they constitute the second of the three groups of key analytical concepts of this module.

Environmental risks include those to nature as well as those to people. We have seen that the risks of the degradation of common land and of climate change can each be explained as tragedies caused when people behave in line with a perceived notion of self-interest rather than the common interest. Although we often talk of the need to reduce risks we must also take risks: we have to assess the likely consequences of different courses of action, and select those options that we judge will have the most beneficial outcomes. Climate change involves risks, but so too do policies to tackle climate change. There is the risk, for example, that environmental policies will not work as intended or quickly enough to solve the problem. We have seen that globalisation can transmit environmental risks around the globe, but can also promote international political cooperation to address these risks.

Uncertainty is a problem for scientists and social scientists alike, especially when the calculation of risks is concerned. The greater the degree of uncertainty, the more difficult it is to calculate risks. An absence or lack of knowledge on a risk does not mean that the risk does not exist, although it does make it more difficult for people to plan properly for risk management. With climate change, for example, there is considerable uncertainty about the rate of climatic change, its likely impacts and how the risks will be differentiated across different spaces and timescales. The scientific and social variables that cause climate change are so many and so complex that, while there is consensus over general trends, the predictions of the timing, impact and consequences of climate change are uncertain. Prediction inevitably becomes more uncertain the further ahead one peers into the future. In this respect, uncertainty is an unavoidable condition, and the best that policy makers can do is to seek to minimise uncertainty as much as they can.

Another question is what level of risk is acceptable? Ultimately this is a political question. In the case of the nuclear industry, a common notion of acceptability is that the risk of a member of the public developing a fatal cancer should be no higher than one person per million per year

(Blowers and Smith, 2003). But inevitably such notions of acceptability are disputed and contested.

# References

Beintema, A. and van Vessem, J. (eds) (1999) *Strategies for Conserving Migratory Waterbirds – Proceedings of Workshop 2 of the 2nd International Conference on Wetlands and Development held in Dakar, Senegal, 8–14 November 1998*, Wetlands International Publication No. 55, Wageningen, The Netherlands.

Bingham, N. and Hinchliffe, S. (2008) 'Mapping the multiplicities of biosecurity', in Lakoff, A. and Collier S. J. (eds) *Biosecurity Interventions*, New York, Columbia University Press.

BirdLife International (2007) *BirdLife Statement on Avian Influenza* [online], http://www.birdlife.org/action/science/species/avian_flu/index.html (Accessed 27 June 2012).

Blowers, A. and Smith, S. (2003) 'Introducing environmental issues: the environment of an estuary', in Hinchliffe, S., Blowers, A. and Freeland, J. (eds) *Understanding Environmental Issues*, Chichester, John Wiley/Milton Keynes, The Open University.

Boere, G. C. and Stroud, D. A. (2006) 'The flyway concept: what it is and what it isn't', in Boere, G. C., Galbraith, C. A and Stroud, D. A. (eds) *Waterbirds Around the World*, The Stationery Office, Edinburgh; also available online at http://jncc.defra.gov.uk/PDF/pub07_waterbirds_part1_flywayconcept.pdf (Accessed 28 June 2012).

Climate-Charts.com (2010) 'Saint-Louis, Senegal: climate, global warming, and daylight charts and data' [online], http://www.climate-charts.com/Locations/s/SG61600.php (Accessed 28 June 2012).

Cline, W. (2007) *Global Warming and Agriculture: Impact Estimates by Country*, Washington, DC, Peterson Institute for International Economics.

Diagne, K. (2007) 'Governance and natural disasters: addressing flooding in Saint Louis, Senegal', *Environment and Urbanization*, vol. 19, no. 2, pp. 552–62.

Diouf, A. M (2002) 'Djoudj National Park and its periphery: an experiment in wetland co-management', in Gawler, M. (ed.) *Strategies for Wise Use of Wetlands: Best Practices in Participatory Management: Proceedings of a Workshop held at the 2nd International Conference on Wetlands and Development*, Gland and Wageningen, IUCN – The World Conservation Union/Wetlands International/World Wide Fund for Nature.

Eccleston, P. (2008) 'Britain "losing its migratory birds"', *The Telegraph*, 21 April, p. 6; also available online at http://www.telegraph.co.uk/news/1896598/Britain-losing-its-migratory-birds.html (Accessed 28 June 2012).

Ericksen, P., Thornton, P., Notenbaert, L., Jones, P. and Herrero, M. (2011) *Mapping Hotspots of Climate Change and Food Insecurity in the Global Tropics*, CCAFS Report no. 5, CGIAR Research Program on Climate Change, Agriculture and Food Security (CCAFS), Copenhagen.

Food and Agriculture Organization of the United Nations (FAO) (2008) *Resolution 4.15 Responding to the Spread of Highly Pathogenic Avian Influenza H5N1, Flyway Conservation at Work – Review of the Past, Vision for the Future*, Agreement on the Conservation of African-Eurasian Migratory Waterbirds, 4th Session of the Meeting of the Parties, 15–19 September 2008, Antananarivo, Madagascar [online], http://www.fao.org/docs/eims/upload//259348/ak075e00.pdf (Accessed 28 June 2012).

Giddens, A. (1990) *The Consequences of Modernity*, Palo Alto, CA, Stanford University Press.

Gray, R. (2010) 'Migratory birds decline in UK due to low African rain', *The Telegraph*, 5 September [online], http://www.telegraph.co.uk/earth/wildlife/7981699/Migratory-birds-decline-in-UK-due-to-low-African-rain.html (Accessed 28 June 2012).

Hardin, G. (1968) 'The tragedy of the commons', *Science*, vol. 162, no. 3859, pp. 1243–8.

Hardin, G. (1994) 'The tragedy of the unmanaged commons', *Trends in Ecology & Evolution*, vol. 9, no. 5, pp. 199.

Latour, B. (1987) *Science in Action*, Milton Keynes, Open University Press.

Normile, D. (2005) 'Are wild birds to blame?', *Science*, vol. 310, no. 5747, pp. 426–8.

Olsen, B., Munster, V., Wallensten, A., Waldenström, J., Osterhaus, A. and Fouchier, R. (2006) 'Global patterns of influenza A virus in wild birds', *Science*, vol. 312, no. 5772, pp. 384–8.

Reuters (2011) 'Mutation of H5N1 virus could revive bird flu threat, says UN', *The Guardian*, 29 August [online], http://www.guardian.co.uk/world/2011/aug/29/mutation-h5n1-virus-bird-flue?INTCMP=ILCNETTXT3487 (Accessed 28 June 2012).

Roberts, J. T. and Parks, B. (2007) *A Climate of Injustice*, Cambridge, MA, MIT Press.

Taubenberger, J. K and Morens, D. M. (2006) '1918 influenza: the mother of all pandemics', *Emerging Infectious Diseases*, vol. 12, no. 1 [online], http://wwwnc.cdc.gov/eid/article/12/1/05-0979_article.htm (Accessed 28 June 2012).

United Nations Environment Programme (UNEP) (1992) *Rio Declaration on Environment and Development* [online], http://www.unep.org/Documents.Multilingual/Default.asp?documentid=78&articleid=1163 (Accessed 28 June 2012).

United Nations Environment Programme (UNEP) (2006) *Restoration of Wetlands Key to Reducing Future Threats of Avian Flu* [online], http://www.unep.org/Documents.Multilingual/Default.asp?DocumentID=475&ArticleID=5255&l=en (Accessed 28 June 2012).

United Nations Statistics Division (2007) *CO$_2$ Emissions per Capita in 2007* [online], http://unstats.un.org/unsd/environment/air_co2_emissions.htm (Accessed 28 June 2012).

# Chapter 3   Shaping and sustaining places

Nigel Clark

# Contents

# 1 Introduction

So far we have encountered a number of ways in which humans respond to changing environmental conditions, including migration and staying in the same place and developing new ways of coping. We have seen that different people in different places bear different levels and types of environmental risk, and that those who bear the risks may not be responsible for causing the problem. Some environmental risks are generated by long-term geological and climatic processes. Others may be generated mainly by humans. Access to the world's resources, we have seen, is highly inequitable. The issue of climate change, for example, raises questions about the deeply unequal use of energy resources.

These are complex issues, and they point to the importance of global connections through which different places have historically been related to each other. In this chapter we explore some of these connections and, in doing so, examine how humans have shaped their environments in sometimes very surprising ways.

# 2   Global connections in an uneven world

In the late eighteenth and nineteenth centuries a small number of countries in Europe and North America, most of which had access to coal, reached a 'take-off' point of economic growth and were able to reap the advantages of early industrialisation (Mitchell, 2009) (Figure 3.1). This take-off was not only a matter of using fossil fuel energy resources (coal, oil and gas). It was facilitated by the wealth and resources extracted from other regions of the Earth during the colonial period. Britain and France had access to coal and had many colonies across the world. French overseas territories included the West African colonies centred on Saint-Louis. Industrialisation and colonisation gave Britain and France **power** on the global stage (Box 3.1).

Figure 3.1   Early industrialisation in England

## Box 3.1  Power

US political scientist Joseph Nye has noted that power is difficult to define and measure, but that simply because the concept is elusive it does not mean it is meaningless (Nye, 2011). Power, Nye observes, comes in many different forms.

The political scientist Robert Dahl examined power as relations between people. He argued that A has power over B if A can get B to do something B would not otherwise do (Dahl, 1957). A may have power over B, but X may have power over A, and B may have power over Y. Power, therefore, is relational: it concerns relationships between two or more actors, each of which may have different interests, values and objectives.

The power of an individual is very different from that of, say, a militarily strong country, a major business corporation or an international investment bank (Figure 3.2). The power of a government is derived from the resources it commands and which it can deploy to influence other governments in pursuit of its objectives. These resources include military resources, natural resources and economic resources such as a skilled workforce and a well-developed infrastructure (Williams, 2005). The USA is a powerful country, while countries such as India and Brazil may be seen as rising powers in terms of their economic activity and productivity. The power of a business is derived from the assets it controls, its sales, its profits and its market value on the stock exchange.

Power may also be seen as the ability to set agendas and to establish ideas that other actors then accept as legitimate, fair and authoritative. One way of expressing this is to use the term discourse. A **discourse** is a body of language that people use when communicating with each other. A discourse may include a powerful idea or set of ideas, shared values and certain understandings that people come to accept. The ability to shape discourses can be seen as a form of power. Actors that can establish discourses can influence what is discussed and how other actors see the world and behave in relation to it. For example, international climate politics is often discussed in terms of the need for justice at a global scale. The framing of climate change as a justice issue is something that the less wealthy countries have successfully put on the international agenda. Many of these countries, it should be noted, are relatively powerless in terms of the resources they command relative to their industrialised counterparts.

**Discourse**
A discourse is a body of language that people use when communicating with each other.

(a)

(b)                                        (c)

Figure 3.2   Power comes in different guises and can be wielded in many different ways. (a) A United States Navy aircraft carrier; (b) United Nations secretary-general Ban Ki-moon; (c) The offices of the international investment bank Goldman Sachs in Jersey City, New Jersey

In the social sciences, then, power is the capability of an actor to achieve influence in support of its interests and objectives. It may be conceived in two ways: possessing and deploying resources, and shaping and promoting discourses.

Those nations which industrialised early had an economic advantage in the early era of globalisation which they have, in most cases, retained, although they are now being challenged by emerging powers in Asia, South America and eastern Europe. Other countries, such as Senegal, have an economy that remains based on the export of primary products. In Senegal's case, this can be traced back to the colonial period of the nineteenth century.

The export of primary products – as well as enslaved human beings – funded a rich cultural life for a small minority of the population in colonial centres like Saint-Louis but did not generate the economic foundations for the rapid economic growth characteristic of western Europe or North America. Senegal's economy remains dependent on unprocessed agricultural products. But the market prices for these products have frequently been unfavourable compared with the markets for industrial commodities or services. Senegal's dependence on these markets gives the large international companies that buy agricultural produce a form of power over the Senegalese economy. And Senegal's future capacity for growing agricultural produce is unclear: along with many of its African neighbours, Senegal finds itself more vulnerable to human-induced climate change than those wealthier nations that enjoyed the benefits of an early industrialisation.

Claims about the fundamental unfairness of the distribution of benefits and costs from fossil fuel burning are made in many different forums. That some countries suffer the negative consequences of the actions of others can be seen as contravening basic principles such as national sovereignty and human rights. How is it possible that this state of affairs is tolerated and perpetuated? This is a question that directs us to consider how power operates globally.

Anthropogenic climate change is driven by some deep-rooted power relations. Because the economies and lifestyles of industrialised nations are dependent on high fossil fuel consumption, many stakeholders and groups have an interest in maintaining their current levels of energy consumption. Over time, power has gathered around the sourcing and distribution of fossil fuels. Oil has become a key power resource, one that is itself secured and controlled by the exercise of political power. Those who have power can perpetuate their position by exercising this power to acquire additional resources. Those whose power is derived from fossil fuel consumption are thus able to impede change. They may do this by seeking to discredit scientific evidence on climate change, lobbying media organisations and exercising influence on political decision makers.

In international climate negotiations, the more heavily industrialised nations have been able to steer international agreements from commitments to shift the energy basis of their economies away from fossil fuels (Timmons Roberts and Parks, 2007). Meanwhile, the relative powerlessness of many developing countries can limit their contributions to the negotiations. Lack of access to legal, technical and scientific expertise can impede effective participation on the part of many countries afflicted by climate change (Newell, 2005). Despite this, many of the least industrialised countries have been able to amplify their impact in climate negotiations through lobbying in unison. In the 1960s, Senegal was a founding member of the Group of 77 Developing Countries (G77), a UN caucus group that now numbers 132 member states. The G77 consistently pushes for wealthier nations to take the lead in cutting their carbon emissions and providing finance and technology to assist poorer states in dealing with climate change (Vihma et al., 2011).

## Activity 3.1   Exercising power

Power may be exercised by building up and linking together various resources and ideas over space and time. Can you recall any examples of how power has been exercised from the first two chapters of this book?

## Comment

Activists from Happisburgh have empowered themselves by forging relations of solidarity with campaigners in other coastal communities (Chapter 1). African countries gained influence in wildlife protection by joining others in the African-Eurasian Water Bird Agreement (Chapter 2). Both cases illustrate that power can be synergistic. In other words, actors can achieve more by cooperating over shared objectives and pooling power than by acting alone.

**Values**
Values refer to what is of worth, merit or importance.

How power is exercised depends in large part on the **values** of an actor. Values are what is of worth, merit or importance in society. Values may be held by individuals. Different features of an environment can be valued differently by different individuals and groups: one community's fossil fuel resources may represent an environmental risk to another; one group's 'pristine' wildlife is another's lost livelihood. Shared values may contribute to discourse formation. They may characterise the moral beliefs of a community and what is considered just or right (and thus what is unjust or wrong). Two actors may have very similar power capabilities in terms of the material resources they command, but if they have different value-based beliefs they will behave very differently. They thus have different agency.

**Agency** may be defined as the difference that a social actor makes to the world. This implies intentionality. An actor will behave in a way that is consciously intended to bring about a certain outcome. For example, an NGO (say the World Wide Fund for Nature) may, in line with its conservationist values, seek to conserve an area of forest. It will deploy its power resources to that end. It may have to compete against other powerful actors with different values, perhaps timber-logging companies that wish to clear the forest.

**Agency**
The difference that a social actor makes to the world.

But human agency does not only encompass the changes we bring about intentionally. Our agency may bring about environmental consequences we do not desire and may not be able to control. As you have seen, human agency has been partially responsible for avian flu outbreaks. These outbreaks were, eventually, contained. But humans may make other environmental changes that may be irreversible and can assume a momentum of their own. A species made extinct cannot be recovered. The life forms living within an ecosystem that humans have disturbed may evolve and adapt in ways we do not expect. Changed weather patterns in one part of the world may have unintended consequences elsewhere. The exercise of human agency can generate risks over time and space that we may not be able to foresee, let alone control. What human agency can achieve, therefore, does not depend only on intentionality. It depends on how the natural world reacts to human interferences and disturbances.

# 3   Agriculture and environmental change

In the Blackwater Estuary and Senegal River delta, considerable efforts have been made to protect habitats that support many different species. Both these landscapes have a long-standing human presence, and much of what is now seen as worthy of conservation bears the imprint of human activity from earlier times. In the past, the natural and social sciences often sought to separate human life from the natural world. Today, however, most approaches tend to view humans and their physical environments as interrelated. 'In this view', as environmental scientist Thomas Tomich and his interdisciplinary team put it, 'there is no more "wilderness" or "nature" without people, and humans and their societies are shaped by and are shapers of landscapes and ecological processes'. Agriculture, they go on to say, is 'a prime example of these interactions' (Tomich et al., 2011, p. 196). We now explore some of the ways that human and natural processes have combined to shape agricultural ecosystems.

## 3.1   The disturbing truth about heathlands

Breckland is a landscape of heathland, forest and farmland of some 940 square kilometres which stretches across the Norfolk and Suffolk border in East Anglia. Heathlands are habitats of uncultivated land with infertile soils dominated by low shrubs. In a recent study that brought together researchers from the University of East Anglia (UEA), Natural England, the Forestry Commission and county councils, researchers gathered data on the biodiversity in Breckland (UEA, 2010).

**Biodiversity**
A measure of the number and variety of species in an area.

**Biodiversity** is a contraction of the term biological diversity. In its most basic sense, biodiversity is a measure of the number and variety of species in an area.

The Breckland Biodiversity Audit set out to collect data on every plant and animal species 'from the smallest gnat and tiniest beetle, through to birds, plants and mammals' (UEA, 2010). The researchers, including some 200 naturalists, knew the area was rich in wildlife but were surprised by the diversity they discovered. Over 12,500 species were identified, including 2000 of national conservation concern. They found that 28 per cent of the UK's rare species inhabit an area covering only 0.4 per cent of the country. The research project then analysed the ecological needs of the 2000 rare species, identifying possible habitat management strategies to protect and restore biodiversity in Breckland. 'Although much of what conservation has achieved is excellent', research leader Paul Dolman observed, 'new approaches are urgently needed or we risk many of these species drifting towards extinction' (quoted in UEA, 2010).

Over time species may become extinct due to disease, predators, geological upheavals, lack of food and climate change. What concerned those investigating Breckland, however, is the possibility of human-driven extinctions that exceed the pre-human (background) rate of extinction. Most species currently threatened with extinction are at risk because of habitat loss or modification. In the case of tropical forests – ecosystems with very high biodiversity – human activities, such as forest burning and conversion to agricultural land, are the major cause of extinction. Similarly, human activity was largely responsible for the estimated 70–90 per cent reduction in European heathlands over the course of the twentieth century. Britain is the location of 44 per cent of the remaining heathlands. Breckland constitutes 1.3 per cent of Europe's overall area of heathland habitat (Dolman and Sutherland, 1992).

But while today humans threaten heathlands, in the past humans played a major role in establishing heathland habitats. In Breckland, major anthropogenic influence can be traced back some 5000 years, when neolithic farmers cleared woodlands for cultivation and grazing. For thousands of years, *shifting cultivation* was practised: land was farmed, then left fallow for a time before farming was resumed. Indeed, breck is a medieval term for a fallow cropped field (Dolman and Sutherland, 1992). Rabbits, believed to have been introduced to the British Isles by the Romans, have played a large part in shaping heathland habitat. Farmed from the thirteenth century through to the 1930s, rabbits also established extensive feral populations. As well as shifting cultivation, human activities such as path making, flint mining, turf cutting and even military exercises have all left an imprint on the landscape of Breckland.

It is the *cessation* of these human activities that threatens the Breckland habitat and the biodiversity it supports. Bird species such as the stone curlew, woodlark and wheatear, and plants such as field wormwood and Breckland thyme prefer disturbed land and conditions supported by a low availability of nutrients (Figure 3.3). In important ways, human agency – burning, clearing, tilling, even mining – can mimic the agency of natural processes, such as glaciation, fires or storms. Both natural and human agency can thus generate mosaic effects with regard to the age and composition of vegetation. Such periodically 'disturbed' ecosystems – with their patchwork of different stages of regrowth or recovery – can support more biodiversity than ecosystems that are more uniform (White and Pickett, 1985). As Dolman states: 'We shouldn't be scared of getting machinery in and making a right mess … physical disturbance isn't always bad, in fact it is essential for many plants and insects' (quoted in UEA, 2010).

(a)   (b)   (c)   (d)   (e)

Figure 3.3   Breckland bird species (a) stone curlew, (b) woodlark and (c) wheatear; and plant species (d) Breckland thyme and (e) field wormwood

So which environmental values should count? A strict notion of environmental protection suggests that environments should be left free from human interference. But had that view prevailed in the past, Breckland, today an area of beauty for many, would not have evolved as it has. Of course, there are different types and degrees of ecological disturbance with varying degrees of risk. An occasional perturbation of an ecosystem is very different from total destruction. Even so, it is clear that what may be seen as risky or uncertain for human actors today may, from a broader historical perspective, play a vital part in the shaping of valued habitats and ecosystems.

## 3.2   Adapting to environmental change in the Sahel

Central to the idea of climate justice as a discourse is the view that it is morally unacceptable for Senegal and other low carbon-emitting nations to bear the consequences of climate change triggered by carbon emissions from early and rapidly industrialising countries in the global North. In international negotiations, Senegal and other countries from the global South have argued that high carbon dioxide-emitting countries should implement mitigation strategies. A **mitigation strategy** is one that seeks to deal with an environmental problem by addressing its causes. In the case of climate change, a mitigation policy would reduce greenhouse gas emissions or enhance greenhouse gas sinks.

**Mitigation strategy**
A strategy that deals with an environmental problem by addressing its causes.

---

### Activity 3.2   Carbon sinks

From your reading in Chapter 2 can you think of some examples of carbon sinks?

### Comment

The forests and oceans are two examples of carbon sinks (see Chapter 2, Section 4).

---

If mitigation is one way of dealing with an environmental problem, another is adaptation. An **adaptation strategy** deals with an environmental problem by addressing its effects. As you have seen, adaptation responses to coastal erosion in East Anglia include hold the line and managed retreat. Many wealthier countries now acknowledge a duty to help less wealthy nations adapt to climate change through financial and technological aid.

**Adaptation strategy**
A strategy that deals with an environmental problem by addressing its effects.

But as Mariam Sow, a programme officer with the NGO Enda Pronat – Protection Naturelle des Ressources reminds us, rural people in the Sahel region have had to adapt to climate change many times in the past. Sow, who works with farmers in Senegal, notes how agricultural producers adapted to severe droughts in the 1970s: 'They started to develop alternatives in agricultural production, in order to survive under the new conditions and sustain at least minimal production' (quoted in Gueye, 2008). Ironically, she notes, international experts now recommend climate change adaptation strategies to the very people who over time have developed their own solutions (Figure 3.4).

Figure 3.4   The people of the Sahel region have learnt to adapt to climate change over many generations (the picture shows Borko village, Mali)

It is now believed that the farming communities of the Sahel have over generations learnt to live with climatic extremes in excess of those predicted by the Intergovernmental Panel on Climate Change (Nyong et al., 2007). Studies of weather knowledge in the region show that local people have developed intricate ways of observing, predicting and responding to climate change (reminding us that it is not only scientists who engage in the practice of constructing 'models'). For pastoral farmers, adaptation includes holding supplies of emergency fodder for animals in case of drought, keeping herds of mixed species whose composition can be changed depending on climatic conditions, and seasonal nomadic movements. In the case of arable farmers, cropping patterns, choice of plants and the timing of planting are all based on what scientist Anthony Nyong and colleagues describe as 'complex cultural models' of weather (Nyong et al., 2007, pp. 793–4).

Living with climatic variability over the long term is not just a matter of humans adapting to a non-human environment. It is also about the transformation of landscapes and living organisms, as we have seen with Breckland. There is nowhere on Earth with a longer history of human habitation than the grasslands of Africa. African farmers have been transforming habitats through fire, and domesticating the native grasses of the savannahs for thousands of years. With a range of crops that include African rice, millets, sorghum, teff and fonio, Africa's native cereals have a diversity unmatched on other continents. Traditional cereals are well adapted to African soils and have natural drought-resistant traits that have been enhanced through selection by generations of cultivators. For example, fonio – a hardy, extremely fast-growing member of the *Digitaria* genus that is rich in the amino acids essential to human health and is used in soups, porridge, couscous, bread and beer – thrives in the sandy soils and semi-arid conditions of West Africa (National Research Council, 1996).

But for decades agricultural development policies in Africa have neglected native grains and food crops in favour of introduced global staples, such as wheat and Asian rice. In Senegal and other African countries, there has been a shift to 'monocultures' (growing a single crop over a large area) to produce food for global markets, in particular for consumers in the global North. Senegalese agricultural policy includes exporting food to richer countries to increase earnings of hard currency. This export-driven agricultural model reliant on a restricted range of crops has tended to displace older traditions of cultivating in close proximity a wide range of plants with varying tolerances of climatic conditions and pests. Those countries that Senegal exports to can be said to have an **ecological footprint** in Senegal. An ecological footprint is the environmental impacts of consumption patterns on ecosystems. The term is often used to describe the impacts of consumption in one geographical space on another space.

**Ecological footprint**
The environmental impacts of consumption patterns on ecosystems.

Examining agricultural production provides some insights into how power operates in the global food industry. International businesses are increasingly buying up land around the world to grow food, not for local people but for distant consumers. The world's food supply, argues Raj Patel (Patel, 2007), is in effect managed by a small number of agricultural business corporations that control the production, distribution and retailing of food in the interests of consumers in the richer developed countries. On this view, global food companies and major food retailers exert an often hidden, but nonetheless pervasive, form of power over ecological spaces in food-producing countries such as Senegal.

# 4   Sustaining ecosystems

The traditional farmers of the Sahel region, as we have seen, have adapted over long time spans in ways that enhance their capacity to cope with climatic variability (Kerssen, 2010). The emphasis has been on crop selection and farming practices that are not suited simply to current conditions but also to a range of possible future changes. The time horizon here is very different from that of contemporary agricultural production systems within global markets. Here there are strong pressures on realising market value to earn profit in the short term, with the global market operating so that food gravitates to those consumers where the potential for profit is greatest.

Furthermore, environmental costs are not factored into the costs of production nor, therefore, into the prices of products. So, for example, a food consumer does not pay for the environmental costs of intensive agriculture. In economic theory it is generally assumed that environmental conditions remain constant. However, if the assumption changes to one that recognises that environmental conditions are likely to change in the future, then rather different time horizons will need to prevail. It suggests that investment preferences will need to move from a focus on short-term profit maximisation towards agricultural production that is sustainable over the long term (Box 3.2).

**Resilience**
The capacity of a system to recover from a disturbance.

One of the key measures of the sustainability of a system is resilience. **Resilience** is the capacity of a system to recover from a disturbance. Initially the concept of resilience was developed in relation to ecosystems, but it is increasingly applied to systems with both social and physical components, such as agricultural ecosystems (agro-ecosystems) (Tomich et al., 2011). In general, the more diverse a system, the more resilient it is. Hence, traditional agriculture, with its emphasis on cultivating different species, is more resilient than modern monocultures. If rapid climate change occurs, some species will not survive because they will not be able to adapt to the changed conditions. The more species cultivated under traditional agricultural methods, the more likely it is that some species at least will survive a changed climate, enabling an adapted form of agriculture to continue. Monocultural agriculture, which is dependent on the cultivation of a few species over large areas, is less resilient, because if these species do not survive climate change, agricultural production will collapse.

## Box 3.2  Sustainability

The term sustainability is central to the concept of sustainable development (Chapter 1, Section 3). It is derived from the Latin *sustinere* (*tenere*: to hold; *sus*: up). Sustainability tends to be conceived in terms of human actors assuming long-term responsibility for their environments and resources. Environmental, social and economic processes should be considered as intersecting domains (Figure 3.5). The carrying capacity (Chapter 2, Section 4) of the Earth is often invoked as a limit to human activity. Most discussions of sustainability stress the qualitative aspects rather than the quantitative, such as income. This is captured in the influential definition: 'sustainability is improving the quality of human life while living within the carrying capacity of supporting eco-systems' (IUCN/UNEP/WWF, 1991).

Like many other important concepts in environmental thought, sustainability is a contested concept, interpreted in different ways by different groups with different values. Whether sustainability can be made compatible with economic development – sustainable development – has been a source of much debate since the 1980s.

Figure 3.5  Sustainability is often conceptualised as a three-legged stool, resting on environmental, social and economic supports. On this view, all three are necessary or the stool will collapse

Whereas earlier theories of resilience put the stress on systems returning to a stable, pre-existing state, more recent interpretations place greater emphasis on the capacity to reorganise, change and adapt. As we have seen, in the Breckland heathlands and in the agro-ecosystems of the

Sahel, episodes of stress or disturbance are recurrent events, and natural and human-induced perturbations have helped shape the distribution and the diversity of living organisms.

But when pressures, such as large-scale human disturbance or climate change, push a system beyond its limits of resilience, the result is usually a dramatic transformation. Beyond a certain threshold, which can be hard to identify in advance, the system ceases to readjust itself and tips into an entirely different state (Scheffer et al., 2001). In the case of ecosystem change, this new state is likely to have a very different composition of species, possibly resulting in the loss of whole populations of organisms. Where the systemic shift is of a very large scale or when the range of the species is narrow, it can result in extinction.

**Tipping point**
A threshold that, if crossed, causes a system to change from one state to another.

As we have seen, human consumption of fossil fuels and other activities are leading to an accumulation of greenhouse gases in the Earth's atmosphere. Many climate scientists believe there is a threshold at which the global climatic system as a whole will be pushed beyond its capacity for resilience and tip into a new climate regime. This is called the **tipping point**. In the conditions that would follow, scientists speculate, a great many physical and social systems would cease to be sustainable (Foley et al., 2010; Lenton et al., 2008).

In the next section we start to consider whether humans can prevent the global climate from reaching its tipping point.

# 5   Biochar – sustainability for the era of global climate change?

As well as forests and the oceans, a major carbon sink is soil (FAO, 2012). If a way can be found to remove carbon from the atmosphere and store it in soils it could contribute to solving climate change.

This is the idea behind one of the most ambitious proposals for addressing climate change: biochar. **Biochar** is a form of charcoal produced by the pyrolysis of trees, agricultural waste and other plant matter. **Pyrolysis** is the treatment of material at high temperatures in an oxygen-deprived environment (Lehmann at al., 2006). Plant matter is rich in carbon that has been removed from the atmosphere by photosynthesis (the synthesis of organic compounds from carbon dioxide and water using solar energy). The absence of oxygen during pyrolysis means that minimal carbon dioxide is produced, the main product being carbon-rich biochar which can be added to soils. Pyrolysis also produces liquid or gaseous products which can be used as fuels (Figure 3.6).

If carried out on a sufficiently large scale, the production of biochar could, in principle, reduce the atmospheric concentration of carbon dioxide. In the natural scheme of things most of the carbon in plant life returns to the atmosphere as carbon dioxide through one of two processes: respiration (the opposite of photosynthesis when plants release carbon dioxide), and combustion (the burning of plant life with oxygen present). So, if more plant life is turned into biochar and mixed with soil, more carbon is removed from the atmosphere. Evidence suggests that when added to soil, biochar can remain there for thousands of years. (The processes of photosynthesis, respiration and combustion are covered in Book 2, Chapters 1–4; see also Box 5.1 in Chapter 5 of this book.)

**Biochar**
A form of charcoal produced by the pyrolysis of trees, agricultural waste and other plant matter.

**Pyrolysis**
Treatment of material at high temperatures in an oxygen-deprived environment.

(a)

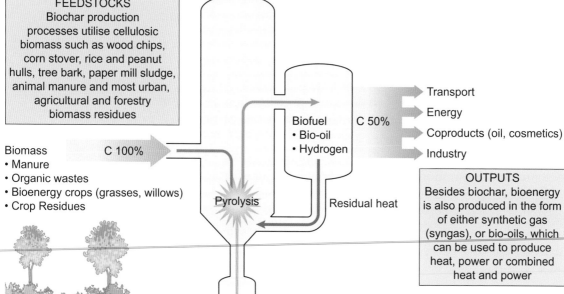

FEEDSTOCKS
Biochar production processes utilise cellulosic biomass such as wood chips, corn stover, rice and peanut hulls, tree bark, paper mill sludge, animal manure and most urban, agricultural and forestry biomass residues

Biomass
• Manure
• Organic wastes
• Bioenergy crops (grasses, willows)
• Crop Residues

C 100%

Pyrolysis

Biofuel
• Bio-oil
• Hydrogen

C 50%

Transport

Energy

Coproducts (oil, cosmetics)

Industry

Residual heat

OUTPUTS
Besides biochar, bioenergy is also produced in the form of either synthetic gas (syngas), or bio-oils, which can be used to produce heat, power or combined heat and power

C 50%

Biochar returned to soil

C = Carbon

(b)

Figure 3.6   (a) Pyrolysis machine for producing biochar; (b) How biochar is produced using a pyrolysis machine

While biochar is highly inert (i.e. it does not readily react with other chemicals), it improves soil fertility by retaining within its structure water and nutrients that would otherwise be leached out of the soil. Soil scientists have found that a traditional Native American practice in parts of the Amazon involved the smouldering and burying of biomass (plant material used as a fuel or energy source) to produce carbon-enriched soils (Figure 3.7). Called terra preta by Portuguese European colonisers, these highly fertile soils have also been referred to as 'Amazonian dark earths' (FAO, 2012; Leach et al., 2012). The original practices – believed to have been operative 500–2500 years ago – no longer survive. Evidence suggests that the soils were formed through a combination of incidental disposal of organic waste and deliberate application of biochar (Lehmann et al., 2006).

Figure 3.7   Terra preta soils support considerable biodiversity

Studies have shown that a hectare of metre-deep anthropogenic dark earth can contain 250 tonnes of carbon, compared with 100 tonnes in unimproved soils from the same location: the extra carbon being found not only in the concentration of biochar but also in soil bacteria (Winsley, 2007). Soils enriched in this way greatly increase crop yields and enhance biodiversity both in the soil and in the vegetation it supports (Figure 3.8). Enhanced biodiversity, in turn, can contribute to more resilient ecosystems (FAO, 2012).

Figure 3.8    Crop yields on carbon-enriched soils

It is not difficult to see that a technology which promises to remove carbon dioxide from the atmosphere and improve agricultural yields – particularly in the weathered soils of the tropical regions – could have immense appeal. Biochar production could also reduce deforestation by replacing wood with waste biomass as a fuel source. Climate activist Bill McKibben exclaims: 'We can, literally, start sucking some of the carbon that our predecessors have poured into the atmosphere down through our weeds and stalks and stick it back in the ground. We can run the movie backward. We can unmine some of the coal, undrill some of the oil' (quoted in Leach et al., 2012, p. 286).

Biochar can be produced in temperate regions as well as in tropical regions. A report commissioned by the East of England Development Agency (EEDA) found that the systematic application of biochar to the soils of East Anglia could significantly increase crop yields by improving soil nutrient retention and enhancing soil moisture-holding capacity. It would reduce carbon emissions from the agricultural sector by reducing the need for synthetic fertilisers. It was estimated that 'a massive and dedicated programme of biochar production and sequestration in the UK could potentially sequester around 8 to 9 % of UK carbon [dioxide] emissions' (Collison et al., 2009, p. 12).

Too good to be true? Let's take a closer look at the biochar debate and examine the politics of a claimed technological solution to climate change.

## 5.1   Putting biochar production into practice

Biochar technology can operate at different spatial scales, from large industrial-sized installations to village, farm or household units. A pilot project is operating in Ross Bethio in Senegal. The trial scheme was set-up by Brazilian NGO Pro-Natura in 2008 using a prize-winning pyrolysis machine which aims to turn 'waste' biomass such as rice husks and invasive weeds into biochar. The project provides training and financial incentives to local farmers to adopt the technique, and contributes to scientific research on the effects of biochar on crop yields (International Biochar Initiative, 2008). The Ross Bethio scheme is a trial and both the farmers and researchers involved with the project are in the process of learning from the experience.

Operating at a different scale, Pro-Natura is campaigning to have biochar production formally recognised by the United Nations Framework Convention on Climate Change (UNFCCC) as a means of reducing greenhouse gas emissions. Projects which demonstrate success in sequestering biochar in soil – even on a small scale – could be eligible for 'credits'. In other words, Senegalese farmers producing biochar would receive funding from actors outside Senegal (International Biochar Initiative, 2008). These actors might be companies or governments who prefer to purchase credits for carbon sequestered by biochar rather than reduce their own carbon emissions. The suggestion that the UNFCCC recognises biochar is just a proposal at present and the exact details of any such scheme, if agreed, would require some lengthy negotiations.

Some commentators, however, are unconvinced by the proposal. The NGO Biofuelwatch suggests that biochar development in poorer countries is being driven by the need to solve the climate problem created primarily by industrial nations. Actors with high carbon dioxide emissions, it is suggested, should reduce their own emissions rather than look to farmers in other countries to offset the carbon from their emissions. On this view the sequestration of carbon by Senegalese farmers perpetuates global power inequalities, in effect exploiting people and land in less wealthy parts of the world. It represents another example of an ecological footprint, with the land of Senegalese farmers being used not in the interests of the local population but of powerful governments and businesses elsewhere.

There is also uncertainty about the claimed benefits of biochar to agricultural productivity. In the west central African nation of Cameroon, researchers looked at a high-profile biochar project run with local maize farmers by Belgian NGO Biochar Fund. The increased crop yields claimed by project organisers proved difficult to substantiate, and farmers seem to have been left confused and disappointed when the trial was abandoned and their initially high expectations were left unfulfilled (Ndameu and Biofuelwatch, 2011).

Biofuelwatch warns of the risk of a 'one-size-fits-all' biochar approach that pays little attention to local conditions and people's needs. The organisation argues that biochar is an example of exploitation of communities, another example being the purchase of land around the world to grow crops for use in **biofuels** to substitute for fossil fuels. Biofuels are fuels derived from plant matter, such as palm oil and ethanol from sugar cane (Figure 3.9). They are considered to be carbon *neutral* as the carbon dioxide emitted when they are burned is balanced by the carbon dioxide taken up from the atmosphere when the plants are grown. Proponents argue that biofuels are an example of sustainable development; motor vehicles can be fuelled without contributing to climate change. But Biofuelwatch cautions that technologies such as biofuels and biochar are poorly understood and

**Biofuels**
Fuels derived from plant matter that are intended to be carbon neutral.

will likely encourage expansion of industrial monocultures, result in more 'land grabs' and human rights abuses, further contribute to the loss of biodiversity, and undermine an essential transition to better (agro-ecological) practices in agriculture and forestry.

(Biofuelwatch, 2011, p. 9)

(a)

(b)

Figure 3.9   (a) A field growing sugar cane in Brazil; (b) An ethanol fuel pump at a petrol station in Brazil

Biofuels and biochar are examples of technology. **Technology** may be defined as the technical means that humans use to interact with their environment and with each other. Technology is a means for ordering

**Technology**
The technical means that humans use to interact with their environment and with each other.

103

and transforming raw materials, objects, ideas, or even people and other living things, for a particular purpose. In different ways, both the pro-biochar NGOs Pro-Natura and Biochar Fund and the critical voice of Biofuelwatch suggest that developing and applying a new technology such as biochar is a risky and uncertain process that needs to be done cautiously, if at all.

---

## Activity 3.3   Technology and unforeseen consequences

We noted earlier in this chapter that human interventions in the environment can have unintended consequences. Can you think of any examples of technology having unforeseen consequences?

### Comment

Three examples from your work so far are the technologies for utilising fossil fuels as an energy source which are leading to climate change, poultry-raising techniques that precipitated a viral outbreak, and the unexpected impact of engineering the diversion channel in the Senegal River. On a more positive note, technologies of land transformation in Breckland have unintentionally supported biodiversity. Technology may be seen as a *double-edged sword*. It may cause some environmental problems, yet offer solutions to others.

---

Technology is frequently used with the intention to control an event or a process. One reason why technology may have unforeseen consequences is that it is invariably operated within a larger environmental and social context that cannot always be confidently controlled, or even known. For example, while the conversion of coal or oil into mechanical and electrical power is quite predictable, there is a much greater degree of uncertainty about the effects on the environment of burning these fossil fuels. Uncertainty is likely to be increased when a technology is transferred from the context in which it was developed to a different context. In this respect, Pro-Natura and Biofuelwatch are aware that the technology which produced the terra preta soils of Amazonia can only be transferred sustainably to Africa if careful attention is paid to the local environment and ways of life.

Technology can be a source of political and economic power. Those who have technology and other resources can exercise authority and influence over those who do not. Pro-Natura's offer of training and financial incentives to Senegalese farmers to produce biochar is a form of power, in that Pro-Natura is able to persuade the farmers to do something that it wants. Technologies also embody the values of those who have designed or developed them. These values may be very different from the values of those who end up operating the technology. What Biofuelwatch fears is that biochar technology is being introduced into African countries in accordance with the values of those who wish to profit from the predicament of climate change, but who may have little commitment to the communities who will work with the technology. If biochar production is deployed in order to generate carbon credits for reducing greenhouse gas emissions, the NGO argues, it could have negative consequences for local livelihoods and ecosystems that are anything but 'sustainable'.

# 6   Summary

We have seen that human interventions in ecological systems can shape both the landscapes and life forms with which we share our dynamic planet, even down to the soil beneath our feet. And as we have explored how we shape and sustain the places where we live, we have worked with three concepts: *values*, *power* and *agency*. Together they combine to yield the third, and final, group of key analytical concepts that we will work with in the weeks ahead.

Different actors may value the environment in different ways. Moreover, an individual may be capable of holding different values. People have mixed motives and may behave altruistically in some respects; selfishly in others. A person's deep-seated, emotional attachment to a landscape may also coincide with an appreciation of the income such natural 'resources' may provide.

Power, we have seen, is unevenly distributed. Power comes in different guises. Some people, groups and societies have more power at their disposal than others. They may control and deploy resources to persuade other actors to change their behaviour. Resources may also be deployed to coerce, or even threaten, other actors in order to change their behaviour. Power, therefore, operates using consensual and coercive means ('the carrot and the stick').

Power is also the ability to set agendas and shape discourses. An actor that can promote a discourse – a way of seeing the world – that other actors accept is better able to achieve its objectives. Discourses can enable powerful actors to claim a legitimacy that other less powerful actors accept. Understanding how power operates can help us to explain why some actions and policies are more likely to succeed than others. But possession of power does not necessarily imply that it is exercised. An actor may have power, yet desist from using it. But when power is deployed effectively an actor exercises agency, in line with its values.

The exercise of power influences the distribution of environmental and economic resources. Inequalities may arise when powerful actors are able to act to defend their own environments and to exercise control over the environments of more distant and less powerful communities. Climate change is one of the examples that have been used to illustrate the exercise of power and how those who bear the risks of a problem need not necessarily be those who caused it.

We are living through an era where human agency can make itself felt in almost every part of the world, yet humans do not act alone. The relationship between human agency and natural process has been a recurring theme in our exploration of the environment. While ecosystems are resilient and can adapt to some of our disturbances, we now know that our agency can lead to irreversible and long-lasting environmental changes.

So, our concepts for this module are:

| Time and space | Risk and uncertainty | Values, power and agency |
| --- | --- | --- |

Working with these concepts will enable us to move between different environmental issues. Each concept has a broad degree of applicability. Working with and applying the concepts will enable us to interrogate and examine any environmental issue: from the past, present and future. By using these concepts fluently and flexibly, we will be able to move from environmental issues we are familiar with into new fields of environmental contention. In a world in which environmental problems seem to be multiplying, often taking us by surprise, having a common toolkit of concepts offers us a useful way to engage with environmental issues.

# References

Biofuelwatch (2011) *Biochar: A Critical Review of Science and Policy* [online], http://www.biofuelwatch.org.uk/wp-content/uploads/Biochar-Report3.pdf (Accessed 2 July 2012).

Collison, M., Collison, L., Sakrabani, R., Tofield, B. and Wallage, Z. (2009) *Biochar and Carbon Sequestration: A Regional Perspective – A Report Prepared for East of England Development Agency (EEDA)*, Norwich, University of East Anglia [online], http://www.uea.ac.uk/polopoly_fs/1.118134!LCIC%20EEDA%20BIOCHAR%20REVIEW%2020-04-09.pdf (Accessed 11 October 2012).

Dahl, R. A. (1957) 'The concept of power', *Behavioural Science*, vol. 2, no. 3, pp. 201–15.

Dolman, P. M. and Sutherland, W. J. (1992) 'The ecological changes of Breckland grass heaths and the consequences of management', *Journal of Applied Ecology*, vol. 29, no. 2, pp. 402–13.

Foley, J., Daily, G. C., Howarth, R., Vaccari, D. A., Morris, A. C., Lambin, E. F., Doney, S. C., Gleick, P. H. and Fahey, D. W. (2010) 'Boundaries for a healthy planet, *Scientific American*, vol. 302, no. 4, pp. 54–7 [online]. Available at Academic Search Complete, EBSCOhost (Accessed 2 July 2012).

Food and Agriculture Organization of the United Nations (FAO) (2012) *Terra Preta –Amazonian Dark Earths (Brazil)* [online], http://www.fao.org/nr/giahs/other-systems/other/america/terra-preta/detailed-information2/en/ (Accessed 2 July 2012).

Gueye, M. (2008) 'Global warming: waiting for culprits to act', *D+C Development and Cooperation* [online], http://www.dandc.eu/articles/082771/index.en.shtml (Accessed 2 July 2012).

International Biochar Initiative (2008) *Pro-Natura: Green Charcoal for Sustainable Development* [online], http://www.biochar-international.org/Pronatura (Accessed 2 July 2012).

IUCN/UNEP/WWF (1991) *Caring for the Earth: A Strategy for Sustainable Living*, Gland, Switzerland, IUCN/UNEP/WWF.

Kerssen, T. (2010) 'Saving Africa's seeds: farmers fighting for diversity', *Food First* [online], http://www.foodfirst.org/en/node/3224 (Accessed 2 July 2012).

Leach, M., Fairhead, J. and Fraser, J. (2012) 'Green grabs and biochar: revaluing African soils and farming in the new carbon economy', *Journal of Peasant Studies*, vol. 39, no. 2, pp. 285–307.

Lehmann, J., Gaunt, J. and Rondon, M. (2006) 'Bio-char sequestration in terrestrial ecosystems – a review', *Mitigation and Adaptation Strategies for Global Change*, vol. 11, pp. 403–27.

Lenton, T. M., Held, H., Kriegler, E., Hall, J. W., Lucht, W., Rahmstorf, S. and Schellnhuber, H. J. (2008) 'Tipping elements in the Earth's climate system',

*Proceedings of the National Academy of Sciences of the United States of America*, vol. 105, no. 6, pp. 1786–93.

Mitchell, T. (2009) 'Carbon democracy', *Economy and Society*, vol. 38, no. 3, pp. 399–432.

National Research Council (1996) 'Fonio (Acha)', in *Lost Crops of Africa: Volume 1: Grains*, Washington, DC, National Academies Press [online], http://books.nap.edu/openbook.php?record_id=2305&page=59 (Accessed 2 July 2012).

Ndameu, B. and Biofuelwatch (2011) *Biochar Fund Trials In Cameroon: Hype And Unfulfilled Promises*, November [online], http://www.biofuelwatch.org.uk/wp-content/uploads/Biochar-Cameroon-report1.pdf (Accessed 2 July 2012).

Newell, P. (2005) 'Race, class and the global politics of environmental inequality', *Global Environmental Politics*, vol. 5, no. 3, pp. 70–94.

Nye, J. S. (2011) *The Future of Power*, New York, Public Affairs.

Nyong, A., Adesina, F. and Osman Elasha, B. (2007) 'The value of indigenous knowledge in climate change mitigation and adaptation strategies in the African Sahel', *Mitigation and Adaptation Strategies for Global Change*, vol. 12, no. 5, pp. 787–97.

Patel, R. (2007) *Stuffed and Starved: Markets, Power and the Hidden Battle for the World Food System*, London, Portobello Books.

Scheffer, M., Carpenter, S., Foley J. A., Folkes, C. and Walker, B. (2001) 'Catastrophic shifts in ecosystems', *Nature*, vol. 413, no. 6856, pp. 591–6.

Timmons Roberts, J. and Parks, B. C. (2007) *A Climate of Injustice: Global Inequality, North–South Politics, and Climate Policy*, Cambridge, MA, MIT Press.

Tomich, T. P., Brodt, S., Ferris, H., Galt, R., Horwath, W. R., Kebreab, E., Leveau, J. H., Liptzin, D., Lubell, M., Merel, P., Michelmore, R., Rosenstock, T., Scow, K., Six, J., Williams, N. and Yang, L. (2011) 'Agroecology: a review from a global-change perspective', *Annual Review of Environment and Resources*, vol. 36, pp. 193–222.

University of East Anglia (UEA) (2010) 'Pioneering study reveals nationally important biodiversity hotspot', Press Releases, 30 November [online], http://www.uea.ac.uk/mac/comm/media/press/2010/nov/breckland (Accessed 2 July 2012).

Vihma, A., Mulugetta, Y. and Karlsson-Vinkhuyzen, S. (2011) 'Negotiating solidarity? The G77 through the prism of climate change negotiations', *Global Change, Peace & Security*, vol. 23, no. 3, pp. 315–34.

White, P. S. and Pickett, S. T. A. (1985) 'Natural disturbance and patch dynamics: an introduction', in Pickett, S. T. A. and White, P. S. (eds) *The Ecology of Natural Disturbance and Patch Dynamics*, Orlando, FL, Academic Press.

Williams, M. C. (2005) *The Realist Tradition and the Limits of International Relations*, Cambridge, Cambridge University Press.

Winsley, P. (2007) 'Biochar and bioenergy production for climate change mitigation', *New Zealand Science Review*, vol. 64, no. 1, pp. 5–10; also available online at http://www.biochar-international.org/images/NZSR64_1_Winsley.pdf (Accessed 25 July 2012).

# Chapter 4   Securing food, sharing land

Nigel Clark and Parvati Raghuram

# Contents

# 1 Introduction

We human beings (*Homo sapiens sapiens*) are a terrestrial species. While we have developed technologies that enable us to travel on and underneath the oceans, through the atmosphere and in outer space, we are in essence land-dwellers. We live on the land, we travel across its surface, we cultivate it and we build our homes and workplaces there.

In this chapter we look at some of the conflicts that arise over land ownership. We explore the question of whom land belongs to, and how it may be legitimately acquired. We examine some of the shifting patterns of land occupancy which operate across spatial boundaries. In particular, we investigate the phenomenon of land acquisition (sometimes referred to more pejoratively as 'land grabbing') by which powerful actors may take control of land at the expense of others who formerly owned or used this land. In examining conflicts over land ownership and acquisition we make use of the analytical concepts that you have started to work with over the previous three chapters:

- time and space
- risk and uncertainty
- values, power and agency.

# 2   Cash cows? Buying farms overseas

'Chinese swoop on 16 dairy farms in New Zealand' announced a headline in the UK's *The Independent* newspaper in January 2012.

The article described how a Chinese company – Shanghai Pengxin – successfully outbid a local consortium to purchase an 8000-hectare block on New Zealand's North Island (*The Independent*, 2012). The sale of the land, capable of supporting 5000 cattle, was legal under New Zealand law and was approved by the New Zealand government. The transaction took place after China and New Zealand signed a free-trade agreement in 2008, the first China had entered into with a developed country. China is now New Zealand's second largest export market, after Australia, and the largest buyer of New Zealand dairy products, reflecting a growing demand for animal proteins, in the form of yogurt, cheese, butter and milk, among China's expanding middle class (Perry, 2012).

Shanghai Pengxin is one of many Chinese firms moving into agriculture. In 2005, the corporation bought a majority interest in a large soybean and corn farm in Bolivia for $20 million (Withers and Sedgman, 2012). However, acquiring land in New Zealand proved more difficult. The defeated 'local' consortium, led by businessman Michael Fay, and which included Maori investors, appealed against the sale in the New Zealand high court. There was also popular opposition to the deal, thus putting local environmentalists, left-wing activists and Maori land rights campaigners on the same side as Fay, a merchant banker (now domiciled in Switzerland) who had acquired a fortune by capitalising on New Zealand's free-market economic policies. The high court overturned the sale on the grounds that Shanghai Pengxin, a real estate company, could not demonstrate adequate knowledge about the dairy industry, and thereby failed to meet a legal prerequisite for the overseas purchase of agricultural land in New Zealand (BBC News, 2012).

Two months later the foreign purchase of dairy farms was back in the news. This time the investor was Fonterra, a New Zealand cooperative that is one of the world's largest dairy exporters, while the farmland was in China. Fonterra spent over $NZ 100 million purchasing two farms in China's Hebei province, adding to an earlier acquisition of dairy farmland in 2007. After the sale, Fonterra announced its intention to develop the capacity of China to supply the local market with up to a billion litres of milk every year by 2020. This would require the purchase of around 30 more farms in China stocked with herds of some 100,000 cows (McBeth, 2012). Like Chinese investors, New Zealand agribusiness interests are also expanding into South America. Fonterra owns a 99.4 per cent share of Soprole, Chile's largest dairy processor, and a New Zealand syndicate has purchased a 19,000-hectare block, Chile's largest farm.

These purchases point to the shifting demands for agricultural produce in global markets. Investing in farmland around the world is one way of responding to these demands. However, land acquisition is a complex process involving a range of different actors in different countries. In this chapter we use the analytical concepts of the module to gain a sense of the broader coordinates of land acquisition and to understand its political, social and environmental dynamics.

# 3   Spatial patterns of land acquisition

While land acquisition is taking place in many parts of the world, by far the greatest volume of transactions is taking place in Africa. The two main companies referred to above – Shanghai Pengxin and Fonterra – have interests in sub-Saharan Africa. Shanghai Pengxin acquired a majority interest in a copper deposit in the Democratic Republic of Congo in 2009, while Fonterra has been in partnership with South Africa's largest dairy company since 2005. Figure 4.1 gives a breakdown of acquisitions by region for the years 2000–2010. The total figure of 203.4 million hectares is an area over eight times the size of the UK (Anseeuw et al., 2012).

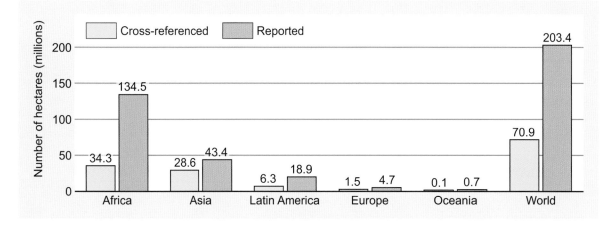

Figure 4.1   Land acquisitions by region, 2000–2010 (Source: based on Anseeuw, et al., 2012, p. 23, Figure 4)

---

## Activity 4.1   Land acquisitions around the world

Two data sets are shown in Figure 4.1: 'reported' and 'cross-referenced'. The 'reported' category includes reports of land acquisition published in any format, whereas 'cross-referenced' data refers to those reported transactions whose reliability has been checked through referencing from multiple sources (Anseeuw et al., 2012). Why do you think the volume of reported deals is so much higher than that for cross-referenced deals?

## Comment

The disparity points to the difficulty of accurately establishing land acquisition data. It takes time to check and authenticate the reliability of reported land acquisitions. Some governments are reluctant to release data on land acquisitions, and some researchers claim that even the cross-referenced data cannot always be taken as verified. This reflects a lack of transparency around land acquisition, with no formal registry of transactions taking place around the world (Zagema, 2011).

Both the cross-referenced and the reported data suggest that more transactions are occurring in the African continent than elsewhere. However, it is important to recognise that levels of 'reported' data reflect in part the attention of the global media. Media interest has been strongly focused on Africa, especially on deals involving countries which are considered newsworthy because they receive food aid or because there is conflict. Transactions in wealthier regions, such as North America and Australasia, which often involve deals between private owners, may not be recorded (Anseeuw et al., 2012).

So, while the aim here is to describe the spatial patterns of land acquisition, uncertainty quickly arises. This is because the data on which our descriptions are based is itself tentative and incomplete, reflecting the conditions and circumstances under which it has been compiled. The data in Figure 4.1 was drawn from different countries with different political systems and systems of land registration. It is open to question. Some awareness of the uncertainty about data is always needed when seeking to describe social or physical processes objectively.

Today many land acquisitions take the form of legal purchases using the law of the country in question. The state (i.e. the parliament and government of a country, its ministries and civil servants) establishes the laws of land ownership and how property rights may be acquired and sold. A **property right** may be defined as a law, created by a government, on how individuals may come into ownership of property and how they may transfer it to others. The theory of the modern state and its role in establishing property rights owes much to the British political philosophers Thomas Hobbes (1588–1679) and John Locke (1632–1704) (Figure 4.2). According to Hobbes, people agree to hand their rights over to a sovereign government which then governs on behalf of the people. Hobbes argued that there were no property rights prior to the creation of the state (Tuck, 2002). The state alone decides the rules of private property ownership and an individual may claim ownership over property only to the extent that the state permits it (Hobbes, 1985 [1651]).

**Property right**
A law, created by a government, on how individuals may come into ownership of property and how they may transfer it to others.

(a)                                    (b)                                    (c)

Figure 4.2   (a) Thomas Hobbes (1588–1679); (b) John Locke (1632–1704); (c) Georg Hegel (1770–1831)

Locke argued that people have rights to life, liberty and property. To Locke, while the state should govern property rights, such rights existed prior to the authority of the state. His views have been interpreted by George Sabine and Thomas Thorson (1973, p. 486) thus: 'a man [*sic*] has a natural right to that with which he has "mixed" the labor of his body, as for example by enclosing and tilling land.' In this respect, Locke parts company with Hobbes, who argued that no property rights existed prior to the establishment of the state (Locke, 1975 [1690]).

The German political philosopher Georg Hegel (1770–1831) also contributed to the debate on the state and property (Figure 4.2). According to Hegel the state is a higher moral and rational political authority and its power is absolute. The state can impart freedoms and  rights to its citizens through the legal and ethical institutions that the community supports. Hegel argued that one of the goals of the individual was to own property, and that the state should establish the conditions under which property can be acquired through laws (Hegel, 2008 [1820]; Singer, 2001).

The debates on property and the role of the state, and in particular whether property rights can be said to exist before the creation of the modern state, help us to understand contemporary debates on land ownership and acquisition. We saw in Chapter 2 that the French had established colonies in West Africa by the seventeenth century and claimed some of the land of the region for the French state and colonial authorities. From the 1880s to the beginning of the First World War in 1914, Western imperial powers competed among themselves to annex vast tracts of Africa, usually by use or threat of force. In what became known as the 'scramble for Africa', almost the entire continent was divided up between the European empires (Packenham, 1992). During this period, land acquisition was strongly resisted by local communities across most of the African continent (as it was in other parts of the world: the Americas, Asia and Australasia). Its logic and morality was also frequently questioned in Europe itself. The traditional and communal forms of land ownership that existed in pre-colonial Africa had been developed by the peoples of the continent over generations and were considered legitimate and authoritative by the local communities.

During the colonial period the European powers introduced European forms of government and the European notion of property rights to their colonies and divided their areas into territories that in the post-Second World War era became self-governing states. By the time these territories were granted independence they had assumed the form of a modern state, with a centralised government and a trained civil service and police force. The terms under which independence was agreed varied enormously, but as far as land ownership was concerned the political elites of the newly independent countries agreed for the most part to uphold and respect as legal those private property rights granted by the colonial powers. In this way, some of the best farmland remained in European hands post-decolonisation, leading, according to some thinkers, to colonial relations persisting in new forms after independence in a global economy dominated by the United States and the former European colonial powers. This has been termed neo-colonialism (Sebastian, 2007).

Furthermore, any land not under private ownership at independence was considered as belonging to the state of the newly independent countries. This has brought the post-colonial state in many African countries into conflict with local communities who had lived on and farmed land for generations, regarding themselves as the legitimate custodians of the land.

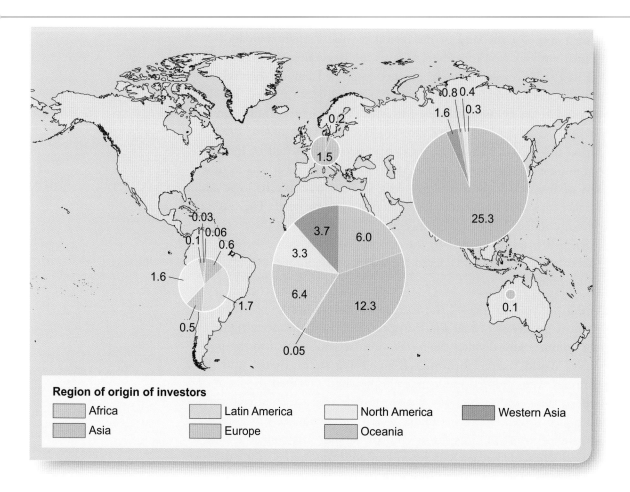

Figure 4.3 Home regions of land acquirers in each region (number of hectares (millions) cross-referenced) (Source: Anseeuw et al., 2012, p. 22, Figure 3)

## Activity 4.2 Who is buying the world's land?

Figure 4.3 shows the home regions of those who are buying land around the world. The data refers only to cross-referenced deals. Using Figure 4.3, determine the main regions that are buying land, and any other significant regional characteristics.

## Comment

Asian businesses are major players in land acquisition, in part owing to China's strong push to acquire land in other regions. But other patterns may be noted. To varying degrees there is a strong presence of actors making land acquisitions within the same region. These intra-regional transactions reflect the rising economic powers in each region: Brazil in South America; South Africa in Africa; and China, India, Indonesia and

South Korea in Asia. Other considerations which facilitate transactions across or within regions include cultural factors, such as the links between Muslim countries, including between the oil-rich Gulf States, such as Saudi Arabia and Qatar, and Pakistan, Sudan and other states in the Sahel (Anseeuw et al., 2012).

The evidence we have examined suggests that land acquisition is significant at a global scale. The data, however, tells us little about who benefits from land acquisition and what it is like to experience this process locally. To consider this, we now examine some of the causes of land acquisition. In doing so we complement the understanding of the spatial patterns of land acquisition we have developed so far with an understanding of time, in particular the rhythms of land acquisition in relation to the dynamics of the global economy.

# 4   Land demand in times of change

In October 2011 there were reports of violent clashes in the small agricultural community of Fanayé in the Senegal River valley. In the resulting struggles, one person was killed and two others seriously injured. The cause of the dispute was the prospect of thousands of hectares of land passing into the control of an Italian investor who intended to use the land to produce crops for biofuel (Figure 4.4). The villagers protested that the deal would result in the loss of local grazing land and their displacement from the area (Radio France Internationale, 2011).

Figure 4.4   In Senegal, thousands of hectares of land have been sold by the government to an Italian company to produce biofuels

Around the world, land acquisitions by overseas interests were low until about 2005, before rising, with a dramatic spike of activity, in 2009 (Figure 4.5). To understand why land conflicts may occur it is important to get a sense of the rate at which land acquisition is occurring, and why.

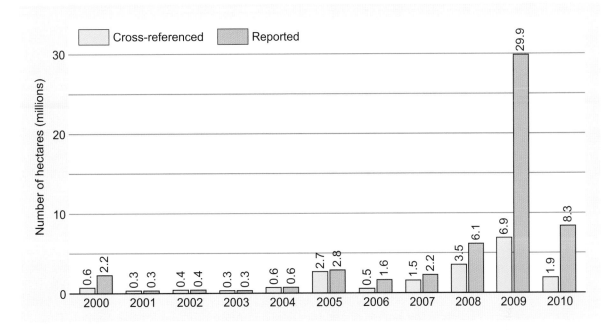

Figure 4.5    The global pace of land acquisitions, 2000–2010 (Source: Anseeuw et al., 2012, p. 20, Figure 2)

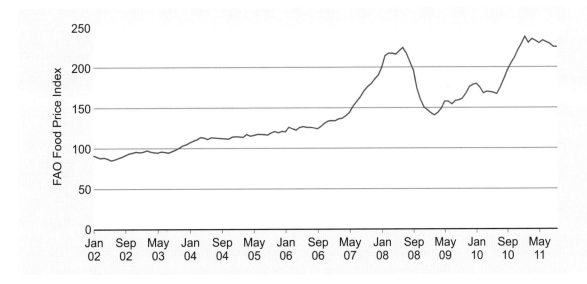

Figure 4.6    The FAO's food price index, January 2002 to May 2011 (Source: Our Finite World, 2011, Figure 6; compiled using data from the UN Food and Agriculture Organization's Food Price Index)

---

## Activity 4.3   Explaining land acquisitions

What might explain the surge in land acquisitions in 2009? To consider this question, look at Figure 4.6, a graph based on an index of world food prices compiled by the UN Food and Agriculture Organization (FAO). The index measures changes in international prices of a 'basket' of food commodities comprising cereal, dairy products, oils and fats, meat and sugar. What do you think the relationship is between food prices and the increase of land acquisitions? You might find it helpful here to consider the distinction between cause and correlation introduced in Chapter 2, Section 2.1, Box 2.2.

### Comment

Around 2007–08, there was a sharp rise in food prices (Figure 4.6). This correlates closely with the rapid rise in land acquisition the following year (Figure 4.5). The increase in food prices led to an increase in supply. Existing agricultural producers, as well as new producers, sought to profit from the higher prices by supplying more produce for the market. This led to increased demand for agricultural land, and thus an increase in land acquisitions. Food prices declined again in 2009, and land acquisitions again followed this trend (as shown in Figure 4.5).

---

The events of 2007–08 came to be viewed as a 'global food price crisis'. Senegal was one of many countries affected. Grain prices in local markets increased by 50 per cent, while the price of rice tripled. Given that the average family allocates some 60 per cent of its income to buying food, the price rise had disastrous consequences. As in many other countries in the global South, rising prices sparked 'food riots' across Senegal (OneWorld, 2012). The inflated prices of staple foods was a factor in the popular uprisings in Tunisia and Egypt in 2010–11 (Walsh, 2011).

But what triggered the rise in global food prices? A number of explanations have been offered, including poor harvests in Australia and the USA (both major grain exporters which have suffered drought), a longer-term decline in overall reserves of food staples which left global supplies vulnerable, and increasing speculation on foodstuffs in global commodity markets. While these may have been contributory factors, there is some consensus that rising oil prices were also significant. As Figure 4.7 shows, there is a close correlation between food and oil

prices over the years 2002–2011. (Note that the Brent oil price index is
an international benchmark of light crude oil prices.)

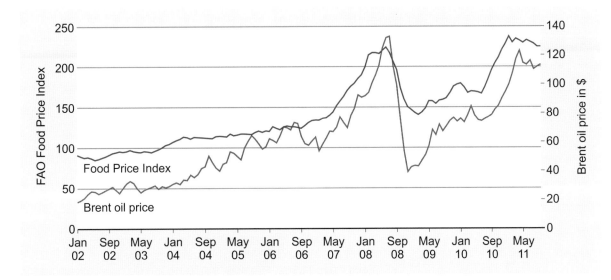
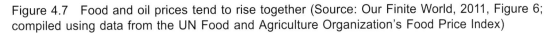

Figure 4.7   Food and oil prices tend to rise together (Source: Our Finite World, 2011, Figure 6;
compiled using data from the UN Food and Agriculture Organization's Food Price Index)

There are good reasons why food prices are related to oil prices. Most
of the food that enters global markets is produced in heavily
industrialised agro-ecosystems that are reliant on fossil fuel-driven
mechanisation and fertilisers synthesised from fossil fuels. Food is
usually transported by fossil fuel-driven transport. Oil price increases
thus directly impact on food production costs. But in recent years, oil
price hikes have also impacted in a less direct way on agricultural
production costs.

Especially in industrialised and rapidly industrialising regions, concerns
over climate change and diminishing oil reserves have prompted a focus
on renewable biomass-based alternatives to fossil fuels. The European
Union, for example, has a target of fuelling 10 per cent of its transport
from renewable sources by 2020. This has led to pressure to use more
agricultural land for biofuel production (Zagema, 2011). A rapid
increase in the overall acreage devoted to biofuel crops has displaced
food production from agricultural land and was a factor in the 2007–08
food price increases and subsequent land acquisitions. Of cross-
referenced land acquisitions between 2000 and 2010, where land use is
known, around 37 per cent has been devoted to biofuel production
(Figure 4.8). Demand for biofuels is driven not only because of concern

about climate change but also because accessible fossil fuel reserves are being depleted. The demand for biofuel is thus related to concerns over energy security.

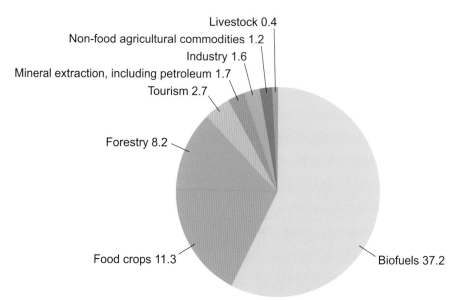

Figure 4.8   Global land acquisitions 2000–2010, by sector (number of hectares (millions) cross-referenced) (Source: Anseeuw et al., 2012, p. 24, Figure 5)

Unsurprisingly, the idea that land previously used to grow food in the global South – especially in regions where malnutrition is still prevalent – is being committed to fuelling the automobiles of wealthy northern populations has provoked controversy. The situation, however, is more complex. Not all advocates of biofuels are in the global North. Brazil, in particular, has made major investments in biofuels (Dauvergne and Neville, 2009). China is expanding its production of biofuels, for both domestic and foreign markets. In 2009, Chinese agribusiness company ZTE secured a million hectares in the Democratic Republic of Congo to set up the world's largest palm tree plantation to produce biofuels (Beiping, 2009). Other governments have been enthusiastic about producing biofuels for export, including the government of Senegal.

We have seen how causal connections between oil prices and food supply help explain food price changes and subsequent changes in land acquisition. However, the 2007–08 food price crisis no longer appears to be an isolated event, and neither does the accompanying surge in securing overseas land. To understand the dynamics of land acquisition and its long-term implication for the communities involved, it is necessary to look beyond the triggers of the food crisis to wider changes in land use at the global scale. To do so we bring the concepts of time and space together with those of risk and uncertainty to see how land acquisitions can be understood in the context of global environmental change.

# 5   Land use in a climate of risk and uncertainty

An important factor that influences demand for food, and thus prices, is the increasing global human population. Although the rate of growth is slowing, world population is expected to grow from 7 billion in 2011 to 9 billion by 2050. What is important, however, is not just the total numbers of people, but what they consume. China's growing middle classes are turning towards a diet high in animal proteins, a trend shared by other rapidly growing economies. Because land is needed for animal feed, each kilo of animal protein produced requires a much greater area of land than the equivalent quantity of vegetable protein. But the overall amount of available agricultural land is decreasing, as is the quality of this land. Urbanisation and various commercial uses are encroaching on farmland, while in many regions overuse or inappropriate agricultural practices degrade soil fertility.

## Activity 4.4   Changing dynamics of land use

Looking back over this and earlier chapters in this book, can you think of further reasons why demands for productive land might be increasing?

## Comment

It is often difficult to put a precise weighting on the various factors that shape the demands for productive land: they are often context dependent and difficult to tease apart. However, there is evidence that changing global climate will impact on agricultural production worldwide. It is predicted that heat, drought, extreme weather events and sea-level rise will negatively affect agricultural productivity in many regions. Coupled with population growth, these threats contribute to a growing sense of food insecurity, with increased demand for new land acquisitions, especially near secure water supplies such as rivers and aquifers. In many parts of the world, demand for water now exceeds supply. Especially in arid regions, climate change is likely to exacerbate water scarcity.

Over the decades of intensifying globalisation, increasing amounts of agricultural products have been traded internationally. Investment has tended to flow towards those commodities whose market value has been relatively high. Increasingly, there has been futures market speculation on the price of commodities, including food and land-based products. A **futures market** is a market where participants agree to buy and sell products, at a price agreed today, on a stipulated date in the future. If a seller can agree a price for a product and the market price subsequently falls, the seller will receive more money than she would have done when the deal matures. In effect, the seller took a risk and bet on the price falling. Similarly, if a buyer agrees a price and the price subsequently rises, the buyer will pay less than the market price when the deal matures. In effect, the buyer has bet on the price rising. The situation becomes more complex when a market player undertakes different futures deals, buying from a seller at one price and selling to a buyer at another price with the intention of making a profit.

**Futures market**
A market where participants agree to buy and sell products, at a price agreed today, on a stipulated date in the future.

In short, powerful actors in global markets for land and other commodities take risks, based on calculations of the probability that prices will go up or down. New forms of financial speculation on food, raw materials and other commodities mean that astute investors can make large profits even when supplies decline (Cooper, 2010; Pryke, 2007). The decisions taken on future markets can have significant consequences for the environment and for communities, shaping the agricultural produce that will be grown in different agricultural spaces around the world.

The surge in land acquisition suggests a new dynamic is emerging. The 2007–08 food crisis came as a shock: a foretaste of global market uncertainties. Global markets are now seen as an increasingly risky way of making decisions on agricultural production and making profits for market players. Securing additional land emerges as the best option. As Olivier De Schutter, UN Special Raporteur on the right to food, explains:

> The global food price crisis of 2007–2008 convinced many governments and private commodity buyers that international markets would be less reliable and more volatile in the future, and that these markets could not be trusted to provide a stable supply of food commodities: in order to achieve food security or stability of supply, buying farmland – outsourcing food production – was seen as more interesting than buying on the international markets.

The acquisition of farmland became popular among certain governments worried about their future ability to feed themselves.

(De Schutter, 2011, p. 251)

It can be argued that the very nature of risk itself is changing. Whereas food, water, energy supplies and other commodities were previously imagined in terms of economic or financial risk, they are now being reimagined in terms of environmental risk. The difference is that where economic or financial risk involves profits and losses in monetary terms, environmental risk entails something more substantial. It involves a more profound insecurity about whether populations have adequate food, water and energy.

Another way of putting this is that the degree of uncertainty under which actors operate in the global economy has heightened. We are now looking at conditions under which significant global change is known to be taking place: one in which future major 'shocks', both environmental and economic, are to be expected. This level of uncertainty requires a new and different kind of management of food production. Land acquisition appears to be key to this new regime of management.

But if powerful governmental and corporate interests are in a position to take control of land across spatial boundaries, where does this leave less powerful actors? What are the consequences of land acquisition for local people and their ways of life? To answer these questions we use the concepts of value, power and agency.

# 6 Valuing agricultural land

So far we have seen that escalating insecurity in global food supplies is transforming how land is used in a global context. This helps explain the patterns of foreign investment in land that we have observed. This investment comes not only from the global North but also from emergent economic powers outside Europe and North America. As well as having large and growing urban populations, nations such as China, India, Indonesia, Qatar and Saudi Arabia are more vulnerable to the effects of hotter – and in some cases drier – weather than temperate nations. For example, in 2008, Saudi Arabia, formerly a major wheat producer, made the decision to conserve water by reducing its domestic cereal production and to compensate for this by increasing its investment in agriculture abroad (De Schutter, 2011).

If gaining access to overseas land is one way of managing environmental insecurity for 'investor' nations, what then are the perceived benefits for the 'host' nations? In the case of a Saudi Arabian company which is currently acquiring land in Senegal, Benin and Mauritania, the Senegalise company spokesman Momar Gueye explains it as follows: 'What we are trying to do here is raise the quality of rice that's being produced locally. We bring new technology, like new seeds to improve production' (quoted in Hinshaw, 2011). Or, in the words of Zhang Peng of ZTE, the Chinese agribusiness company active in the Democratic Republic of Congo: 'We will plant palm trees here and convert palm oil into biodiesel. The one-million-hectare palm plantation will eventually provide thousands of jobs for the local Congolese people' (quoted in Beiping, 2009).

The assumption seems to be that host nations – especially in the global South – have abundant land (and labour), while suffering from restricted access to financial resources, markets, and scientific and technological expertise. Both investors and host governments tend to see land as 'idle', 'underutilised' or 'marginal'. The land is perceived as having a significant value that is not being realised.

However, while much agricultural land in the global South has not realised its full productive potential in terms of the global market, the land is often productive for local markets. In Senegal, local people have worked smallholdings for generations, producing agricultural produce for local markets. In many cases these people lack legal title to the land. The central government in Dakar has tended not to invest in these smallholdings, which comprise the majority of the agricultural sector, preferring instead to invest in large-scale industrial agriculture for export. Policy makers, it can be argued, have failed to appreciate the social, economic and environmental value of small-scale agricultural production. This has left countries such as Senegal less self-sufficient in food production than they might otherwise have been, leaving them vulnerable to food price hikes.

The claim that land is 'idle' or 'underutilised' is vigorously contested. As a 2011 Oxfam briefing paper on land acquisition points out, what overseas investors generally want is the best land: fertile soil that is close to water, transport infrastructure and markets so that any investment is as profitable as possible (Zagema, 2011). Water is especially important, leading one commentator to suggest that what is happening in Africa is as much a 'water grab' as a land grab (Provost, 2011). As the chairman of Nestlé, Peter Brabeck-Letmathe, has commented on the land acquisitions: 'With the land comes the right to withdraw the water linked to it, in most countries essentially a freebie that increasingly could be the most valuable part of the deal' (quoted in Provost, 2011). This raises questions on the uses to which water should be put, especially in a country like Senegal which has a significant semi-arid land area.

Even land that is relatively infertile can be of great importance to customary users. Based on satellite imagery, the World Bank has claimed that there are hundreds of millions of hectares of unutilised land across the global South. Contesting this claim, Oxfam argues that this imaging is not picking up land uses such as shifting cultivation, pastoralism, hunting and gathering (Zagema, 2011). Indeed, the very notion of idle land needs to be questioned. As an Oxfam researcher in Senegal, Lamine Ndiaye, puts it: 'The myth that's brought so many investors is this thinking that there is so much empty land in Africa. The land is not empty. They're being occupied by the community, it's just that they're not recognized as owners of that land' (quoted in Hinshaw, 2011).

What Ndiaye is arguing is that much of the land in Africa is held and used in common.

## Activity 4.5   The tragedy of the commons revisited

Can you recall the main points of Hardin's tragedy of the commons? And can you draw out some differences between the theory of the tragedy of the commons and the phenomenon of land acquisition we have considered in this chapter?

### Comment

Hardin argued that resources open to all have a tendency to be overused, as each individual user seeks to maximise their own gains. Critics noted that Hardin was not writing about a genuine local common in which members of a community cooperate to share and regulate access to the resource, including restricting access to outsiders, but an open-access regime in which there is no regulation and, in effect, a free-for-all.

An important difference between the tragedy Hardin describes and land acquisition is that whereas there is overuse of land in the case of the former, in the latter land is legally acquired by outside groups, who can then fence it off and legally exclude the traditional communities. Land acquisition thus involves a fundamental tension between two different notions of legitimate land ownership. The first is the notion of traditional common land that has been managed by a community, usually for several generations, and which is considered as 'belonging' to the community. The second is the notion of private land ownership that is recognised by the state as having a legal status. These two forms of ownership are not mutually exclusive. Around the world many communities have successfully applied for and received legal title to their ancestral land. However, when this is not the case, and when the land concerned legally belongs to the state, communities invariably face eviction when the state sells the land to a private owner. The work of political theorists such as Hobbes, Locke and Hegel provides the philosophical underpinning to the role of the state in land ownership.

Note that Locke's point, noted in Section 3, that 'a man has a natural right to that with which he has "mixed" the labor of his body' is not an argument to support the rights of commoners who have worked the land collectively, but an argument for the individual private ownership of land. Locke argued for the enclosure of the commons by individuals provided enough is left for others. To Locke an act of commons appropriation that leaves sufficient for other people results in everyone being better off overall (Kymlicka, 2002).

While many communities in Africa have been collectively using and managing land for generations, only around 10 per cent of such land is held in formal title. Political economist Liz Alden Wily argues that it is not so much the lack of title that is the problem but the failure of many national governments and overseas actors to acknowledge and respect the rights of the customary occupiers of common lands (Alden Wily, 2011).

Lack of recognition of the commons was a contributory factor in the appropriation of land in Africa by European colonial powers from the sixteenth century until the early twentieth century. This has continued to be the case during the current wave of post-independence land acquisition. Failure to respect the rights of customary users was also a contentious issue in European history (Box 4.1).

---

### Box 4.1   Enclosure in early modern Britain

Driven partly by rising demands for land, enclosure turned open fields into fenced lands and converted commonly held land into private ownership. Enclosure began at least as early as the eleventh century, shortly after the Norman Conquest. It placed outside the law those people who continued to try to access their former commons. The legend of the English folk hero Robin Hood relates the resentment of commoners regarding the royal forest laws that legalised commons appropriation for royalty and the nobility (Figure 4.9). The legend strikes a populist note as Robin Hood plays a role in wealth redistribution: by robbing from the rich and giving to the poor he helps to right the historical wrong of land seizure from commoners by the aristocracy (Humphreys, 2006). Commons enclosure incited considerable popular resistance from smallholders and labourers accustomed to relying on communal lands for a range of uses including grazing of cattle, sheep and fowl, pig foraging, berry picking and firewood gathering. For some critical historians, enclosures were instrumental in ending the English peasantry and creating a landless working class (Thompson, 1991).

---

Figure 4.9   A statue of Robin Hood in the English city of Nottingham

The argument that much land in Africa and elsewhere in the global South is underutilised is not just a legal matter. It is also a matter of an undervaluation of the land, with the main focus of the state being on market value rather than the cultural and social value of the land to local communities. For the communities who have occupied land over many generations, what it can produce is only one way it can be valued: the land also has cultural or symbolic meanings. But as these values are expressed only in the lives of local people, they do not register with decision makers at a national level. In summing up the way traditional farmers relate to the lands they live and work on, Oxfam's report on land acquisition offers a helpful description of how different land values are closely bound up:

Land is not just an important productive asset. Even for families who have stopped living directly off the land, it often serves as an important safety net to fall back on when other economic ventures fail or when the economy fails to provide opportunities. Land has multiple other … uses as well, which are vital to family livelihood security. It can provide fodder, nuts, fruits, roots, medicinal and kitchen herbs, dyes, rope, timber, and roofing and fencing materials. Many of these resources are available on common lands, and are often especially important for women. Land also provides a space for social, cultural, spiritual, and ceremonial events, and as such is essential for sustaining the identity and well-being of a community and its members.

(Zagema, 2011, p. 9)

A similar set of claims could be made for the multiple ways of valuing the land that was subjected to acts of enclosure in Britain (Box 4.1). There is now concern that global land acquisition threatens the livelihoods of the half a billion small-scale farmers in sub-Saharan Africa and the approximately one-and-a-half billion smallholders worldwide (De Schutter, 2011).

# 7   Power, agency and land rights

In contemporary land acquisitions, as in the case of early modern Britain, the capacity of the state and its allies to appropriate land from customary occupiers is due to uneven power relations. These power relations cannot simply be reduced to a conflict between a powerless 'local' people and overbearing 'global' forces. National, and even local, elites are often closely involved in land acquisition, and in some cases elites have themselves acquired land with the intention of selling it on to overseas investors. National and local elites may also provide services – for a price – brokering deals with foreign investors (Anseeuw et al., 2012). Small farmers are often excluded from these deals.

This power imbalance is partly due to the material resources that local elites have at their disposal. Elites are often allied with national government, which offers access to information, the police and legal support. Elites are also in a position to join forces with overseas investors to shape the discourses which present land as 'idle' and 'underutilised', thereby framing land deals as win–win situations. As we saw in Chapter 3, discourses play a role in shaping the ideas actors use to communicate and legitimise power relations. For example, the word 'investor' may at first sight seem neutral and uncontentious. However, because of the way tax breaks, concessions and subsidies operate, many foreign-based actors bring very little in the way of financial investment to their host countries, even in the case of large-scale operations. Moreover, the experience of land acquisition to date suggests that while investors often promise infrastructural improvement, technology transfer and employment opportunities, these often fail to materialise.

Pro-land acquisition discourses rarely give recognition to the vast 'investments' that smallholders have put into their land. As we saw in Chapter 3, farmers in sub-Saharan Africa have been investing time and energy in the land for many generations, working with local resources and devising responses to variable environmental conditions. The agency of women in the agriculture sector is deserving of special acknowledgement: not only have women played a key role in cultivating plants and raising livestock, they have in some cases contributed to the very formation of the soil. Women in smallholder communities are also likely to bear the greatest burden of losing access to land. This is both because of their responsibility for feeding their families, and because their own land tenure tends to be even more insecure than that of men, despite the fact that they are the majority of farmers (Zagema, 2011).

The agency of smallholders can extend beyond shaping local agro-ecosystems. In many places, customary landholders have struggled to assert their rights both during and after the period of colonial control. But, as Alden Wily notes in the context of sub-Saharan Africa, 'Modern rural communities are more educated, politicized and nationally and internationally connected than their predecessors' (Alden Wily, 2011, p. 753). Moreover, she notes, local involvement in a range of civil conflicts, together with demonstration of popular resistance in North Africa from 2010 onwards, is encouraging rural people to resist land acquisition.

Figure 4.10   During the first Forum on Food Sovereignty, participants visited some local rice farmers outside the town of Nyéléni

Farming communities are increasingly forging their own connections across spatial boundaries. In 2011, the town of Nyéléni in Mali hosted the first Forum on Food Sovereignty, bringing together representatives of traditional farmers from over 30 countries (Figure 4.10). Collectively, the multinational participants at the conference drafted the Mali Declaration, which began:

> We, women and men peasants, pastoralists, indigenous peoples and their allies, who gathered together in Nyéléni from 17–19 November 2011, have come from across the world for the first time to share with each other our experiences and struggles against

land-grabbing ... [W]e are determined to defend food sovereignty, the commons and the rights of small scale food providers to natural resources.

(Mali Declaration, 2011)

The Mali Declaration went on to acknowledge the range of countries – across both the global North and South – in which 'land grabbing' corporations were based, and noted that both land and water are being appropriated. The declaration stressed the need for local capacity building to inform and strengthen rural communities in the struggle against land and water grabbing.

# 8    Summary

Contemporary land acquisition involves a range of actors, processes and commodities, some of which move across spatial boundaries. By analysing the complex dynamics of land acquisition using the concepts of time and space, risk and uncertainty, and values, power and agency, we have seen how a complex problem can be divided up into more readily understood segments.

Global land acquisition, this chapter has argued, is a new kind of response to the risks and uncertainties associated with global environmental change and food production. Major economic actors are attempting to smooth out the volatile rhythms and fluctuations of price changes by taking control of large tracts of land. A form of 'securing space' is taking place in an attempt to mitigate the uncertainties of a changing world. However, in opposition to this process smallholders are mobilising to defend their customary rights to land by insisting on more secure forms of land tenure. Both the customary management of common land and the mobilisation of community groups concerned about land grabbing in Mali can be seen as forms of sharing: collective responses that have been worked out in the context of dynamic environmental conditions.

The Mali conference returns us to the concept of space by another route. When smallholders from different nations join forces to resist land acquisition, they are effectively extending their own power and agency to the same scale at which powerful international actors operate. This should serve as a reminder that the analytical concepts we have been considering do not simply work sequentially: rather, we need to wield these concepts flexibly, and recognise that they are useful at different moments, and in a range of different ways.

# References

Alden Wily, L. (2011) "'The law is to blame": Taking a hard look at the vulnerable status of customary land rights in Africa', *Development and Change*, vol. 42, no. 3, pp. 733–57.

Anseeuw, W., Alden Wily, L., Cotula, L. and Michael Taylor, M. (2012) *Land Rights and the Rush for Land: Findings of the Global Commercial Pressures on Land Research Project*, Rome, International Land Coalition Secretariat.

BBC News (2012) 'New Zealand halts farm sale to China's Shanghai Pengxin', 15 February [online], http://www.bbc.co.uk/news/business-17037406 (Accessed 4 July 2012).

Beiping, T. (2009) 'Chinese agribusiness company in DR Congo to offer thousands of jobs for locals', *China View* [online], http://news.xinhuanet.com/english/2009-07/10/content_11686244.htm (Accessed 4 July 2012).

Cooper, M. (2010) 'Turbulent worlds: financial markets and environmental crisis', *Theory, Culture & Society*, vol. 27, nos 2–3, pp. 167–90.

Dauvergne, P. and Neville, K. J. (2009) 'The changing North–South and South–South political economy of biofuels', *Third World Quarterly*, vol. 30, no. 6, pp. 1087–102.

De Schutter, O. (2011) 'The green rush: the global race for farmland and the rights of land users', *Harvard International Law Journal*, vol. 52, no. 2, pp. 504–59.

Hegel, G. W. F. (2008 [1820]) *Outlines of the Philosophy of Right* (trans. T. M. Knox, ed. S. Houlgate), Oxford, Oxford University Press.

Hinshaw, D. (2011) 'The great African landrush', *The Atlantic*, 14 April [online], http://www.theatlantic.com/international/archive/2011/04/the-great-african-land-rush/237260/ (Accessed 29 May 2012).

Hobbes, T. (1989 [1651]) *Leviathan*, London, Penguin.

Humphreys, D. (2006) *Logjam: Deforestation and the Crisis of Global Governance*, London, Earthscan.

The Independent (2012) 'Chinese swoop on 16 dairy farms in New Zealand', *The Independent*, 28 January [online], http://www.independent.co.uk/news/world/australasia/chinese-swoop-on-16-dairy-farms-in-new-zealand-6295945.html (Accessed 4 July 2012).

Kymlicka, W. (2002) *Contemporary Political Philosophy: An Introduction*, Oxford, Oxford University Press.

Locke, J. (1975 [1690]) *An Essay Concerning Human Understanding* (ed. Peter H. Nidditch), Oxford, Oxford University Press.

Mali Declaration (2011) *Stop Land Grabbing Now*, November [online], http://www.reclaimthefields.org.uk/2012/04/05/conference-declaration-stop-land-grabbing-now/ (Accessed 4 July 2012).

McBeth, P. (2012) 'Business Desk: Fonterra flags $100M spend on two more Chinese dairy farms in push for farm hub with 15,000 cows', *Interest.co.nz* [online], http://www.interest.co.nz/rural-news/58823/businessdesk-fonterra-flags-100m-spend-two-more-chinese-dairy-farms-push-farm-hub-1 (Accessed 4 July 2012).

OneWorld (2012) *Food Security in Senegal: Briefing* [online], http://uk.oneworld.net/guides/senegal/food_security (Accessed 4 July 2012).

Our Finite World (2011) '2012: reaching "limits to growth"', *Our Finite World*, 24 October [online], http://ourfiniteworld.com/2011/10/24/2012-reaching-limits-to-growth/ (Accessed 4 July 2012).

Packenham, T. (1992) *The Scramble for Africa*, London, Abacus.

Perry, N. (2012) 'Anxiety in New Zealand as Chinese buy dairy farms', *Yahoo! Finance* [online], http://finance.yahoo.com/news/anxiety-zealand-chinese-buy-dairy-064627889.html (Accessed 4 July 2012).

Provost, C. (2011) 'Africa's great "water grab"', *Poverty Matters Blog*, 24 November [online], http://www.guardian.co.uk/global-development/poverty-matters/2011/nov/24/africa-water-grab-land-rights (Accessed 4 July 2012).

Pryke, M. (2007) 'Geomoney: an option on frost going long on clouds', *Geoforum*, vol. 38, pp. 576–88.

Radio France Internationale (2011) 'Senegal: biofuels boost land-grab conflict in country', *AllAfrica*, 28 October [online], http://allafrica.com/stories/201110281172.html (Accessed 4 July 2012)

Sabine, G. H. and Thorson, T. L. (1973) *A History of Political Theory* (4th edn), Hinsdale, IL, Dryden Press.

Sebastian, T. (2007) *Globalization and Uneven Development: Neocolonialism, Multinational Corporations, Space and Society*, Jaipur, Rawat.

Singer, P. (2001) *Hegel: A Very Short Introduction*, Oxford, OxfordUniversity Press.

Thompson, E. P. (1991) *The Making of the English Working Class*, London, Penguin.

Tuck, R. (2002) *Hobbes: A Very Short Introduction*, Oxford, Oxford University Press.

Walsh, B. (2011) 'Why biofuels help push up world food prices', *Time Magazine*, 14 February [online], http://www.time.com/time/health/article/0,8599,2048885,00.html#ixzz1iru3QXqO (Accessed 4 July 2012).

Withers, T. and Sedgman, P. (2012) 'Chinese developer wins approval to buy 16 New Zealand farms', *Businessweek*, 29 January [online], http://www.

businessweek.com/news/2012-01-29/chinese-developer-wins-approval-to-buy-16-new-zealand-farms.html (Accessed 4 July 2012).

Zagema, B. (2011) *Land and Power: The Growing Scandal Regarding the New Wave of Investments in Land*, Oxford, Oxfam International; also available online at http://policy-practice.oxfam.org.uk/publications/land-and-power-the-growing-scandal-surrounding-the-new-wave-of-investments-in-l-142858 (Accessed 4 July 2012).

# Block 2　Life

# Chapter 5   Life and the ocean

Philip O'Sullivan and Donal O'Donnell

# Contents

# 1   Introduction

Human life evolved from earlier forms of life, and it remains utterly dependent on the web of biological life. However, in many different ways human demands and lifestyles are putting increasing pressure on other forms of life. Why is it that human activities increasingly weigh so heavily on other living things and the ecosystems they comprise? And which environmental changes matter to humans, and which do not?

Over the next four chapters we look at how concern over environmental change can be triggered, leading, under certain circumstances, to environmental issues. In particular, we examine what makes an environmental issue in relation to the challenges that arise out of sharing the planet with other forms of biological life. So far in the module we have looked at a range of case studies in which the changing relationship between people and their environments has provoked a political response of some sort. This is what is usually referred to as an environmental issue. But not all environmental change becomes an 'issue'. Whether environmental change becomes an issue depends in large part on how people view and value the world around them.

To begin exploring the block question *What is an environmental issue?*, we start where scientists believe it is most likely that life itself began around 3900 million years ago: the ocean.

# 2   In deep water

We typically refer to our planet as 'Planet Earth', yet as the science fiction writer Arthur C. Clarke once remarked, we might call a globe with 71 per cent water cover and more than 99 per cent of its living biosphere in marine waters 'Planet Ocean' (quoted in Snelgrove, 2010, p. 3). The ocean constitutes the largest habitat on Earth and comprises 71 per cent of the planet's surface, an area of 361 million square kilometres. The global volume of ocean water is 1370 million cubic kilometres. This immense volume of seawater has a major influence on the Earth's climate (Angel and Rice, 1996). While the deepest ocean trenches extend to 11 kilometres deep, overall the average depth is 4.3 kilometres (NOS, 2011). This means that although the oceans constitute the largest reservoir of water on the planet – with 96 per cent of all the water on Earth – they are no more than a thin layer on the surface of the Earth, about the same relative thickness as the layer of skin on an apple. The ocean has an average thickness of 0.058 per cent of the planet's overall radius of some 6371 kilometres (Snelgrove, 2010, p. ix).

Given the vastness of the ocean, how do we know when human activities are impacting negatively on its life forms? This is a difficult question, not just because of the scale of the ocean, but because it is dynamic and constantly changing. What do we need to know about the ocean and the life it supports in order to make clear claims about human impacts? We now begin to engage with this question, starting with what is widely believed to have been a disaster for marine life: the Deepwater Horizon oil accident of 2010.

# 3   Deepwater Horizon: what's the issue?

On 20 April 2010 a blowout at the Macondo wellhead at the Deepwater Horizon drilling rig in the Gulf of Mexico killed 11 workers (Figure 5.1). Two days later, on 22 April, ironically on International Mother Earth Day (Figure 5.2), the 58,000-tonne mobile rig sank. This incident was the world's largest accidental oil spill and it took 85 days to cap the wellhead, some 1680 metres beneath the surface. By the time it was capped an estimated 779 million litres of oil (or 4.9 million barrels) had been released into the ocean.

Figure 5.1   The $560 million Deepwater Horizon drilling rig burns after the April 2010 well blowout

In this chapter we refer to this event as the Deepwater Horizon oil spill, or Deepwater Horizon for short. This is not just a matter of semantics or minor detail. When it comes to apportioning responsibility for this event, the parties involved could not even agree on the name of the issue, as the words used may frame, or imply, responsibility. The media commonly referred to the accident as the 'BP oil spill' after the company (formerly known as British Petroleum) which owned the licence to drill at the site. BP, however, argued that it was not solely responsible, as two other companies, Transocean (the rig's owner) and Halliburton (an oilfield services company), shared corporate responsibility for the cause of the accident and, therefore, any financial restitution. BP referred to the 'Deepwater Horizon accident' (the name of the rig), while Transocean referred to the event 'at the Macondo Well' (the name of the well at the head of which a blowout preventer failed, leading to the explosion). From this, we can see how even the language used to frame an environmental issue can be contested from the very start.

Figure 5.2   President Evo Morales of Bolivia addressing the UN General Assembly on 22 April 2009. Following a proposal from Morales the United Nations designated 22 April International Mother Earth Day. Exactly one year later the Deepwater Horizon oil rig sank

By August 2010, US government scientists estimated that the clean-up operation had removed a quarter of the oil while another quarter had evaporated or dissolved into scattered molecules. But a third quarter had been dispersed in the water as small droplets, posing an increased toxic risk to marine life. And the last quarter – around five times the amount released by the *Exxon Valdez* oil tanker spill in Alaska in 1989 – remained as slicks or sheens on the water or tar balls on the beaches. The Deepwater Horizon spill had become the largest accidental spill of oil into the ocean in history, surpassed only by the intentional 1991

Gulf War spill in Kuwait (Bourne, 2010). The Minerals Management Service (MMS) – the federal agency in the USA that regulated offshore drilling at the time – claimed that the probability of a blowout was less than one per cent and that, even if one did happen, it wouldn't release much oil. But they were wrong.

---

## Activity 5.1 Revisiting risk

If the probability of a blowout at the Deepwater Horizon rig was less than one per cent, does that mean drilling at the rig was a low-risk activity? You may find it helpful to think back to your learning on risk in Chapter 2, Section 2.1.

## Comment

Risk is calculated by multiplying the probability of an event by the magnitude of the hazard of the event. It is now clear that the risk of oil drilling at Deepwater Horizon was higher than anticipated because, although the probability of a blowout was very low, the hazard in terms of oil released was considerably greater than originally thought.

---

# 4   Oil spills as environmental disasters

Media coverage of the Deepwater Horizon oil spill initially focused on the oil rig blowout and the death and injury inflicted on the rig workers. The incident was not at first a major media event. As a news story it 'simmered for several days before an expanding oil slick grabbed worldwide attention' (Kerr et al., 2010, p. 674). From this point on, global news media provided extensive coverage of the growing slick, the repeated attempts to cap the wellhead, and the impacts of the oil on wildlife and human livelihoods in the Gulf of Mexico region.

As philosopher of science Isabelle Stengers has noted, there are certain kinds of event which unfold in such a momentous way that they 'have the power to force unanimous recognition' (Stengers, 2010, p. 4). Not all environment changes have this power to force widespread recognition, however. In Chapter 2, for example, we touched on the question of how much effort it has taken to put the issue of global climate change on the international agenda, and to keep it there. But in the case of an expanding oil slick, the news media brought the reality of environmental change into our living rooms and workspaces.

## Activity 5.2   The imagery of environmental disasters

You might want to pause at this point and recall your own early impressions of the Deepwater Horizon oil spill, or a similar event involving oil contaminants. What images come to mind, and what responses do they elicit?

## Comment

As well as dramatic shots of blazing oil, you may recall photographs of struggling oil-drenched birds, dead fish and desperate clean-up efforts. Although each event like this is 'new' – and therefore 'newsworthy' – it is also likely that you found the event, in some ways, familiar. Oil spills and their immediate consequences are part of a repertoire of visual images of dramatic environmental change which media audiences are by now well accustomed to viewing and interpreting (Figure 5.3).

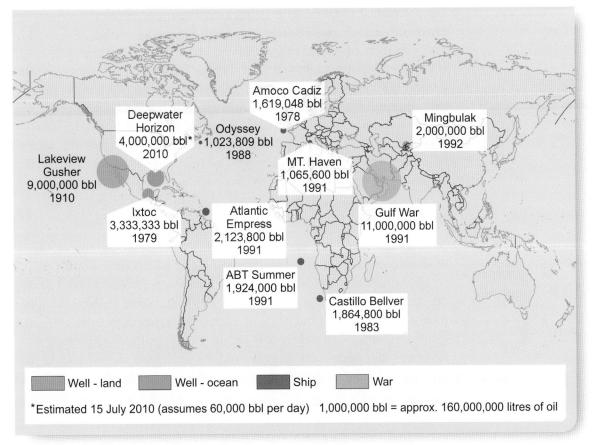

(a)

(b)                                              (c)

Figure 5.3   (a) Map showing the world's largest oil spills; (b) Prior to the 1990–91 Gulf War, the largest oil spill was the Lakeview Gusher in California in 1910, which spilled some 1431 million litres (9 million barrels) before it played itself out naturally; (c) In 1978 the Amoco Cadiz ran aground off the coast of Brittany, France, leading to what was then the largest oil spill at sea

Environmental concern, as a widespread social and political phenomenon, has been closely associated with news media representation of visible and disturbing environmental change. Environmentalism is just one of a number of social movements (others include the civil rights movement, feminism and the peace movement) that emerged in the 1960s, and which represented a new kind of political activity. These movements weren't based on class or regional lines, but arose from groups of people with shared concerns and values organising to campaign for change. The news media is one of the main arenas where these social movements have contested existing mainstream opinion. Media reporting has also helped to recruit and sustain supporters (Dunlap and Mertig, 1991; Smith, 2003).

At recurrent points, oil spills have played a key role in the rise of the modern environment movement. Some major events include the oil slick that resulted from the grounding of the supertanker *Torrey Canyon* off the south-west coast of the UK in 1967, the Santa Barbara oil spill from a drilling rig off the coast of southern California in early 1969, the ignition of oil-soaked debris that set the heavily polluted Cuyahoga River in Ohio alight later in 1969, and the spill from the grounding of the *Exxon Valdez* tanker off Alaska in 1989 (Hirokawa, 2011; Sheail, 2007). But these events are by no means the largest oil spills to have occurred.

Even in the case of such highly visible environmental catastrophes, widespread public concern needs to be seen in terms of emerging awareness of the consequences of environmental degradation and changing values rather than as a direct outcome of the events themselves. The Cuyahoga River, which flows into Lake Erie, for example, had reputedly caught fire a dozen or so times, from 1868 onwards, before the 1969 blaze which *Time* magazine deemed worthy of attention (Figure 5.4). As environmental lawyer Keith Hirokawa reminds us: 'there was a time when a colourful surface sheen on the water, or a brownish tint, or even the complete absence of aquatic life, would not cause public alarm' (Hirokawa, 2011, p. 545). Although there have often been dissenting voices, there is a long history of accepting degraded environments as an unavoidable consequence of wealth-generating economic activity. However, the rise of the environmental movement in the 1960s and the new values this movement promoted mean that environmental conditions that were previously accepted were now contested. The burning of the Cuyahoga River came to be seen as undesirable by a section of the population who argued for tougher anti-pollution laws. Pollution into the river had become an environmental issue.

Figure 5.4   The Cuyahoga River in Cleveland, USA, pictured in 1970. At the time the river was a fire hazard due to the quantities of oil deposited there by industries in the Cleveland area

The important point here is that environmental change does not necessary translate into an environmental issue. A pre-existing environmental condition may become an issue due to a change in broader social values. **Social values** are the beliefs and principles shared by people within a society. They express what is considered desirable in a society and are based on a society's religious, cultural and political traditions. They might include, for example, belief in the right to a free health service, respect for elders, a belief in majority rule, discipline, animal rights and compassion. Social values may be contested and redefined over time, with new values emerging. The news media, environmental campaigners and a range of other actors all play a part in promoting and disseminating these values to the wider public. By the time of the Deepwater Horizon oil spill, news media reporting of visible and spectacular environmental disasters had been established for over four decades, as had the expression of popular outrage over such events.

**Social values**
The beliefs and principles shared by people within a society.

The Deepwater Horizon oil spill was quickly identified as 'one of the worst human-caused environmental disasters in American history'

(Hirokawa, 2011). It triggered the largest emergency response to a marine oil spill in history, one that involved massive application of chemical dispersants, controlled burns of oil, skimming and siphoning of the spill, containment booms, and large-scale coastline clean-ups (Atlas and Hazen, 2011; Azwell et al., 2011). The slick was spread by wind and current movements. The Louisiana Governor declared a state of emergency on 29 April 2010, and part of the Gulf of Mexico was closed to commercial and recreational fishing. A succession of extensions to this zone brought the closed area to approximately 240,000 square kilometres by late June. Initially, oil containment and clean-up measures were run by BP, but on 28 April the US military joined the operation. As well as volunteering in the official containment and remediation programme, communities along the Gulf coast organised beach clean-ups and wildlife rescuing missions. In June 2010, a US$20 billion fund was set up by BP to compensate victims of the oil spill (Hirokawa, 2011).

Mass-media images and information played an important role in the framing of the event as a disaster, and in turning the Deepwater Horizon oil spill into an occasion for public involvement. However, as interest in the environmental impacts of the spill deepened, it soon became apparent that news media were only showing part of the picture. While an event such as an oil rig blowout or an expanding oil slick is newsworthy, it is rare for news media to devote similar attention to the underlying causes and processes that led to the problem (Smith, 2003). The environmental impacts of both the oil spill and the chemicals used to break down the oil require an understanding of marine ecosystems. This is complicated, for in order to begin to make sense of the consequences of a massive influx of petroleum hydrocarbons on ecosystems, we need to know about the composition and state of the ecosystems at the time of the disaster. But ecological systems themselves are constantly changing: as well as knowing about their pre-disaster state, we also need to understand the dynamics of life and its ocean environment. These questions have implications that extend far beyond the Deepwater Horizon oil spill and that take in all human impacts on marine and coastal ecosystems.

# 5   Environmental impacts of Deepwater Horizon

The question that marine scientists posed and sought to answer in 2010 was: what will be the long-term effects of the oil spill on life in the sea? Despite countless interim reports from marine biologists, oceanographers and NGOs, as well as official governmental reports, the short answer is that we do not yet know for certain. In order to understand why there is such uncertainty, we now examine three main aspects of biological life: its diversity, its adaptability and its interconnectivity.

## 5.1   The diversity of life

Mainstream media coverage of the environmental impacts of the Deepwater Horizon oil spill tended to focus on a number of familiar and photogenic species, including pelicans, dolphins, whales and turtles (Schmidt, 2010) (Figure 5.5). This heightened attention to a small range of iconic species – sometimes referred to as 'charismatic megafauna' – has long been a staple of mobilisation of concern around endangered wildlife. However scientific research takes into account a far wider range of living things.

Variety is one of the crucial ways in which the living environment differs from the non-living environment. There are approximately 1.75 million known living species of plants and animals (UNEP, 2002). Even today, new species from the deep oceans and tropical rainforests are being discovered and described. Estimates of species yet to be discovered vary from 10 million to as many as 100 million, whereas there are only about 92 known naturally occurring chemical elements. (Scientists sometimes disagree on the precise number because there is some debate over whether traces of some of the elements that humans have created in laboratories have been detected in minerals.)

Over recent decades, the concept of biodiversity – a contraction of biological diversity – has been increasingly used to express life's variability. The United Nations Convention on Biological Diversity agreed the following definition of biodiversity in 1992: 'The variability among living organisms from all sources including, *inter alia*, terrestrial, marine and other aquatic ecosystems and the ecological complexes of which they are a part: this includes diversity within species, between species and of ecosystems' (United Nations, 1992, Article 2).

(a)                                              (b)

Figure 5.5   Two species harmed by the Deepwater Horizon oil spill: (a) pelican; (b) drum fish

**Species richness**
The number of species in a given area.

One way to measure biodiversity is **species richness**: the number of species in a given area. Although this is quite an easy measure to obtain, it is not necessarily an accurate reflection of diversity. This is because it is not just the total number of species that is important in determining diversity but the relative proportions of individuals of each species and the number of species. Ecologists combine these two measures of species richness and relative abundance into a single figure known as a diversity index.

Assessing the impacts of the Deepwater Horizon oil spill was assisted by the fact that a comprehensive survey of marine life in the Gulf had been completed and made available in the year prior to the blowout. With the help of 140 taxonomic experts from 15 countries, the Harte Research Institute for Gulf of Mexico Studies completed a species inventory of the Gulf of Mexico. Although the researchers conceded that there were likely to be many species yet to be discovered in the Gulf, from this database they estimated that the quadrant of the Gulf where the spill occurred contained 8332 species of plants and animals. With regard to the major **taxa** of animals, this included 1461 molluscs, 604 polychaetes (marine worms), 1503 crustaceans, 1270 fishes, 4 sea turtles, 218 birds and 29 marine mammal species (Shirley et al., 2010).

Both official and community-based efforts at managing the spill concentrated on the affected beaches, wetlands and estuaries. These are vital habitats and nursery areas for many marine species, as Harte Research scientists point out, but they are not the only important habitats. One of the major contributions the database made was to help make the case that spill management also needed to take full account of the species that live in varying depths of the water column in the ocean (Shirley et al., 2010).

Overall, oceanic life can be divided into two categories: species that live on the sea floor, the benthic environment; and species that live in the open ocean, the pelagic environment. **Pelagic species** can live anywhere from the sea surface to the deepest depths. **Benthic species** are restricted to the sea floor. Within the pelagic environment are two types of animals and plants: those that drift with ocean currents, called plankton, and those that can swim, called nekton – for example, fish and aquatic mammals. The Gulf of Mexico species inventory was helpful not only in assessing numbers of species at risk from the spill, but also in showing the levels of the pelagic and benthic environments at which these species were located (Shirley et al., 2010).

Understanding the distribution of marine life across the depths of the ocean is especially important in the context of the Gulf spill. This is because of the way that oil has been dispersed, both by natural processes and by the effects of the chemical compounds that were applied to the oil to accelerate its dispersal (Figure 5.6). As environmental scientists Azwell et al. (2011) explain:

> The net effect of both natural and chemical dispersion was that much of the oil was transformed into tiny droplets with diameters less than 100 microns. Such droplets face significant flow resistance from the water column in their effort to rise to the surface. They are trapped in the deep Gulf environment until degraded by bacteria and are more likely to interact with marine life.
>
> (Azwell et al., 2011, pp. 2–3)

**Taxa**
The plural of taxon, a taxonomic category of species.

**Pelagic species**
Animals and plants that live anywhere in the open ocean.

**Benthic species**
Animals and plants that live on the sea floor.

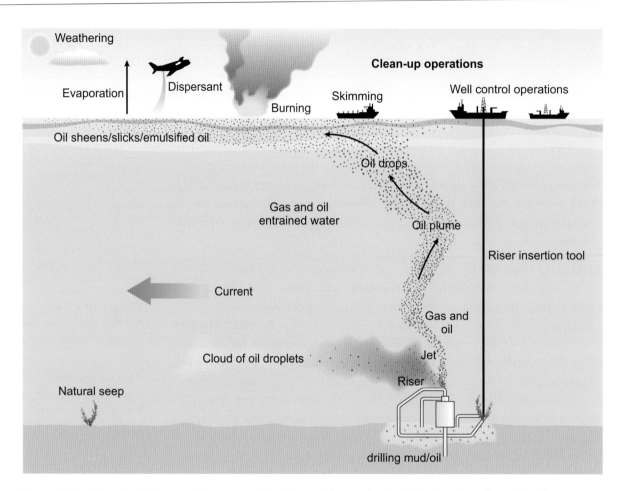

Figure 5.6  Chemical dispersants were applied from ships and aircraft to break up the oil spill

In official governmental reports on the environmental impacts of the spill, the dispersal of oil in the deep ocean and benthic environment was not initially considered. However, independent scientists who analysed the affected Gulf waters at a much deeper level were able to expand the scope of environmental impact assessment to take into account the depth of oil plumes and the sedimentation of oil on the sea floor (Azwell et al., 2011). Oceanographer Samantha Joye and her colleagues explored the benthic layer around the wellhead, and found that the impact was devastating: 'filter-feeding organisms, invertebrate worms, corals, sea fans, all of those were substantially impacted – and by impacted, I mean essentially killed' (quoted in Palmer, 2011).

The most crucial impacts of the spill, however, may lie even further from visibility than these deep-water species. Although, as environmental journalist Brandon Keim puts it, 'Nobody's going to shed a tear for an oiled microbe' (Keim, 2010), research suggests that the most significant impacts of the spill may indeed be on marine microorganisms (Schmidt, 2010; Widger et al., 2011). These are the life forms at the base of the marine ecosystem and the descendents of some of the earliest life forms on Earth.

While we do not know for sure where life began, or when, the scientific consensus is that life began 3900 to 4000 million years ago in the oceans. For around 3000 million years, all life on Earth was microscopic, mostly comprising single-celled microorganisms. By about 3500 million years ago, some of these organisms had developed the ability to photosynthesise: they could use the energy of sunlight to build and maintain plant tissue (Box 5.1).

---

### Box 5.1   Photosynthesis and respiration

Metabolism is the set of chemical reactions that take place in the cells of living organisms to sustain life.

In plant photosynthesis, carbon dioxide combines with water (using sunlight as an energy source) to produce carbohydrate (a complex carbon-containing compound) plus oxygen. Respiration is the opposite of photosynthesis, with oxygen taken in by the plant combining with the carbohydrate to produce the energy for life, releasing carbon dioxide and water. These two fundamental life processes are, in effect, mirror images and may be expressed:

carbon dioxide + water $\leftrightarrow$ carbohydrate + oxygen

with photosynthesis going from left to right, and respiration from right to left.

Carbohydrate produced by photosynthesis can be metabolised within the plant in two ways. It can be combined with other raw materials from the soil to form proteins, fats, and so on. And some of the original carbohydrate is used up in the process of cellular respiration to supply the energy that is essential for tissue building.

We return to the chemistry of photosynthesis and respiration in Book 2, Chapter 1.

---

Sunlight, however, is only one of a number of energy sources that bacteria and other microorganisms are able to use, and this, as we shall shortly see, has profound implications for the impacts of the oil spill.

While evidence mounted about the fatal impact of the oil on many species in the Gulf, research also showed that some bacteria were flourishing in the presence of petroleum hydrocarbons in their environment. This is because certain sub-families of bacteria are capable of consuming compounds in the oil (Hazen et al., 2010). To understand how it is that some organisms are able to thrive and multiply in the presence of chemical compounds which are toxic to others takes us beyond the diversity of life and into questions about life's adaptability.

## 5.2   The adaptability of life

Although spills of crude oil are highly toxic for many forms of life, oil itself is a natural product derived from marine algae that lived millions of years ago. Human activity such as oil drilling can lead to accidental release, but oil (consisting of hydrocarbons) may also escape naturally and can be found in varying concentrations in all marine environments. Over millions of years, many microorganisms, including bacteria, archaea and fungi, have evolved the capacity to utilise hydrocarbons as a source of energy (Atlas and Hazen, 2011). Microorganisms with the capacity to metabolise oil are only a small part of the overall microbial community in any marine environment. Many other microscopic organisms can be highly vulnerable to excessive amounts of oil. Some environments have a higher proportion of oil-consuming microorganisms than others. As microbiologists Ronald Atlas and Terry Hazen note, the Gulf of Mexico has more natural oil seepage than any other marine area in North America, which means that its bacteria and other microbiota are likely to be better adapted to oil than are those in other marine environments. Moreover, the long history of oil drilling – and associated oil spilling – in the Gulf of Mexico has also favoured microorganisms that can metabolise or tolerate oil (Atlas and Hazen, 2011).

The ability of some microorganisms to thrive under conditions which are toxic to other organisms requires an understanding of the way life changes in response to changing environmental conditions. While the response of bacteria to the oil spill offers an example of the process of artificially induced change, there is also a theory for natural change that applies to all living things – and was initially developed through the study of larger, more observable organisms (Box 5.2).

---

## Box 5.2   The theory of evolution by natural selection

The theory of evolution by natural selection originated in the middle of the nineteenth century with the independent work of natural historians Charles Darwin (1809–1882) and Alfred Russel Wallace (1823–1913) (Figure 5.7). As it is known today, the Theory of Natural Selection is based on three major criteria:

- Variation in the characteristics or traits shown by individual organisms within a population (such as the capacity to tolerate or to metabolise petroleum hydrocarbons).

- Higher reproductive success (defined by producing greater numbers of viable offspring) of individuals as a direct result of the trait that is evolving. Those individuals with higher survival rates in the context of a particular environmental condition are more likely to produce offspring, whether by sexual reproduction (two parents) or asexual reproduction (one parent). Bacteria reproduce using both methods.

- The traits must be genetically determined and heritable. How this occurred was not well understood until the 1950s when scientists confirmed the role of DNA (deoxyribonucleic acid) in inheritance, a finding which provided an explanation for how traits could be passed from one generation to the next. DNA is passed on from parents to offspring during reproduction. In each individual, DNA is arranged into units called genes. Each gene or group of genes is responsible for a different structure or function. Those individuals with a higher rate of survival are able to pass on to the next generation those genes responsible for the traits which have increased their chance of survival.

---

The theory of evolution by natural selection is based on a substantial body of evidence, including observations and collections, studies of different species in natural and laboratory conditions, mathematical models and knowledge of genetics. An important aspect of evolution is that it owes a lot to chance. Chance genetic mutations – each one a random occurrence – give rise to the variation of characteristics or traits among individuals in a given population. This initial element of chance means that the speed at which evolution occurs is highly variable. Because microorganisms generally reproduce far more quickly than larger, multicellular organisms (every 20 minutes in some bacteria), their rate of genetic mutation and evolution by natural selection also tends to be much more rapid.

(a)                                                    (b)

Figure 5.7   Independent research by (a) Charles Darwin and (b) Alfred Russel Wallace in the nineteenth century led to the development of the theory of evolution by natural selection

Evolution is specific to individuals' surroundings. In order to fully appreciate how evolution has produced many millions of species over time, we must think about the phenomenal diversity of environments on Earth that have been continuously changing since life began. If we imagine millions of species adapting through evolution (or failing to adapt) to a variety of dynamic environments over many millions of years, then we begin to understand how so many species have evolved (and become extinct) throughout history.

Human impacts such as accidental oil spills are examples of the changing environmental conditions that select for different traits and characteristics in other organisms. Early support for Darwin's theory of evolution by natural selection came from observations of changes in the population of the peppered moth (*Biston betularia*) as a result of the impact of industrial pollution on the English countryside during the nineteenth century. As researchers noted, when pollution darkened trees, the once rare dark form of the moth became less visible to predators, and the more common pale or peppered form became more vulnerable to predation – resulting in significant changes in the observed frequency of the darker variation (an almost 1000 per cent increase in some cases) (Freeland, 2003).

## Activity 5.3  Human changes to the environment and natural selection

Can you think of examples from earlier in the module where human changes to the environment may have played a part in the selection of different traits and characteristics of other organisms?

### Comment

In Chapter 3 we saw that some agricultural practices in Breckland selected for species tolerant of disruption and infertile conditions. We also saw how farmers in the Sahel regions have selected plants and animals tolerant of the climatic variation of semi-arid lands. In addition, poultry-raising practices may have played a part in the emergence of the H5N1 avian flu virus (Chapter 2). These last two examples may be viewed as a form of artificial selection (not natural Darwinian selection), although there is some disagreement over whether or not viruses should be considered to be living organisms.

Because the microscopic size of bacteria makes it hard to detect the changing frequency of variable traits, and because not all bacteria can be clearly delineated into species, there are uncertainties in tracking processes of natural selection. Until recently this required the isolation and breeding (or culturing) of individual microorganisms. However, computerised techniques for sequencing and identifying genes now make it possible to calculate the frequency of particular genes or gene sequences in a sample of water or soil containing millions of bacteria, without the need for culturing. This has resulted in the discovery of thousands of previously unknown genes and metabolic pathways in populations of bacteria (Widger et al., 2011).

In a research project conducted in 2010, microbial ecologist Terry Hazen and colleagues used these advanced molecular techniques to analyse deep water samples taken from within a 10 km radius of the Deepwater Horizon wellhead. By comparing samples from within the oil plume with control groups from outside the plume, they built up a picture of the impact of oil and chemical dispersants on diverse microbial communities. Analysis of the samples showed that 951 distinct bacterial taxa were present. Of these, 16 taxa appeared to have been 'significantly enriched' through their exposure to the hydrocarbons leaked during the spill (Hazen et al., 2010, p. 205). These 16 taxa are all known to have species capable of consuming and degrading hydrocarbons.

In samples taken from within the oil plumes, over 90 per cent of the gene sequences analysed belonged to a single taxon of bacteria believed to be most closely related to the Oceanospirillales family; the same taxon made up only 5 per cent of the control group samples taken outside the oil-impacted zone (Hazen et al., 2010). Using computerised molecular techniques, Hazen and colleagues compared the frequency of hydrocarbon degrading genes in microbial communities exposed to higher concentrations of oil with those outside the contaminated areas. As the researchers explained:

> Analysis based on individual genes showed that the changes of many hydrocarbon degradation genes are significantly correlated with the concentrations of oil contaminants ... These results indicated that a variety of hydrocarbon-degrading populations exist in the deep-sea plume and that the microbial communities appear to be undergoing rapid dynamic adaptation in response to oil contamination.
>
> (Hazen et al., 2010, p. 207)

What these results indicate is that microbial communities that can degrade oil in the deep waters of the Gulf were likely to have played a key role in disposing of the influx of hydrocarbons from the Deepwater Horizon oil spill (Hazen et al., 2010). News media reports were quick to pick up on the hopeful idea that, as a typical headline put it, 'Microbes ate BP oil deep-water plume' (Zabarenko, 2010) (Figure 5.8).

However, other researchers found that the bloom of bacteria was only consuming certain components of the spill, especially the more easily digestible methane, and leaving the majority of the oil plume undecomposed (Edwards et al., 2011; Teehan, 2011). Furthermore, the dramatically changing composition of the microbial communities in the vicinity of the spill raised questions about long-term changes in the overall composition of ecosystems in the Gulf and beyond. The complexity of food webs implies that there is much more at stake than recognising that certain families of organisms are able to adapt to the

sudden influx of hydrocarbons. This brings us to the third aspect of
life: the interconnectivity of living things.

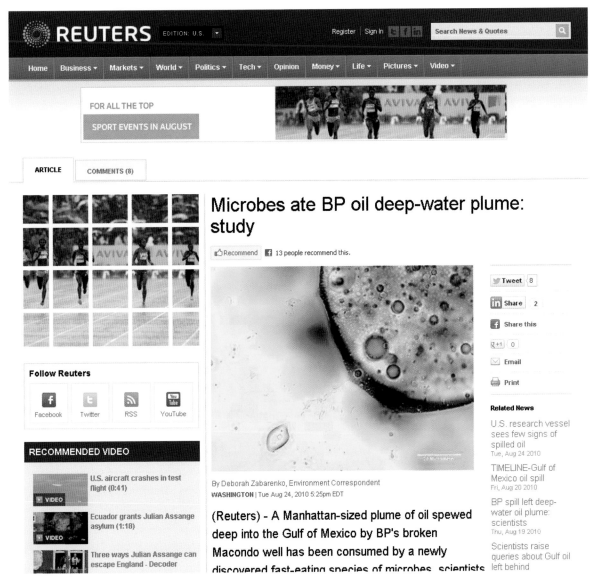

Figure 5.8   A Reuters website reporting the presence of oil-degrading microbes in the Gulf of Mexico

## 5.3   The interconnectedness of life

Some microorganisms are able to metabolise hydrocarbons, resulting in
the decomposing of some leaked oil and the rapid proliferation of
certain families of bacteria. But what does this mean for the multitudes

of other organisms in and around the Gulf? To begin to get a sense of possible consequences, especially over the longer term, we need to understand the basic relationships between different kinds of organisms.

In any ecosystem, whether on land or in the sea, the type of vegetation is an integral part of the environment for all other inhabitants. Plants, algae or bacteria that are capable of photosynthesis are the **primary producers**: those which are the basic food source on which all other life ultimately depends. The biological material generated by photosynthesising organisms provides food for **herbivores** (organisms that eat plants, algae or other primary producers) and **detritivores** (organisms that eat dead organic matter). Herbivores in turn may provide a food source for **carnivores** (animals, and occasionally plants, that eat animal tissue). This set of connections between plants, animals, algae, bacteria and other organisms is called a **food web** – which is the basis of an ecosystem (Figure 5.9).

**Primary producers**
Plants, algae or bacteria which are capable of photosynthesis, on which all other life ultimately depends.

**Herbivores**
Organisms that eat plants, algae or other primary producers.

**Detritivores**
Organisms that eat dead organic matter.

**Carnivores**
Animals, and occasionally plants, that eat animal tissue.

**Food web**
Set of connections between plants, animals, algae, bacteria and other organisms that is the basis of an ecosystem.

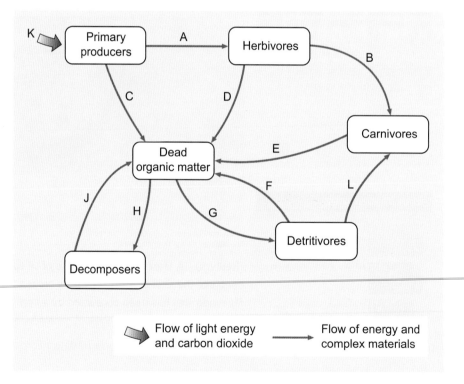

Figure 5.9  The basic components and interlinkages of an ecosystem

---

## Activity 5.4   Flows within the food web

Species consume other species for food, and thus energy. Which of the flows A–J in Figure 5.9 correspond to the following actions:

1   a giraffe eating grass

2   a dead leaf falling from a tree in autumn

3   a mole eating an earthworm

4   an earthworm eating a dead leaf.

You will find the answers at the end of the chapter.

---

As the primary producers of the marine world, **phytoplankton** (plankton capable of photosynthesis) are often referred to as the 'grass' of the sea, although, as most of the photosynthesis on Earth takes place in the ocean, it might be more accurate to call grass the phytoplankton of the land. Until a few decades ago, it was generally believed that there was a more or less linear chain of smaller organisms being consumed by larger organisms in the oceans: one that started with phytoplanktonic algae called diatoms, moved up to small crustaceans (a larger form of plankton) and from there to fish (Sherr and Sherr, 1991). In this view, bacteria were seen as little more than detritivores, mopping up dead or excreted organic matter. Recent decades have seen a major revision of this view, resulting in a much more complex view of the marine food web. Bacteria of many kinds – including photosynthesising microbes far smaller than diatoms – are now considered to play a vital role in both marine and freshwater ecosystems (Sherr and Sherr, 1991). Microscopic bacteria are now known to be abundant in all oceans, forming their own highly complex food webs of producers, herbivores, carnivores and detritivores. This microbial food web plays an important part in the 'grass' or 'pastures' of the sea: feeding slightly larger carnivorous organisms – mesozooplankton – which in turn feed small crustaceans which are consumed by marine metazoans – the larger marine organisms, including fish and whales (Sherr and Sherr, 1991; Mitra et al., 2012).

As we saw above, new techniques are helping scientists to understand the composition and behaviour of microbial communities. But there is still much which is unknown, especially with regard to the role of microbes in deep-sea food webs (Peterson et al., 2012). This makes it extremely difficult to predict the long-term effects on ocean ecosystems

**Phytoplankton**
Plankton capable of photosynthesis.

of an increased concentration of hydrocarbons and a sudden rapid growth of hydrocarbon-consuming bacteria of the kind that resulted from the Deepwater Horizon oil spill.

One of the major concerns has been that petroleum hydrocarbons and other pollutants present in the spill would gradually move through the food web. Rapid response research carried out in the north of the Gulf of Mexico in 2010, shortly after the arrival of oil slicks in the area, used carbon isotopes as a signature of oil-carbon in the marine food web (Graham et al., 2010). Researchers showed that, far from 'disappearing' when decomposed by oil-metabolising bacteria, contaminants moved relatively quickly through the food web. The evidence indicated that at the time of the study the oil consumed by marine bacteria had already moved several levels through the food web to reach the zooplankton which 'graze' on more microscopic organisms (Graham et al., 2010; see also Mitra et al., 2012). As researcher Monty Graham reported: 'We showed with little doubt that oil consumed by marine bacteria did reach the larger zooplankton that form the base of the food chain. These zooplankton are an incredibly important food-source for many species of fish, jellyfish and whales' (quoted in Soos, 2010).

Other research has begun to look at the wider repercussions of the blooming of oil-consuming bacterial populations, with particular attention to the effects of oxygen depletion caused by the metabolising of oil by bacteria, on marine ecosystems. One study used computerised DNA sequencing of samples from coastal waters and beach soil samples from Louisiana and Mississippi to research the changing make-up of the microbial community before and after the oil spill in June 2010 (Widger et al., 2011). As well as providing additional evidence about the ability of certain kinds of bacteria to benefit from the surge in hydrocarbon contaminants, this research found evidence of a corresponding loss of bacterial biodiversity, including photosynthesising bacteria. The researchers suggested that this could be due to the direct impact of oil pollution on oxygen-producing microorganisms, such as the photosynthesising bacteria of the genus *Synechococcus*. But they went on to suggest that this could also be an effect of oxygen depletion caused by the massively enhanced oxygen consumption of those bacteria that were consuming and degrading hydrocarbons from the spilled oil, a metabolic process whose final product is carbon dioxide (Widger et al., 2011).

As the researchers argued, the changing composition of the community of marine microorganisms has potentially profound implications for marine ecosystems:

> Our observations lead us to the conclusion that oil strongly influenced microbial population dynamics, had a striking impact on the phytoplankton and other flora present prior to the appearance of oil, and that the microbial community had not recovered to pre-spill conditions by the end of our observational period … Microbial communities are an essential but vulnerable part of any ecosystem …. Abrupt and severe changes in the microbial metabolism can produce long-term effects on the entire ecosystem.
>
> (Widger et al., 2011, pp. 2–3)

However, when it comes to ascertaining exactly what these long-term effects might be, a clear theme in scientific research on the Deepwater Horizon oil spill to date is one of uncertainty (Widger et al., 2011). Part of this uncertainty is due to the fact that the appreciation of the role of microorganisms in the marine food web is still relatively new and much remains to be discovered, as we saw earlier. In this sense, one of the few positive outcomes of the Deepwater Horizon blowout is that it has provided an urgent imperative for investigating the interconnectivity of microscopic life (such as bacteria which can be seen only with magnification) and macroscopic life (which can be seen by the naked eye). But the point has also been made that there was insufficient attention to deep-water and benthic ecosystems after the accident, with rapid response scientific research focusing disproportionately on the more visible, accessible and better understood shoreline and sea-surface ecosystems. One explanation offered for this is that coastal and sea-surface ecosystem services and their value to people are already well appreciated, whereas those of the deep ocean and sea floor still remain relatively unknown and under-appreciated (Peterson et al., 2012).

However, understanding the environmental impacts of the Deepwater Horizon oil spill is more than a matter of valuing deep-ocean communities and their complex food webs. It is also about recognising that effects can take a long time to work their way through food webs and fully impact on ecosystems. As environmental scientists Charles Peterson and his colleagues conclude: 'Assessing impacts acting through food web modifications, persistence of toxicants, and biogeochemical transformations may require relatively long time frames as lagged indirect effects play out over multiple years' (Peterson et al., 2012, p. 465).

Perhaps the key term Peterson and colleagues use is 'food web modification'. The changes brought about by the sudden, dramatic increase in some microbial life at the expense of other vital macro- and microorganisms in the oceanic food web may end up causing an effectively permanent change in the Gulf marine ecosystem. As we saw in Chapter 3, when extreme or sustained perturbation pushes an ecosystem over a certain threshold or tipping point, the result can be a dramatic transformation in the overall state of the system (Keim, 2010, 2011).

# 6  Summary

Our discussion on the oceans and how life responds to human interferences reveals some interesting points on uncertainty. When the effects of a major perturbation event cascade through ecosystems, uncertainty is not simply a matter of the incompleteness of scientific knowledge. It is also about the inherent inability of researchers to predict exactly how complex webs of different organisms will change, both through natural selection and in response to changing physical conditions, including those brought about by human interference (artificial selection). Different species may respond in different ways to ecosystem disturbance. What may pose a risk for the survival of one species may be an opportunity for another.

We have also seen that environmental changes or predicaments do not automatically generate issues. Rather, issues are constructed by people. People's values may change over time and vary from one part of the world to another. Thus what becomes an environmental issue and how the issue is perceived will, to some extent at least, vary over time and space according to social values.

The first stage of the construction of an issue is that a particular state of the environment must become visible to those people who might potentially be concerned enough to do something about it. The mass media may play an important part in broadcasting an environmental predicament to a broad audience, and scientific knowledge, despite its unavoidable uncertainties, can play a crucial part in providing information that substantiates environmental concerns. Initially, the most visible impacts of the Deepwater Horizon oil spill were central to the formation of the issue but, as time went on, scientific researchers – through the publicity their work attracted – were able to put previously little-known and largely invisible microorganisms on the agenda.

What the Deepwater Horizon case shows clearly is that while pre-existing scientific knowledge can play a big part in the shaping of an environmental issue, a major environmental event can also give impetus to new research projects, generating new knowledge that may redefine the issue. As environmental scientist and researcher Sean Anderson puts it: 'The Gulf Coast has become something of a living lab to explore the effects of human activities on the coast' (quoted in California State University Channel Islands, 2012).

# References

Angel, M. V. and Rice, A. L. (1996) 'The ecology of the deep ocean and its relevance to global waste management', *Journal of Applied Ecology*, vol. 33, pp. 915–26.

Atlas, R. M. and Hazen, T. C. (2011) 'Oil biodegradation and bioremediation: a tale of the two worst spills in U.S. history', *Environmental Science & Technology*, vol. 45, no. 16, pp. 6709–15 [online], DOI: 10.1021/es2013227 (Accessed 10 July 2012).

Azwell, T., Blum, M. J., Hare, A., Joye, S., Kubendran, S., Laleian, A., Lane, G., Meffert, D. J., Overton, E. B., Thomas, J. and White, L. E. (2011) *The Macondo Blowout Environmental Report*, Deepwater Horizon Study Group, January [online], http://ccrm.berkeley.edu/pdfs_papers/DHSGWorkingPapersFeb16-2011/MacondoBlowoutEnvironmentalReport-TA_DHSG-Jan2011.pdf (Accessed 10 July 2012).

Bourne, J. K. (2010) 'Is another Deepwater disaster inevitable?', *National Geographic Magazine*, October, p. 42, [online], http://ngm.nationalgeographic.com/2010/10/gulf-oil-spill/bourne-text (Accessed 10 July 2012).

California State University Channel Islands (CSUCI) (2012) 'CI professor leads national research panel on Deepwater Horizon oil spill' [online], http://www.csuci.edu/news/releases/2012-deepwateroilspill.htm (Accessed 10 July 2012).

Dunlap, R. E. and Mertig, A. G. (1991) 'The evolution of the US environmental movement from 1970 to 1990: an overview', *Society and Natural Resources*, vol. 4, no. 3, pp. 209–18.

Edwards, B. R., Reddy, C. M., Camilli, R., Carmichael, C. A., Longnecker, K. and Van Mooy, B. A. S. (2011) 'Rapid microbial respiration of oil from the *Deepwater Horizon* spill in offshore surface waters of the Gulf of Mexico', *Environmental Research Letters*, vol. 6, pp. 1–9.

Freeland, J. (2003) 'Are too many species going extinct? Environmental change in time and space', in Hinchliffe, S., Blowers, A. and Freeland, J. (eds) *Understanding Environmental Issues*, Milton Keynes, The Open University/Chichester, John Wiley.

Graham, W. M., Condon, R. H., Carmichael, R. H., D'Ambra, I., Patterson, H. K., Linn, L. J. and Hernandez Jr., F. J. (2010) 'Oil carbon entered the coastal planktonic food web during the Deepwater Horizon oil spill', *Environmental Research Letters*, vol. 5, no. 4, pp. 1–6; [online], http://iopscience.iop.org/1748-9326/5/4/045301 (Accessed 10 July 2012).

Hazen, T. C., Dubinsky, E. A., DeSantis, T. Z., Andersen, G. L., Piceno, Y. M., Singh, N., Jansson, J. K., Probst, A., Borglin, S. E., Fortney, J. L., Stringfellow, W. T., Bill, M., Conrad, M. E., Tom, L. M., Chavarria, K. L., Alusi, T. R., Lamendella, R., Joyner, D. C., Spier, C., Baelum, J., Auer, M., Zemla, M. L., Chakraborty, R., Sonnenthal, E. L., D'haeseleer, P., Holman, H., Osman, S., Lu, Z., Van Nostrand, J. D., Deng, Y., Zhou, J. and Mason, O. U. (2010)

'Deep-sea oil plume enriches indigenous oil-degrading bacteria', *Science*, vol. 330, 8 October, pp. 204–8.

Hirokawa, K. H. (2011) 'Disasters and ecosystem deprivation: from Cuyahoga to the Deepwater Horizon', *Albany Law Review*, vol. 74, no. 1, pp. 543–61 [online], http://www.albanylawreview.org/articles/14_HIROKAWA.pdf (Accessed 10 July 2012).

Keim, B. (2010) 'Gulf Coast may be permanently changed by oil spill', *Wired Science*, 5 May [online], http://www.wired.com/wiredscience/2010/05/gulf-tipping/ (Accessed 10 July 2012).

Keim, B. (2011) 'Deepwater Horizon's impacts found in bacteria', *Wired Science*, 3 March [online], http://www.wired.com/wiredscience/2011/03/deepwater-horizon-bacteria/ (Accessed 10 July 2012).

Kerr, R., Kintisch, E. and Stokstad, E. (2010) 'Will Deepwater Horizon set a new standard for catastrophe?', *Science*, vol. 328, 7 May, pp. 674–5.

Mitra, S., Kimmel, D. G., Snyder, J., Scalise, K., McGlaughon, B. D., Roman, M. R., Jahn, G. L., Pierson, J. J., Brandt, S. B., Montoya, J. P., Rosenbauer, R. J., Lorenson, T. D., Wong, F. L. and Campbell, P. L. (2012) 'Macondo-1 well oil-derived polycyclic aromatic hydrocarbons in mesozooplankton from the northern Gulf of Mexico', *Geophysical Research Letters*, vol. 39, L01605, pp. 1–7 [online], DOI: 10.1029/2011GL049505 (Accessed 10 July 2012).

National Ocean Service (NOS) (2011) *Ocean Facts* [online], http://oceanservice.noaa.gov/facts/oceandepth.html (Accessed 10 July 2012).

Palmer, J. (2011) 'Gulf spill's effects "may not be seen for a decade"', *BBC News*, 21 February [online], http://www.bbc.co.uk/news/science-environment-12520630 (Accessed 10 July 2012).

Peterson, C. H., Anderson, S. S., Cherr, G. N., Ambrose, R. F., Anghera, S., Bay, S., Blum, M., Condon, R., Dean, T. A., Graham, M., Guzy, M., Hampton, S., Joye, S., Lambrinos, J., Mate, B., Meffert, D., Powers, S. P., Somasundaran, P., Spies, R. B., Taylor, C. M., Tjeerdema, R. and Adams, E. E. (2012) 'A tale of two spills: novel science and policy implications of an emerging new oil spill model', *BioScience*, vol. 62, no. 5, pp. 461–9 [online], http://www.jstor.org/stable/10.1525/bio.2012.62.5.7 (Accessed 10 July 2012).

Schmidt, C. W. (2010) 'Between the devil and the deep blue sea: dispersants in the Gulf of Mexico', *Environmental Health Perspectives*, vol. 118, no. 8, A338–A344 [online], http://www.ncbi.nlm.nih.gov/pmc/articles/PMC2920105/ (Accessed 10 July 2012).

Sheail, J. (2007) 'Torrey Canyon: the political dimension', *Journal of Contemporary History*, vol. 42, no. 3, pp. 485–504.

Sherr, E. B. and Sherr, B. F. (1991) 'Planktonic microbes: tiny cells at the base of the ocean's food webs', *Trends in Ecology and Evolution*, vol. 6, no. 2, pp. 50–4.

Shirley, T. C.; Tunnell Jr, J. W., Moretzsohn, F. and Brenner, J. (2010) 'Biodiversity of the Gulf of Mexico: applications to the Deep Horizon oil spill', press release, May, Harte Research Institute for Gulf of Mexico Studies, Texas A&M University-Corpus Christi [online], http://www.harteresearchinstitute. org/images/press_releases/biodiversity.pdf (Accessed 10 July 2012).

Smith, J. (2003) 'Making environment news', in Bingham, N., Blowers, A. and Belshaw, C. (eds) *Contested Environments*, Milton Keynes, The Open University/ Chichester, John Wiley.

Snelgrove, P. V. R. (2010) *Discoveries of the Census of Marine Life: MakingOcean Life Count*, Cambridge, Cambridge University Press.

Soos, A. (2010) 'The food chain in the gulf', *Environmental News Network*, 9 November [online], http://www.enn.com/top_stories/article/41980 (Accessed 10 July 2012).

Stengers, I. (2010) 'Including nonhumans in political theory: opening Pandora's Box', in Braun, B. and Whatmore, S. (eds) *Political Matter: Techno Science, Democracy, and Public Life*, Minneapolis, MN, University of Minnesota Press.

Teehan, S. (2011) 'Deepwater Horizon oil spill was a boon for bacteria, study finds', *Cape Cod Times*, 12 August [online], http://www.capecodonline.com/ apps/pbcs.dll/article?AID=/20110812/NEWS/108120327 (Accessed 10 July 2012).

United Nations (1992) *Convention on Biological Diversity* [online], http://www.cbd. int/convention/text/ (Accessed 10 July 2012).

United Nations Environment Programme (UNEP) (2002) *Global Environmental Outlook 3: Past, Present and Future Perspectives*, London, Earthscan.

Widger, W. R., Golovko, G., Martinez, A. F., Ballesteros, E. V., Howard, J. J., Xu, Z., Pandya, U., Fofanov, V. Y., Rojas, M., Bradburne, C., Hadfield, T., Olson, N. A., Santarpia, J. L. and Fofanov, Y. (2011) 'Longitudinal metagenomic analysis of the water and soil from Gulf of Mexico beaches affected by the Deep Water Horizon oil spill', *Nature Precedings*, 28 February [online], http://precedings.nature.com/documents/5733/version/1/files/ npre20115733-1.pdf (Accessed 10 July 2012).

Zabarenko, D. (2010) 'Microbes ate BP oil deep-water plume: study', *Reuters*, 24 August [online], http://www.reuters.com/article/2010/08/24/us-oil-spill-microbes-idUSTRE67N5CC20100824 (Accessed 10 July 2012).

## Answers to Activity 5.4

1 Primary producer to herbivore (A)

2 Primary producer to dead organic material (C)

3 Herbivore to carnivore or detritivore to carnivore, depending on what the worm itself eats (B or L)

4 Dead organic matter to detritivore (G)

# Chapter 6   Political life: making environmental issues public

Philip O'Sullivan

# Contents

# 1   Introduction

The Deepwater Horizon oil spill is an example of a change in the environment which became a major environmental issue because it was considered undesirable by some actors. The role of social values was important in shaping the issue (Chapter 5). We also saw that, through the work of scientists, what was 'at issue' about the spill altered over time as new scientific knowledge was generated.

This chapter returns to the Gulf of Mexico to explore the political work that turned an undesirable state of the environment into an issue: to place it 'on the agenda' as a matter of political concern. It is not only scientists who make matters of concern visible to wider audiences. It is also in the interests of those people who feel they are harmed by a specific condition or change in the environment to make their values, views and proposed solutions visible to others. In this chapter we look at the way that the communities and organisations around the Gulf mobilised in response to the Deepwater Horizon crisis, and what can be learnt from this. This means examining the relationship between turning an environmental predicament into an 'issue' and gathering a 'public' around this issue.

## 2   Putting Deepwater Horizon in context

In its opening pages, the Obama administration's 2010 report *America's Gulf Coast: A Long Term Recovery Plan after the Deepwater Horizon Oil Spill* has this to say:

> Today, the well is dead, oil no longer flows into the Gulf, and the attention of the media and the public is beginning to shift elsewhere. But as the President said on June 15, 2010, we will not forget what occurred, and we will not forget the promise made to the people of the Gulf Coast to help them restore their ecosystems and economy to health. The effects of the oil spill may reverberate in the region and across the country for years to come.
>
> (Mabus, 2010, p. i)

As the report suggests, the environmental challenges of the Gulf are much more long-standing and extensive than the Deepwater Horizon oil spill. The current state of the Gulf shows the effects of 'a multitude of storms and years of environmental decline' (Mabus, 2010, p. 1). Indeed, just a month before the blowout of the Macondo wellhead, the White House's Council on Environmental Quality released a report on ecosystem restoration of the Louisiana–Mississippi Gulf Coast, entitled *Roadmap for Restoring Ecosystem Resiliency and Sustainability*, which noted that the region faced profound challenges that have 'direct and indirect impacts on the economy, communities, and environment of the regions' (White House Council on Environmental Quality, 2010, p. 1).

Variously known as 'the American Mediterranean', 'America's Sea' and 'the Energy Coast', the Gulf of Mexico is of vital economic importance to the USA. At 1,592,800 square kilometres and with an average depth of 1486 metres, the Gulf is the ninth largest body of water in the world. It is bordered by five US states, six Mexican states and Cuba (Figure 6.1). The northern (US) border of the Gulf is a coastline of 6400 kilometres which includes an array of habitats from coral reefs and lagoons to emergent wetlands and vast seagrass meadows (Harte Institute, 2012).

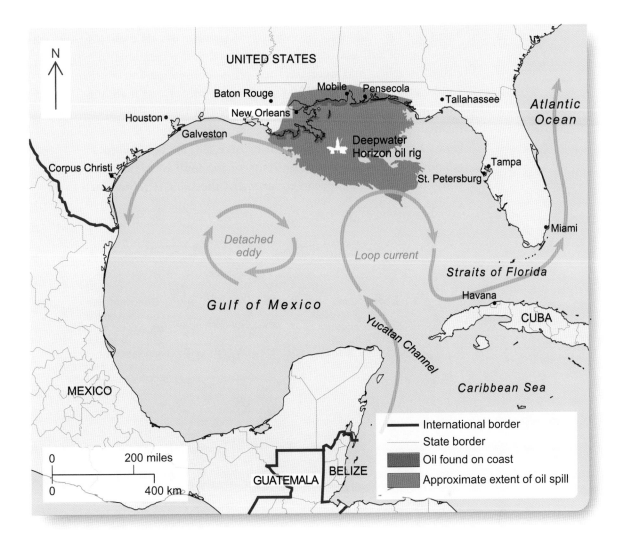

Figure 6.1  Political map showing the Gulf of Mexico in relation to international borders and the five US Gulf states which share its coastline (Source: NOAA, 2011, p. iv)

Ecologically and economically, the Gulf of Mexico is one of the most productive bodies of water on Earth (Beck et al., 2011; Brown et al., 2011; Tunnell, 2009). The region provides more than 90 per cent of US offshore oil and natural gas production, and 33 per cent of the nation's seafood. It hosts 13 of the nation's top 20 ports by tonnage (Gulf Coast Ecosystem Restoration Task Force, 2011). In 2009, the **Gross Domestic Product (GDP)** of the states of the US Gulf Coast was 2.4 trillion dollars or 17 per cent of overall US GDP (NOAA, 2011). Indeed, if the five US Gulf Coast states (Florida, Louisiana, Texas, Mississippi and Alabama) were considered a country it would rank seventh richest in the world in terms of GDP (NOAA, 2011).

**Gross Domestic Product (GDP)**
The value of all final goods and services produced in a country in one year.

The Gulf Coast region's economy is dependent on its natural resources, including oil and gas deposits, commercial and recreational fishing, coastal beaches, and waterways for ports, commerce and tourism. This combination of exploiting oil and gas and conserving maritime environments and ecosystems has resulted in tensions between maintaining a healthy environment and a successful economy (Gulf Coast Ecosystem Restoration Task Force, 2011). The complex relationship between the ecosystems of the Gulf of Mexico, the coastal communities and the ocean economy of the Gulf is represented in Figure 6.2.

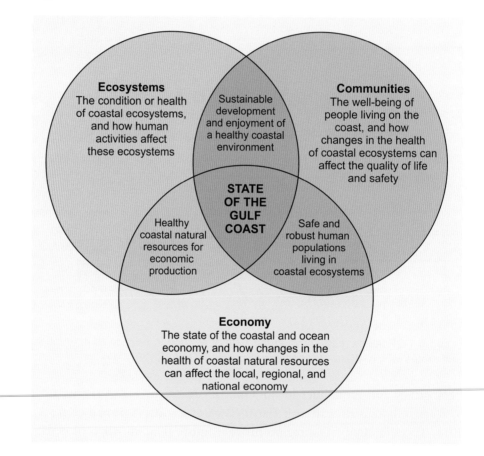

Figure 6.2   A Venn diagram illustrating the complex relationship between the ecosystems of the Gulf of Mexico, the coastal communities and the ocean economy of the region (Source: NOAA, 2011, p. 1)

## 2.1 The Gulf of Mexico ecosystem

Despite its ecological and economic importance, the Gulf has been poorly managed for decades, resulting in 'degraded habitats, poor water quality, stressed fisheries, and altered coastal freshwater inflows' (Brown et al., 2011, p. 1; GOMA, 2009; NOAA, 2010). This pressure on the ecosystems of the Gulf reduces their resilience, which increases the vulnerability of human communities to a multitude of hazards (Brown et al., 2011). As you saw in Chapter 3, the resilience of an ecosystem is its capacity to resist and recover from a disturbance. Highly resilient ecosystems may recover quickly to a state that is close to that before the disturbance. Less resilient ecosystems may tip into a different ecological state following a major disturbance, or may even collapse.

For generations the Gulf's coastal habitats – barrier islands, coastal marshes, mangroves and other coastal forests, seagrass beds and oyster reefs – have supported fishing economies. These habitats also intercept surges created by strong storms, reducing their impact on human settlements. Predictions of rising sea level and intensifying extreme weather events indicate that the risks to coastal habitats are likely to increase (Brown et al., 2011). Understanding the relationship between the different types of risk to the Gulf of Mexico ecosystems is critical to gauging the environmental issues the region faces. The threats include physical, chemical, geological and biological/ecological factors, as well as socio-economic ones.

A **driver** of ecological change is any natural or human-induced factor that directly or indirectly causes a change in an ecosystem. The main natural drivers of ecological change in the Gulf of Mexico are:

**Driver**
Any natural or human-induced factor that directly or indirectly causes a change in an ecosystem.

- *Loop current.* Seawater enters from the Caribbean Sea into the Gulf. Rubbish and pollutants are also brought in by this major current system (Figure 6.3).

- *Freshwater inflow.* Freshwater, nutrients and sediments enter the Gulf via a number of drainage systems, bays, estuaries and rivers. These freshwater inflows provide nutrients to the Gulf system. The freshwater/saltwater mix provides habitat conditions for wintering waterfowl, reproductive nurseries for many marine species, and the brackish-water conditions that support some oyster populations.

- *Hurricanes/tropical storms.* These impact on coastal natural resources and also damage the human built environment. For example, after Hurricane Katrina in 2005, oil prices for motorists increased by 18 per cent and aircraft fuel by 26 per cent because of damage to urban and transport infrastructure (Harte Institute, 2012).

- *Ecological buffers and filters.* The Gulf's wetlands, barrier islands and mangrove forests provide important buffers in the Gulf ecosystems, filtering nutrients and providing habitats for coastal species (Brown et al., 2011).

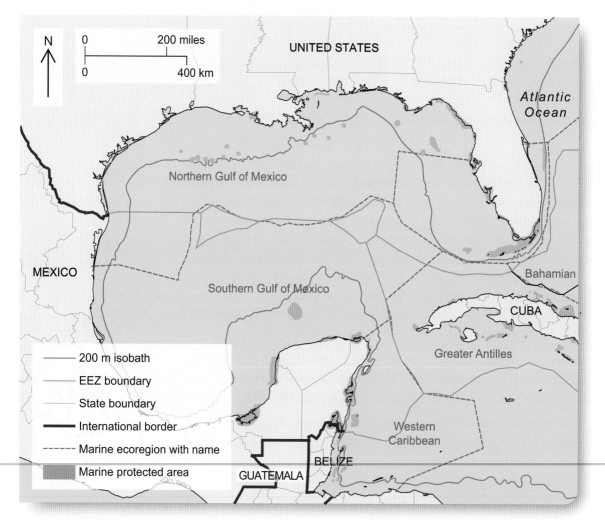

Figure 6.3   Gulf of Mexico Large Marine Ecosystem. The map also shows Economic Exclusion Zone (EEZ) boundaries (the territorial waters of a country), state boundaries, international boundaries, marine eco-regions, and marine protected areas. An isobath is an imaginary line on a map that connects all points of the same depth (Source: Fautin et al., 2010, p. 17, Figure 6)

Anthropogenic (human) drivers often couple with natural or non-human drivers to compound threats and affects. It is to these drivers that we now turn. Box 6.1 summarises the threats to the Gulf of Mexico ecosystem and their direct effects on natural systems and resources.

---

### Box 6.1 Drivers of ecological change in the Gulf of Mexico

| Driver | Effects |
|---|---|
| Agriculture | Can negatively affect water quality and quantity, and cause problems with habitat fragmentation and conversion |
| Changes in freshwater inflow/discharge (amount/rate/timing/channelling) into estuaries around the Gulf | Affects volume of sediment-carrying water, tides and salt levels and thus reproduction and recruitment of many estuarine-dependent species such as crabs, shrimp and fish, and survival and recruitment of many habitats including seagrass, salt marsh/wetlands, and oyster reefs |
| Creation of channels and dredging for navigation | Disrupts water flow; sediment disposal can cause sedimentation of natural habitats; constructing levees (riverside embankments) along rivers also affects sediment dispersion; affects deltaic (marsh) communities, their well-being, growth, and preservation |
| Coastal development and industrial development/expansion | Causes habitat loss due to land conversion from natural to human-built environment; reduces biodiversity, connectivity and resilience; increases habitat fragmentation and storm water run-off |
| Damaging fishing techniques | Habitat destruction, unintentional catches, and wasted by-catch (fish caught unintentionally while trying to catch other fish) |
| Endocrine disruptors (chemicals that interfere with the hormone system in animals), pesticides and other forms of pollution | Endocrine disruptors have their largest effect in estuaries and near shore, primarily affecting early life history stages |

| Engineered shoreline structures | Disrupts the movement of sediment along the coast (long-shore sediment flow), causing erosion elsewhere |
|---|---|
| Global climate change | Affects intensity and duration of cold fronts, storm intensities, ranges and reproductive periods of species, precipitation patterns and resulting freshwater inflows |
| Harmful algal blooms (the rapid increase or accumulation in the population of algae) | Can cause massive fish/invertebrate kills; often interacts with increased nutrient discharge |
| Invasive species (a non-native or alien species to the ecosystem under consideration whose introduction causes, or is likely to cause, economic or environmental harm, or harm to human health) | Includes non-native or invasive wetland and marine organisms, as well as native species occurring outside their natural range or in excess of historic abundance due to anthropogenic activities; food web disruption, displacement of native species |
| Nutrient discharge into rivers and outflows into estuaries and the Gulf | Generates hypoxic (low-oxygen) zones in estuaries and offshore |
| Ocean acidification | Increased atmospheric concentrations of carbon dioxide are leading to increased oceanic uptake of carbon dioxide, causing ocean acidification. Elevated atmospheric carbon dioxide levels affect survival of larval and adult stages of marine life |
| Oil and gas exploration and development | Affects land use, causes environmental degradation directly (e.g. pollutants) and indirectly (e.g. canals accelerating coastal erosion). Offshore releases of oil can affect coastal lands and marine environments well beyond the location of source |
| Overfishing | Affects food webs. A change in the size of one population in a food web will have an effect on other populations; many non-target species are affected and biodiversity may be reduced |

| Sea level rise | Another consequence of global climate change; impacts may be enhanced by groundwater and petroleum product extraction causing subsidence |
|---|---|
| Treated and untreated sewage discharge | Untreated discharges cause water quality problems and diseases. Sewage treatment does not degrade many of the chemicals and drugs placed in waste water (e.g. prescription drugs, caffeine, and other chemicals that may have already passed through humans). Can have negative consequences on marine life. |

Source: based on Brown et al., 2011, pp. 4–5

Many threats at multiple scales have exerted a cumulative negative impact on the Gulf. In some cases the linkage between these various sources of ecological stress is known. In other cases the linkages are unclear. This illustrates the concept of scientific uncertainty: not all aspects of ecosystem functioning are understood, and there are uncertainties about how some ecosystems will respond to human intervention (Brown et al., 2011).

Our discussion has highlighted the different aspects of agency in the physical systems of the Gulf of Mexico. It is clear that the distinction between social and natural drivers is in some respects artificial: there is a strong, close and dynamic interrelationship between the social and natural factors that drive ecological change in the Gulf.

## 2.2   Economic impacts of environmental change

In terms of revenue and employment, the economic value of the Gulf of Mexico states for the USA is enormous. At the time of the Deepwater Horizon oil spill in 2010, the economic value of the Gulf States was estimated at over $US 100 billion per annum, with Gulf resources directly supporting some 645,000 jobs, predominantly in oil and gas, tourism and fishing (Table 6.1). The economic development of the Gulf region thus provides significant economic benefits to business, local actors and the US economy. But development may also lead to various costs, such as depleted fisheries, pollution, and so on. When

**Cost–benefit analysis**
A process for valuing and comparing the anticipated costs and benefits of an economic activity.

weighing up the various options for action, economists seek to value the various costs and benefits to assess whether, overall, a particular economic activity should be carried out. This is called **cost–benefit analysis (CBA)**, which can be defined as the process for valuing and comparing the anticipated costs and benefits of an economic activity.

Table 6.1   The economy of the US Gulf (2010 estimate)

|  | Annual revenue (in $ billions) | Jobs (estimated) |
|---|---|---|
| Oil and gas | 62.7 | 107 000 |
| Tourism | 38.1 | 524 000 |
| Commercial fishing | 0.7 | 14 000 |
| **Total** | **101.5** | **645 000** |

Source: *National Geographic*, Map Supplement, October 2010

## Activity 6.1   Cost–benefit analysis and uncertainty

Can you think of any difficulties in calculating a cost–benefit analysis on an economic activity such as constructing and using an oil rig? You might like to use the module concept of time when thinking through this question.

### Comment

Predicting costs is difficult due to uncertainty over future events. When there is no oil spill, or rather if it is assumed there is no risk of an oil spill, then a CBA is likely to suggest that oil drilling will provide significant economic benefits with low costs (Harte Institute, 2012). However, an oil spill fundamentally changes the ratio of benefits to costs. If the costs from the 2010 spill had been factored into the initial CBA, then the decision to proceed with the Deepwater Horizon rig might not have been taken.

At the time of writing (2012), definitive figures on the economic costs of the Deepwater Horizon oil spill remain hard to ascertain, as long-term effects remain uncertain (Figure 6.4). Environmental economist Rashid Sumaila and colleagues have estimated the potential negative economic effects of the disaster on commercial and recreational fishing across the five US Gulf states (Table 6.2). By computing potential losses throughout the fish value chain, they assessed the effects in terms of total revenues, total profits, wages, jobs and overall economic impact (Sumaila et al., 2012).

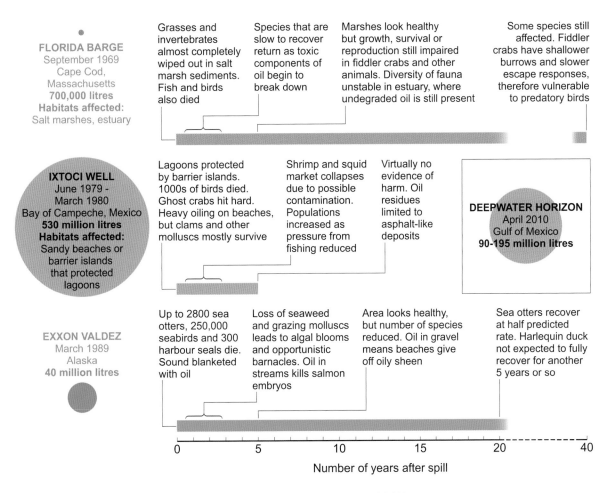

Figure 6.4   How long before recovery? (Source: Aldhous et al., 2010)

Table 6.2    Predicted (midpoint) present value losses in economic indicators for all affected US Gulf states for commercial and recreational fisheries combined

| Sector | Total revenues (million US$) | Total profits (million US$) | Wages (million US$) | Economic impact (million US$) | Employment (jobs) |
|---|---|---|---|---|---|
| Commercial fisheries | 1577 | 823 | 469 | 4888 | 7000 |
| Recreational fisheries | 1949 | 1062 | 715 | 3457 | 14 900 |
| Mariculture | 129 | 61 | 26 | 399 | 280 |
| **Total** | **3655** | **1946** | **1210** | **8744** | **22 180** |

Source: Sumaila et al., 2012, p. 506, Table 8

**Externality**

A value that arises when one actor's actions affect the welfare of others in a way that is not reflected in market prices.

The costs (or benefits) arising from an economic activity that affect somebody other than the people engaged in the original process are referred to as externalities. An **externality** is a value that arises when one economic actor's actions affect the welfare of others in a way that is not reflected in market prices. The British economist Arthur Pigou (1952 [1920]) first introduced the idea of negative external effects, or negative externalities. These are the costs imposed by one actor on to others, for which no compensation is paid. The effects of oil pollution from the Deepwater Horizon spill not yet (or insufficiently) covered by compensation are classic examples of negative externalities (Figure 6.5). One example of a negative externality that Pigou provided was the sparks emitted from steam trains. These sparks often set alight forests and sometimes houses. The railway company's business benefited from running the rail service, but did not bear the costs of the fires, which were borne by the forest and house owners or their insurance companies (van der Straaten and Gordon, 1995).

A positive externality arises when an actor provides a benefit that another actor enjoys, but does not pay for. For example, the bees from bee-keepers who harvest honey will pollinate local fields, which could improve farmers' crop yields. The farmers will not pay for this service although they will enjoy the benefits. For Pigou (1952 [1920]), externalities are part of the difference between the social and private cost price of goods and services. He proposed taxing those who produce negative externalities (such as polluters) and subsidising those who produce positive externalities (such as bee-keepers).

(a)          (b)          (c)

Figure 6.5  Some examples of negative externalities: (a) Factory pollution in rivers can kill aquatic life and contaminate drinking water; (b) Opencast mining can despoil the beauty of landscapes; (c) Construction of a motorway can depress house prices leading to losses for home owners

While they may not articulate it in these terms, communities living and working around the Gulf of Mexico are aware that they are bearing the costs of economic activities that are benefiting others, and have done so for a long time. Prior to the Deepwater Horizon spill, it is estimated that over 79.5 million litres of oil had spilled into the Gulf from some 4000 offshore oil and gas platforms and tens of thousands of kilometers of pipeline located in the Gulf (Robertson, 2010). Another problem is the discharge of nutrients into the Gulf. Some 41 per cent of the area of the contiguous United States feeds into the Mississippi River which feeds into the Gulf. Nitrogen and phosphorous nutrients from agricultural fertilisers have formed 'dead zones' of low-oxygen water conditions (or hypoxia) where the Mississippi flows into the Gulf, reaching up to 22,000 square kilometres (Farber, 2011; Rabalais, 2011).

Both the 'dead zone' and the impact of the oil industry on the Gulf are examples of negative externalities that are often generated some distance from the areas that are affected. For the affected communities, such externalities can have profound economic consequences. But this predicament tends to be much more than a matter of lost income and other economic costs. It is also about people feeling they have no effective role in decision making over the affairs that affect them. The experience of Gulf communities during and after the Deepwater Horizon oil spill is a case in point which offers lessons about how to address disempowerment and loss of agency.

# 3   Power, agency and the Deepwater Horizon oil spill

As law professor Daniel Farber observes: 'The oil spill has threatened Cajun culture because it challenges traditional fishing livelihoods, and threatens to undermine the Cajun tradition of self-reliance' (Farber, 2011, p. 5). Cajuns are of French descent, and took refuge in Lower Louisiana after they were expelled from Canada in the eighteenth century. They are one of many groups and communities who experienced the Deepwater Horizon crisis as one of economic and political disempowerment. The Obama administration's *America's Gulf Coast* report cited earlier makes frequent reference to public engagement with local leaders, tribes, fishermen, small business owners and other local people (Mabus, 2010). But many communities around the Gulf have little trust in federal or state-level decision making and argue that even when public engagement occurs it rarely impacts adequately at policy-making levels (Gordon et al., 2011).

A contributing factor to this scepticism has been the experience of the failure of state-governed federal recovery funds to reach communities which suffered the worst effects of Hurricanes Katrina and Rita in 2005 (Gordon et al., 2011). This erosion of trust appears to have been exacerbated by the Deepwater Horizon crisis. Many coastal residents soon found that they were restricted from accessing contaminated coastline and marine areas, which appeared to have come under the jurisdiction of BP (McClelland, 2010). Fisherfolk and their communities were not consulted about the closure of fisheries (Osofsky et al., 2011). Gulf residents were not only excluded from decisions about how to the treat the spill, but also found that there were legal restrictions on disclosure of the ingredients which made up the chemical dispersants that were being applied to break up the slick (Sheppard, 2010).

The fishing communities recognised that the recovery of their livelihoods was not only a matter of reopening fishing grounds and of marine ecosystem resilience. It ultimately depended on the willingness of consumers to purchase seafood sourced in the Gulf, a confidence that was undermined by uncertainty surrounding the persistent toxicity of chemical dispersants (Osofsky et al., 2011). Fisherfolk were themselves uncertain about the safety of their catch. As an outreach coordinator who works with commercial fisherfolk of the Native American United Houna Nation explains: 'They're afraid of their seafood. Should they bring it home to their families?' (Clarice Friloux, quoted in Sturgis and Kromm, 2012, p. 8).

While the impact of toxic chemicals may be beyond the expertise of Gulf fisherfolk, in other respects fishing communities claim a deep and extensive understanding of the environments and the ecosystems with which they are in constant interaction. Lack of recognition of this knowledge in relation to official responses to the Deepwater Horizon spill has been a major source of frustration. In a public statement made at the height of the crisis, an organisation representing workers in the local fishing industry insisted:

> We Are the Gulf Coast Experts. Our lifelong experience and environmental knowledge have not been utilized to mitigate and solve the impacts of this catastrophic ecological, economic and social disaster. Still, most of us have not yet been employed as 'first responders' to protect our fishing grounds, shore lines, wildlife, and our communities. This is nonsense.
>
> (Gulf Coast Fishermen, Seafood Workers and Maritime Communities, 2010, p. 2)

It's worth noting that fisherfolk trawling for shrimp in the early 1970s first labelled the outflow of the Mississippi a 'dead zone', and it was their reports of a recurrent absence of harvestable marine life at certain times of the year that helped bring the severity of the hypoxia problem into visibility (Rabalais, 2011). We should also note environmental journalist Mike Tidwell's recollections from the early 2000s that Hurricane Katrina was 'routinely predicted by every last Louisiana fisherman I ever met' (Tidwell, 2006, p. 29): a prognosis, he adds, that was based on intimate knowledge of the destruction of local wetlands and the implications of this for the severity of the looming catastrophe (Box 6.2).

> ## Box 6.2   Traditional ecological knowledge
>
> The concept of traditional ecological knowledge is usually used to refer to the ways of knowing and interacting with the local environment developed over many generations by indigenous peoples engaged in hunter-gatherer or peasant ways of life (Berkes, 1999). An argument might be made, however, that the concept of traditional ecological knowledge should be extended to take in modernised forms of 'local' or 'communal' knowledge of ecosystems and environmental resources which also arise out of long-term or intergenerational experience. The intimate knowledge that Gulf of Mexico fishing communities have of their environments would fit into such an expanded notion of traditional ecological knowledge.

Like others who work directly with environmental resources, fisherfolk have an agency that emerges out of interacting on a daily and seasonal basis with dynamic physical and biological processes. But this complex and fine-tuned form of agency does not necessarily translate into power resources or the setting of agendas. However, local or place-based actors always have some degree of discretion in shaping the spatial and temporal processes in which their lives are implicated.

## Activity 6.2   Local knowledge, power and environmental change

Can you recall an example from earlier in the module where local actors have been able to exercise power in response to environmental conditions or changes they found undesirable?

## Comment

One example you may have recalled from Chapter 1 was the Coastal Concern Action Group at Happisburgh. Through this group, people had a discernible impact in the struggle for recognition of the effects of coastal erosion. You might also have noted that African communities are beginning to mobilise against land appropriation, as in the conference of 2011 in Nyéléni in Mali (Chapter 4).

What Liz Alden Wily observed in the context of sub-Saharan Africa (Chapter 4, Section 7) also applies to other parts of the world, including the US Gulf Coast: 'Modern rural communities are more educated, politicized and nationally and internationally connected than their predecessors' (Alden Wily, 2011, p. 753). Drawing on traditional knowledge can enable communities to mobilise in response to environmental changes or threats. But so too can new forms of knowledge and communication, including new ways of making environmental change visible.

## 3.1 Citizen science: making environmental issues visible

A set of guidelines produced in the early days of the Deepwater Horizon oil spill to help local people monitor the effects of the oil spill on wildlife had this to say: 'Our collective ability to avert damage is limited; however, our collective ability to document damages for future mitigation is critical' (LA Bird Response Working Group, 2010, p. 2).

We have seen that one important outcome of the spill was the capacity of scientists to shape and reframe the issue by making previously unseen objects – water columns, benthic life, microorganisms – into matters of concern. This is not only a task taken on by scientific experts. From early on in the crisis, other concerned groups cooperated to make the otherwise obscure effects of oil pollution visible to wider audiences.

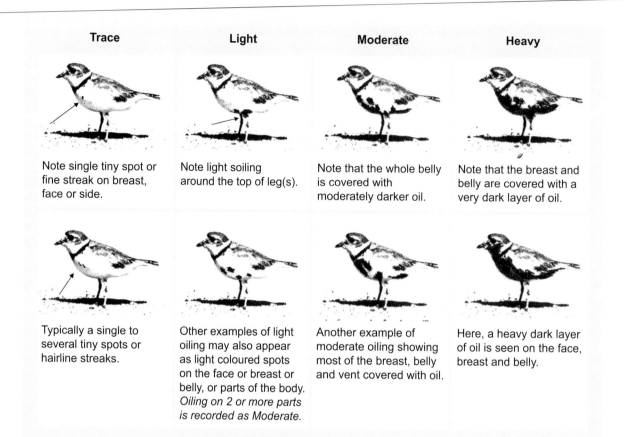

| Trace | Light | Moderate | Heavy |
|---|---|---|---|
| Note single tiny spot or fine streak on breast, face or side. | Note light soiling around the top of leg(s). | Note that the whole belly is covered with moderately darker oil. | Note that the breast and belly are covered with a very dark layer of oil. |
| Typically a single to several tiny spots or hairline streaks. | Other examples of light oiling may also appear as light coloured spots on the face or breast or belly, or parts of the body. *Oiling on 2 or more parts is recorded as Moderate.* | Another example of moderate oiling showing most of the breast, belly and vent covered with oil. | Here, a heavy dark layer of oil is seen on the face, breast and belly. |

Figure 6.6   A guide on bird oiling levels provided by the LA Bird Response Working Group to enable citizen reporting (Source: LA Bird Response Working Group, 2010)

**Citizen science**
Citizen science' a glossed term, with the definition

The washing ashore of the Deepwater Horizon oil slick coincided with migrations and nesting seasons for shorebird and seabird species around the Gulf. Within days, two **citizen science** projects involving birdwatchers – NestWatch and eBird — were converted into programmes for gathering information on the effects of oil contamination on different bird populations (Fitzpatrick, 2012). Citizen science, as the Open University's Jonathan Silvertown explains, involves volunteers contributing to scientific inquiry by collecting data and sometimes helping to process it: a practice greatly facilitated by the use of new technologies for gathering and disseminating information (Silvertown, 2009). It is proving particularly successful in ecology and the environmental sciences. There are projects in place all around the world, ranging from Khoi-San animal trackers in Southern Africa using mobile wireless technologies to report on wildlife distribution through to the Open University's iSpot, a social networking site in which amateur natural historians receive community and professional help in identifying sightings of plants and wildlife (Silvertown, 2009).

The NestWatch and eBird projects quickly developed a system of specialised tools and protocols through which local observers could input information – such as the degree of oil contamination visible on the plumage of individual birds – to centralised databases (LA Bird Response Working Group, 2010) (Figures 6.6 and 6.7). Over the summer of 2010, some 4000 local participants provided over 120,000 observations (Gardiner, 2011). Oil Reporter – another citizen science project which used downloadable applications for smartphones – involved participants uploading photos and videos of oil slicks and wildlife affected by oil pollution (Oil Reporter, 2010).

Citizen science is not just about wildlife and habitats, however. The emergence of new initiatives associated with the Deepwater Horizon event built on a much longer tradition of popular participation in scientific data gathering in the Gulf region, one that has a strong environmental justice orientation. A major actor in the documentation of the oil spill was the Louisiana Bucket Brigade (LABB) (Box 6.3). The LABB is an influential environmental health and justice organisation which collaborated with local communities and other organisations to produce an interactive oil spill crisis map which recorded both oil sightings and health problems believed to be associated with the spill (LABB, 2012a).

# OILED BIRD MONITORING FORM

DATE (MM/DD/YYYY): _____   NAME:_____

LOCATION:_____   PHONE & EMAIL:_____

WIND:_____   PRECIP:_____   CLOUD COVER (%):_____   START TIME:_____   END TIME:_____

TRAVEL DISTANCE (MI):_____   START LAT/LONG:_____   DIRECTION TRAVELED:_____

BINOCULARS: Y / N      SPOTTING SCOPE: Y / N      SURVEY BY: foot / car* / boat / stationary

BEACH CONDITIONS: WRACK:_____   HUMANS:_____   GARBAGE:_____   TAR BALLS:_____   OIL:_____

LOCATION NOTES: _____

| SPECIES | COUNT | OIL CONTAMINATION | BEHAVIOR | NOTES |
|---|---|---|---|---|
| | | | | |
| | | | | |
| | | | | |
| | | | | |
| | | | | |
| | | | | |
| | | | | |
| | | | | |

Figure 6.7   A monitoring form provided by the LA Bird Response Working Group for citizens reporting oiled birds following the Deepwater Horizon oil spill (Source: LA Bird Response Working Group, 2010)

## Box 6.3 The environmental justice movement and the bucket brigades

An environmental justice movement emerged in the southern states of the USA in the early 1980s in response to a growing awareness that environmentally polluting or hazardous economic activities – such as oil refineries and waste dumps – were disproportionately located close to African American, Hispanic, indigenous and other low-income communities (Bullard, 1994). These communities often appeared to suffer higher incidences of health problems than their more privileged counterparts. The corridor of oil refineries and petrochemical plants lining the Mississippi River between New Orleans and Baton Rouge – known locally as 'Cancer Alley' – was one of the epicentres of the emergence of the movement (Berry, 2003; Godsil et al., 2009) (Figure 6.8). Environmental sociologist Robert Bullard, whom you read about in relation to the critique of Nimbyism (Chapter 1, Section 3), is a key figure in the campaign for environmental justice, which draws inspiration from the American civil rights movements of the 1950s and 1960s.

Grassroots community resistance to undesirable environmental activities has played a central role in the environmental justice movement (Bullard and Johnson, 2000). A crucial strategy of the movement has been the deployment of 'bucket brigades' in which local people use simple, cheap devices to take air samples which are then sent off to be analysed in laboratories. The Louisiana Bucket Brigade (LABB) was formed in 1999, to capitalise on a successful campaign in the community of Mossville, where samples taken by local residents revealed atmospheric levels of the carcinogenic chemical benzene 220 times higher than the state standard. LABB trains communities to take samples and submit reports, as well as lobbying state and federal decision makers (LABB, 2011). Bucket brigades have since achieved successes throughout Louisiana, across the USA and as far away as Durban, South Africa.

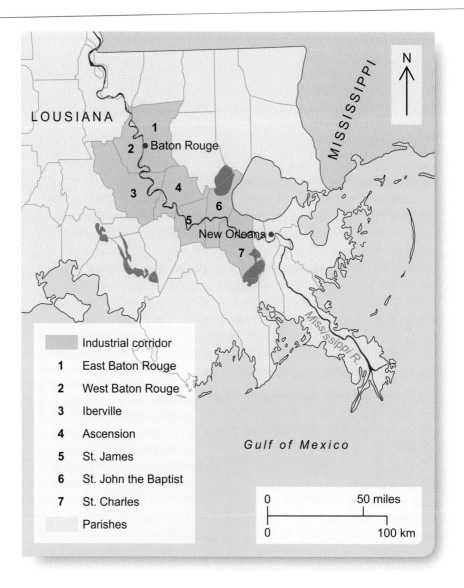

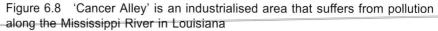

Figure 6.8   'Cancer Alley' is an industrialised area that suffers from pollution along the Mississippi River in Louisiana

The LABB followed up its citizen participation activities on the spill with a major community survey of health and economic impacts of the disaster on four coastal Louisiana parishes. The survey found that nearly half the respondents reported health symptoms consistent with chemical exposure, 44 per cent reported that the primary economic provider in the home had been affected by the crisis, while 64 per cent indicated concerns about seafood contamination (LABB, 2012b).

One of the remarkable features of popular engagement with the Deepwater Horizon crisis was the widespread participation in the construction and interpretation of maps. SkyTruth is a non-profit organisation that uses satellite images to gather evidence about the environmental consequences of human activity across the planet, which it makes available to environmental and citizens groups. As its website explains: 'Satellite images allow us to see what's happening in places that we could never visit in person, and on a grand scale that only astronauts experience firsthand' (SkyTruth, 2007). In the early days of the crisis, SkyTruth successfully challenged BP and federal official estimates of the volume of oil being released, resulting in revised daily estimate some five times higher (Cart, 2010).

Another innovative project used low-cost aerial photography to counter official under-reporting of the spill, and to work around the restriction on flying over the affected area imposed by the Federal Aviation Authority after the accident. Working closely with the Louisiana Bucket Brigade, the Public Laboratory for Open Technology and Science (PLOTS) group used cameras rigged to kites and balloons to produce extensive photographic maps of spill-impacted areas (PLOTS, 2011a). The project involved training local community groups to take their own airborne photographs – using aerial rigs costing under $200. Volunteers uploaded over 11,000 images between May and July 2010 (Warren, 2010). As well as being able to bridge the scale between ground-based observations and satellite images, the composite maps produced by the project provided detailed 'before and after' shots which helped track the impact of the oil on ecosystems and economies (Warren, 2010, pp. 70–1). As ecologist John Fitzpatrick concluded in the aftermath of the spill, 'While the longer term ecological consequences of the Deepwater Horizon disaster remain unclear at this writing, the immediate and large-scale monitoring of its specific, short-term impacts became a milestone achievement in citizen science' (Fitzpatrick, 2012, p. 240).

In previous chapters we have explored the importance of the concepts of space and time for understanding the dynamics of physical and social processes. Space and time, however, are more than just tools we can utilise for gauging and tracking complex processes. We can see from citizen science mapping projects in the Gulf that how space and time are represented is itself open to contestation. Working at a range of different spatial scales and time intervals, campaigners have demonstrated that it is possible to generate their own framings of space and time, which may contest the 'official' views put forward by large corporations or state agencies. As PLOTS activists have put it: 'Maps are often used by those in power to exert influence over territory, or control territorial narratives. "Grassroots mapping" attempts to invert this dynamic by using maps as a mode of communication and as evidence for an alternative, community-owned definition of a territory' (PLOTS, 2011b). Or to put it another way, how space and time are framed and experienced is also a matter of power. Working together, well-organised groups of citizens – who may have only limited resources – may be able to substantially influence environmental discourses. New political agendas can be established by bringing otherwise obscure events and processes into visibility – and making sure they stay visible.

# 4   Forming issues, convening publics

Through our examination of the Deepwater Horizon oil spill we have explored the concept of an **environmental issue**. We may now define an environmental issue as *an undesired condition or change in the environment which prompts actors to engage publicly.* As we have seen, to make an environmental condition or an environmental change into an issue requires that it be made visible. To present something as an 'issue' is more than just suffering in silence. Those who are affected – directly or indirectly – by an environmental problem must seek to make others aware of it.

**Environmental issue**
An undesired condition or change in the environment which prompts actors to engage publicly.

The commonsensical view of 'making an issue' of something is that an appeal is made to 'the public'. Recall, for example, the claim made in the *America's Gulf Coast* report: 'the attention of the media and the public is beginning to shift elsewhere' (Mabus, 2010, p. i). Such a view assumes that 'the public', at least in a (more or less) democratic society, is already out there. 'The public', in this sense, is seen as a pre-existing collective body. There is, however, a social science view, not of 'a public' (singular) but of 'publics' (plural), that is somewhat different. On this view, there is not one big preformed public 'out there' waiting to be sparked into life by bacterial blooms, chemical residues or balloon photography. Rather, a 'public' is group of interested or troubled people who come together over objects of concern, such as these different components which made up the 'issue' of the Deepwater Horizon spill (Barnett, 2008; Marres, 2007).

There are, in this sense, different, although often overlapping, publics for different issues. And where there is not yet an issue, or where an issue has fizzled out, there is – effectively – no concerned public. According to this way of thinking, issues and publics are co-constituted. A public is a group that convenes in order to make an issue visible; an issue is what emerges as a public works itself into existence over a matter of common concern. This is what we mean by an issue prompting actors 'to engage publicly' (Figure 6.9).

(a)                                                                    (b)

Figure 6.9   Two examples of a public seeking to make an issue visible: (a) Protesters in the UK demonstrating against nuclear weapons, organised by the Campaign for Nuclear Disarmament (CND); (b) A protest against the expansion of Heathrow Airport, at the Houses of Parliament in London

This has implications not just for how we think about publics, but for how we conceive of politics generally. On this view, the mutual formation of publics and issues becomes the very pivot around which the more conventional or 'official' aspects of political processes revolve. As sociologist Bruno Latour has argued, when it comes to deciding what counts as politics, the processes through which issues and publics take shape are at least as important as the more formal procedures involving elections, parliamentary debates and policy making that we tend to think of as the definitive features of politics. What we need to do, he argues, is to 'make politics turn around topics that generate a public around them' (Latour, 2007, p. 814). Or, as another sociologist, Noortje Marres, emphatically puts it, 'No issue, no politics!' (quoted in Latour, 2007, p. 815).

This is closely related to the idea of power as discourse (Chapter 3, Section 2). It is through the mutual formation of publics and issues that new matters of concern arise, and it becomes possible to speak of new issues that have not previously been on the political agenda. The idea that the emergence of publics and issues is the key to modern politics is not entirely new, for it draws on the writing of American pragmatist philosopher John Dewey. Dewey's *The Public and Its Problems* (1927) is concerned with the ways in which publics form in response to the consequences of human agency in modern societies. As he puts it, 'the public consists of all those who are affected by the indirect consequences of transactions, to such an extent that it is deemed necessary to have those consequences systematically cared for' (Dewey, 1927, pp. 15–16).

Marres (2007) draws out the contemporary significance of Dewey's thoughts on issue-driven politics. Dewey, she points out, had a prescient understanding of the way that issues emerge precisely out of contexts in which conventional political procedures and topics of debate cannot cope. Modern technological societies generate new kinds of events, Dewey recognised, which are not the kind of things that conventional parliamentary politics was intended to deal with. Dewey, writing in the 1920s, refers to changes associated with new 'inventions in means of transit, transportation and intercommunication' (1927, p. 44), while Marres, writing 80 years later, gives the examples of genetically modified food, radioactive fallout and climate change (Marres, 2007, 2010). As Marres (2010) puts it, issues arise when the procedures and assumptions of institutionalised politics are exceeded by events – especially those that are harmful, indirect, extensive and enduring.

'Harmful, indirect, extensive and enduring' is an apt description of the social and environmental consequences of the Deepwater Horizon disaster. Indeed, it's a neat summing up of many contemporary environmental conditions. It captures the risks and uncertainties associated with environmental issues, as well as the disturbing way that effects seem to move across space and time. Well before the rise of the modern environmental movement, then, Dewey came to the realisation that the conditions that spark public issues – groups of actors experiencing the negative impacts of events and actively seeking to do something about them – were constantly being produced in the everyday life of the modern world.

Dewey was also aware, however, that the kinds of new material or technological developments that can generate harmful consequences also provide opportunities for forming publics and holding them together. For Dewey, the media play a crucial role in forging and sustaining public involvement. He argues that the publics that configure around the harmful consequences of human action depend for their survival and their effectiveness on publicity media (Dewey, 1927; see also Marres, 2010). In this way, changes in what Dewey called 'material culture' (1927, p. 44) generate new problems; but they also help actors to gather, communicate and extend their values and concerns to others near and far.

## 4.1   Ingredients of issue formation and publicity

The approach to environmental issues and their formation developed in Chapters 5 and 6 directs attention to the processes by which publics and issues are formed, and to the different 'ingredients' out of which public issues are composed (Mahony et al., 2010).

This approach encourages us to see that environmental issues are inevitably composed of more than human things. They include harmful and risky activities that trigger anxious responses. As we have seen, there are often real challenges in rendering objects of environmental concern visible. In the case of the Deepwater Horizon spill, the process of issue formation and knowledge production has brought previously obscure bacteria and benthic life into visibility. Gulf communities have publicised the ongoing effects of oil and chemical pollution by presenting evidence of the mutations in harvested marine creatures, such as eyeless shrimps and clawless crabs (Jamail, 2012) (Figure 6.10).

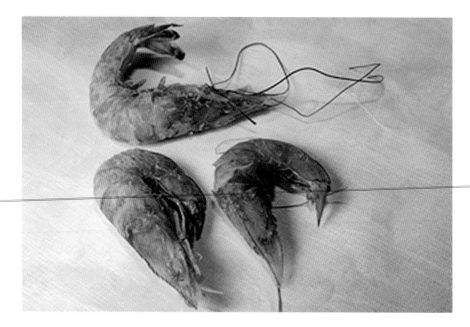

Figure 6.10   Eyeless shrimps in the Gulf of Mexico are believed to have suffered mutations as a result of the 2010 Deepwater Horizon oil spill

As well as bringing undesirable environmental states and changes to light, issue formation and definition also entails establishing cause-and-effect relations. We have seen that citizens have been active in this respect. From the use of air-sampling 'buckets' through to monitoring oil-contaminated wildlife or the human health consequences of exposure to oil and chemical dispersants, different 'apparatuses' have been employed to make contentious objects visible, and to substantiate their harmful or dangerous impacts (Latour, 2005; Stengers, 2010). This is partly a scientific process, by which expert scientists and citizen scientists present the evidence they have gathered. But it also has an element of drama or performance through which the existence and effects of harmful objects are 'acted out' in order to attract the attention of other actors.

When a group of concerned people gather together to make an environmental change or condition 'visible', they are, in the process, also making themselves 'visible', both to other citizens with shared interests, and to those whose attention and commitment they are trying to attract. When balloon-mapping activist Jeffrey Warren describes the experience of documenting the Deepwater Horizon oil spill, he consciously evokes a process of forming groups and identities:

> Throughout the project, we made partnerships with a variety of other organizations to share boat trips, imagery, and to collaborate directly on capturing imagery – among these were the Blue Seals, Greenpeace, Americorps, and many individuals who volunteered their time, money and abilities. This dense web of collaborations has formed a backbone of support for the effort, and ensured its regularity and sustainability. While the urgency of the disaster itself surely played a role in forging such a network of mutual support, such strong local participation must be an integral part of any participatory mapping effort which expects to be sustained beyond an initial burst of enthusiasm.
>
> (Warren, 2010, p. 75)

In this account, groups of individuals are weaving themselves together to compose a public. Actions such as surveying the people or wildlife affected by oil pollution, attaching cameras to balloons or collecting air samples in 'buckets' are also performances. Like protest marches or street theatre, they are activities that build solidarity among those who are already involved, while at the same time seeking to attract the attention of those who are not yet involved.

The approach suggested here also points to the significance of venues where publics can convene to work up, and work on, issues. This includes conventional public meeting places such as town halls or city squares. It may also include the wetlands where evidence is being gathered or the beaches where community clean-ups are taking place. Or it could involve the websites or smartphone networks through which information is assembled, collated and shared. More than a matter of sustaining conversation between those already concerned, the process of achieving and gaining 'publicity' also involves attempts to communicate messages to wider audiences. In this regard, experiments with new participative or interactive media – using, for example, smartphones or web-based grassroots maps – are ways of deepening involvement. But they can also serve to attract the interest of the mass media, and further broaden the audience base.

# 5   Summary

The Deepwater Horizon crisis needs to be viewed within the wider context of a range of environmental drivers and threats operating in the Gulf of Mexico. In response to the oil spill and other undesirable environmental conditions and changes in the Gulf region, local people have communicated and cooperated in a variety of different ways in order to make the environmental problems they face visible to the wider world. Environmental issues and the publics who are concerned about these issues emerge together. In this respect they are co-constituted. We have seen that the formation of an environmental issue and the emergence of a public around such an issue are likely to include the following elements:

- the ecological and social processes that trigger anxiety or concern
- the procedures for bringing unfamiliar or disturbing things into visibility
- the people who are affected, or at risk of being affected, who consider the environmental condition or change to be unacceptable
- a desire on the part of at least some of these people to contest the environmental problem politically
- the venues at which concerned people gather
- the claims through which effects are linked to causes
- the media and the performances through which concerned people communicate with each other and with the wider world.

# References

Alden Wily, L. (2011) '"The law is to blame." Taking a hard look at the vulnerable status of customary land rights in Africa', *Development and Change*, vol. 42, no. 3, pp. 733–57.

Aldhous, P., McKenna, P. and Stier, C. (2010) 'Gulf leak: biggest spill may not be biggest disaster', *New Scientist*, no. 2764, 12 June, pp. 6–7 [online], http://www.newscientist.com/article/dn19016-gulf-leak-biggest-spill-may-not-be-biggest-disaster.html (Accessed 14 July 2012).

Barnett, C. (2008) 'Convening publics: the parasitical spaces of public action', in Cox, K. R., Low, M. and Robinson, J. (eds) *The Sage Handbook of Political Geography*, London, Sage.

Beck, M. W., Brumbaugh, R. D., Airoldi, L., Carranza, A., Coen, L. D., Crawford, C., Defeo, O., Edgar, G. J., Hancock, B., Kay, M. C., Lenihan, H. S., Luckenbach, M. W., Toropova, C. L., Zhang, G. and Guo, X. (2011) 'Oyster reefs at risk and recommendations for conservation, restoration, and management', *BioScience*, vol. 61, no. 2, pp. 107–16 [online], doi: http://dx.doi.org.libezproxy.open.ac.uk/10.1525/bio.2011.61.2.5 (Accessed 15 July 2012).

Berkes, F. (1999) *Sacred Ecology: Traditional Ecological Knowledge and Resource Management*, Philadelphia, PA, Taylor & Francis.

Berry, G. R. (2003) 'Organising against multinational corporate power in Cancer Alley', *Organization and Environment*, vol. 16, no. 3, pp. 3–32.

Brown, C. K., Andrews, J., Brenner, J. W., Tunnell, C., Canfield, C., Dorsett, M., Driscoll, E. and Johnson, S. K. (2011) *Strategy for Restoring the Gulf of Mexico*, Arlington, VA, The Nature Conservancy.

Bullard, R. D. (1994) *Dumping in Dixie: Race, Class and Environmental Quality*, Boulder, CO, Westview Press.

Bullard, R. D. and Johnson, G. S. (2000) 'Environmental justice: grassroots activism and its impact on public policy decision making', *Journal of Social Issues*, vol. 56, no. 3, pp. 555–78.

Cart, J. (2010) 'Tiny group has big impact on spill estimates', *Los Angeles Times*, 1 May [online], http://articles.latimes.com/2010/may/01/nation/la-na-oil-spill-measure-20100502 (Accessed 14 July 2012).

Dewey, J. (1927) *The Public and Its Problems*, Athens, OH, Ohio University Press.

Farber, D. A. (2011) 'The BP blowout and the social and environmental erosion of the Louisiana coast', *UC Berkeley Public Law Research Paper No. 1740844* [online], http://ssrn.com/abstract=1740844 (Accessed 14 July 2012).

Fautin, D., Dalton, P., Incze, L. S., Leong, J.-A. C., Pautzke, C., Rosenberg, A., Sandifer, P., Sedberry, G., Tunnell J. W., Abbott, I., Brainard, R. E. Brodeur, M., Eldredge, L. G., Feldman, M., Moretzsohn, F., Vroom, P. S., Wainstein, M. and Wolff, N. (2010) 'An overview of marine biodiversity in United States waters', *PLoS ONE*, vol. 5, no. 8 [online], http://www.plosone.org/article/info:doi/10.1371/journal.pone.0011914 (Accessed 14 July 2012).

Fitzpatrick, J. W. (2012) 'Afterword', in Dickinson, J. L. and Rick Bonney, R. (eds) *Citizen Science: Public Participation in Environmental Research*, Ithaca, NY, and London, Comstock Publishing Associates.

Gardiner, L. (2011) 'An oily year for citizen scientists on the GulfCoast', *Talking Science*, 21 April [online], http://www.talkingscience.org/2011/04/an-oily-year-for-citizen-scientists-on-the-gulf-coast/ (Accessed 14 July 2012).

Godsil, R., Huang, A. and Solomon, G. (2009) 'Contaminants in the air and soil in New Orleans after the flood: opportunities and limitations for community empowerment', in Bullard, R. and Wright, B (eds) *Race, Place, and Environmental Justice after Hurricane Katrina*, Boulder, CO, Westview Press.

Gordon, K., Buchanan, J. and Singerman, P. with Madrid, J. and Busch, S. (2011) *Beyond Recovery: Moving the Gulf Coast Toward a Sustainable Future*, Washington, DC, Center for American Progress/Oxfam America [online], http://www.oxfamamerica.org/publications/beyond-recovery-moving-the-gulf-coast-toward-a-sustainable-future (Accessed 14 July).

Gulf Coast Ecosystem Restoration Task Force (2011) *Gulf Of Mexico Regional Ecosystem Restoration Strategy*, December [online], http://www.epa.gov/gcertf/pdfs/GulfCoastReport_Full_12-04_508-1.pdf (Accessed 14 July 2012).

Gulf Coast Fishermen, Seafood Workers and Maritime Communities (2010) 'Statement of Gulf Coast fishermen, seafood workers and maritime communities on the Gulf of Mexico oil drilling disaster' [online], http://www.ehumanrights.org/docs/Fishers_et_al_Statement_10-05-13.pdf (Accessed 14 July 2012).

Gulf of Mexico Alliance (GOMA) (2009) *Governor's Action Plan II: For Healthy and Resilient Coasts 2009–2014* [online], http://www.gulfofmexicoalliance.org/pdfs/ap2_final2.pdf (Accessed 14 July 2012).

Harte Institute (2012) 'Why the Gulf of Mexico?' [online], www.harteresearchinstitute.org/the-institute/why-gulf (Accessed 14 July 2012).

Jamail, D. (2012) 'Gulf seafood deformities alarm scientists', *Al Jazeera*, 20 April [online], http://www.aljazeera.com/indepth/features/2012/04/201241682318260912.html (Accessed 15 July 2012).

LA Bird Response Working Group (2010). *A Citizen Scientist's Protocol for Monitoring Oiled Birds in Louisiana*, Louisiana State University School of Renewable Natural Resources, LSU AgCenter and Baton Rouge Audubon Society [online], http://www.braudubon.org/pdf/volunteer_oil_survey_packet_LA.pdf (Accessed 14 July 2012).

Latour, B. (2005) 'From realpolitik to dingpolitik or how to make things public', in Latour, B. and Weibel, P. (eds) *Making Things Public: Atmospheres of Democracy*, Karlsruhe and Cambridge, MA, ZKM Centre for Art and Media and MIT Press.

Latour, B. (2007) 'Turning around politics: a note on Gerard de Vries' paper', *Social Studies of Science*, vol. 37, no. 5, pp. 811–20.

Louisiana Bucket Brigade (LABB) (2011) 'Oil spill response' [online], http://www.labucketbrigade.org/section.php?id=148 (Accessed 15 July 2012).

Louisiana Bucket Brigade (LABB) (2012a) *iWitness Pollution Map* [online], http://map.labucketbrigade.org/ (Accessed 15 July 2012).

Louisiana Bucket Brigade (LABB) (2012b) *The BP Oil Disaster: Results from a Health and Economic Impacts Survey in Four Coastal Louisiana Parishes* [online], http://www.labucketbrigade.org/downloads/2010_HEStudy_SummaryFINAL_1.pdf (Accessed 15 July 2012).

Mabus, R. (2010) *America's Gulf Coast: A Long Term Recovery Plan after the Deepwater Horizon Oil Spill*, United States Government [online], http://www.restorethegulf.gov/release/2010/09/28/america%E2%80%99s-gulf-coast-long-term-recovery-plan-after-deepwater-horizon-oil-spill (Accessed 15 July 2012).

McClelland, M. (2010) '"It's BP's Oil": running the corporate blockade at Louisiana's crude-covered beaches', *Mother Jones*, 24 May [online], http://www.motherjones.com/environment/2010/05/oil-spill-bp-grand-isle-beach (Accessed 15 July 2012).

Mahony, N., Newman, J. and Barnett, C. (2010) 'Introduction: rethinking the public', in Mahony, N., Newman, J. and Barnett, C. (eds) *Rethinking the Public: Innovations in Research, Theory and Politics*, Bristol, The Policy Press.

Marres, N. (2007) 'The issues deserve more credit: pragmatist contributions to the study of public involvement in controversy', *Social Studies of Science*, vol. 37, no. 5, pp. 759–80.

Marres, N. (2010) 'Front-staging nonhumans: publicity as a constraint on the political activity of things', in Braun, B. and Whatmore, S. (eds) *Political Matter: Technoscience, Democracy, and Public Life*, Minneapolis, MN, University of Minnesota Press.

National Oceanic and Atmospheric Administration (NOAA) (2010) *Report to Congress on the Implementation of the Deep Sea Coral Research and Technology Program, 2008–2009*, Silver Spring, MD, NOAA [online], http://coris.noaa.gov/activities/reportcongress_dscrtp_2010/ (Accessed 15 July 2012).

National Oceanic and Atmospheric Administration (NOAA) (2011) *The Gulf of Mexico at a Glance: A Second Glance*, Washington, DC, US Department of Commerce [online], http://stateofthecoast.noaa.gov/NOAAs_Gulf_of_Mexico_at_a_Glance_report.pdf (Accessed 15 July 2012).

Oil Reporter (2010) *Oil Reporter* [online], http://oilreporter.org/ (Accessed 15 July 2012).

Osofsky, H. M., Baxter-Kauf, K. M., Hammer, B., Mailander, A., Mares, B., Pikovsky, A., Whitney, A. and Wilson, L. (2011) 'Environmental justice and the BP Deepwater Horizon oil spill', *New York University Environmental Law Journal*, vol. 20, no. 1 (forthcoming) [online], http://ssrn.com/abstract=1949421 (Accessed 15 July 2012).

Pigou, A.C (1952 [1920]) *The Economics of Welfare*, London, Macmillan.

Public Laboratory for Open Technology and Science (PLOTS) (2011a) 'Gulf Coast: Deepwater Horizon oil spill mapping 2010–2011' [online], http://publiclaboratory.org/place/gulf-coast (Accessed 15 July 2012).

Public Laboratory for Open Technology and Science (PLOTS) (2011b) 'Balloon & kite mapping' [online], http://publiclaboratory.org/tool/balloon-mapping (Accessed 15 July 2012).

Rabalais, N. N. (2011) 'Twelfth Annual Roger Revelle Commemorative Lecture: Troubled Waters of the Gulf of Mexico', *Oceanography*, vol. 24, no. 2, pp. 200–11; [online], http://www.tos.org/oceanography/archive/24-2_rabalais.pdf (Accessed 15 July 2012).

Robertson, C. (2010) 'Gulf of Mexico has long been dumping site', *New York Times*, 29 July [online], http://www.nytimes.com/2010/07/30/us/30gulf.html?_r=1 (Accessed 4 September 2012).

Sheppard, K. (2010) 'BP's bad breakup: how toxic is Corexit?' *Mother Jones*, September/October [online], http://www.motherjones.com/environment/2010/09/bp-ocean-dispersant-corexit (Accessed July 2012).

Silvertown, J. (2009) 'A new dawn for citizen science', *Trends in Ecology & Evolution*, vol. 24, no. 9, pp. 467–71.

SkyTruth (2007) 'What's new' [online], http://www.skytruth.org/ (Accessed 15 July 2012).

Stengers, I. (2010) 'Including nonhumans in political theory: opening Pandora's Box', in Braun, B. and Whatmore, S. (eds) *Political Matter: Technoscience, Democracy, and Public Life*, Minneapolis, MN, University of Minnesota Press.

Sturgis, S. and Kromm, C. (2012) *Troubled Waters: Two Years After the BP Oil Disaster, A Struggling Gulf Coast Calls for National Leadership for Recovery*, Durham, NC, The Institute for Southern Studies [online], http://www.southernstudies.org/2012/04/troubled-waters-two-years-into-bps-oil-disaster-gulf-communities-struggle-to-recover.html (Accessed 15 July 2012).

Sumaila, U.R., Cisneros-Montemayor, A. M., Dyck, A., Huang, L., Cheung, W., Jacquet, J., Kleisner, K., Lam, V., McCrea-Strub, A., Swartz, W., Watson, R., Zeller, D. and Pauly, D. (2012) 'Impact of the Deepwater Horizon well blowout on the economics of US Gulf fisheries', *Canadian Journal Of Fisheries And Aquatic Sciences*, vol. 69, pp. 499–510.

Tidwell, M. (2006) *The Ravaging Tide: Strange Weather, Future Katrinas, and the Coming Death of America's Coastal Cities*, New York, Free Press.

Tunnell, J. W., Jr (2009) 'Gulf of Mexico', in Earle, S. A. and Glover, L. K. (eds) *Ocean: An Illustrated Atlas*, Washington, DC, National Geographic Society.

van der Straaten, J. and Gordon, M. (1995) 'Environmental problems from an economic perspective', in Glasbergen, P. and Blowers, A. (eds) *Environmental Policy in an International Context: Perspectives*, London, Arnold.

Warren, J. Y. (2010) 'Chapter 8: Case Study: Citizen mapping of the BP oil spill', in *Grassroots Mapping: Tools for Participatory and Activist Cartography*, MSc thesis, Massachusetts Institute of Technology [online], http://unterbahn.com/thesis/ (Accessed 15 July 2012).

White House Council on Environmental Quality (2010) *Roadmap for Restoring Ecosystem Resiliency and Sustainability*, Washington, DC, The White House [online], http://www.whitehouse.gov/administration/eop/ceq/initiatives/gulfcoast/roadmap (Accessed 15 July 2012).

# Chapter 7   Valuing nature

Philip O'Sullivan and Victoria A. Johnson

# Contents

# 1 Introduction

'Disasters provide an important and continuing point of reference by compelling us to revise our perceptions on the value of nature and natural processes' wrote environmental lawyer Keith Hirokawa following the Deepwater Horizon oil spill (Hirokawa, 2011, p. 547). We have seen that dramatic environmental change can help generate new scientific and public understandings of how natural processes operate. Actors concerned about environmental change may forge themselves into a public in the process of bringing an issue into visibility. But in a world of constant change and complex conditions, this still leaves the question of why some conditions or changes are undesired, and some are not. And what prompts people to care enough to take a political stand?

To approach this question we now examine some of the different ways in which people value nature. Many people have well-entrenched values – including ways of valuing nature – in advance of issue formation. An understanding of values thus helps us to understand whether, and in what ways, people care about the environment and how environmental issues arise and are defined. But social and personal values are not static entities; they may themselves change in response to environmental change.

## 2 The all-affected principle

Throughout the module so far, we have examined environmental predicaments in which places are caught up in changes whose causes extend far beyond those places. Indeed, it could be argued that all environmental challenges, to some degree, have causal factors that stretch across space and time beyond the particular sites where they make themselves felt. With regard to changes brought about by Earth and life processes, this has always been the case. In relation to changes that result, at least in part, from social processes, this is increasingly the case in a world that is undergoing globalisation.

### Activity 7.1 Globalisation

Can you recall the definition of 'globalisation' from Chapter 2?

### Comment

Globalisation is the intensification and extensification of social relations around the world, with action in one geographical space influencing events elsewhere.

**All-affected principle**
The idea that all who are affected by an action should participate in decisions on that action.

A general principle has emerged that is now regularly invoked in response to people being affected by actions arising largely or entirely in other places. This is the **all-affected principle** (Barnett and Bridge, 2012; Dobson, 2010). According to this principle, all those people who are affected by actions – irrespective of where those actions and the actors behind them are located – should participate in decisions on the actions in question. To put it simply 'what affects all must be agreed to by all' (Tully, 2008, p. 74; quoted in Barnett and Bridge, 2012, p. 4). So if 'your' oil tanker creates a spill that impacts on 'our' coastline, then 'we' should have a say in the decisions on the presence or otherwise of tankers off our coast. Those who come together over a shared affectedness form a 'community of affected interests' (Dobson, 2010, p. 754): what we have referred to as a 'public'.

Although the all-affected principle is still new and evolving, it is influencing how social scientists work with the ideas of values, power and agency. As a particular value-based idea, the all-affected principle proposes that power and political agency should be distributed across political borders. It assumes that people should be able to have a say in the deliberations of political spaces, such as other countries, in which they are not members (Barnett and Bridge, 2012). In other words, the right to participate in decision making should no longer be exclusively connected to a specified geographical space, such as citizenship of a country. Decision makers in globalised political spaces – such as business corporations, financial service networks and international organisations – are now increasingly being held accountable for their actions by those who are affected by them.

Even though the Deepwater Horizon spill happened off the coast of the USA, the main actor responsible – BP – was a UK-based multinational corporation. But the people of the Gulf Coast demanded, as affected parties, participation in the affairs associated with the spill. This illustrates that issue formation and the gathering of a public is not necessarily bound by national or community boundaries. Rather, it follows lines of cause and effect and includes all those affected by the consequences.

The all-affected principle is now invoked in many different situations worldwide, although it forms more of a general 'intuition' or expectation rather than a legally valid principle.

## Activity 7.2   The all-affected principle

Can you recall other examples from the module where people have taken action arising from a common experience of being affected, rather than on the basis of belonging to a shared political constituency or geographical space?

### Comment

Examples include coastal erosion, climate change, managing the flight paths of migrating birds, and land grabs. The all-affected principle is also key to claims for environmental justice.

The all-affected principle has been behind many political struggles. Environmental problems have an especially pronounced tendency to move across political boundaries and in this sense have played a major role in the growing acceptance of the principle. But the principle itself is more of a beginning than an end; agreeing the principle is far easier than putting it into practice in a meaningful way (Dobson, 2010).

Note that so far we have been focusing on other people participating in affairs that affect them. But the consequences of actions extend not just over space within the present generation; they also extend over time to affect future generations. So, and as political philosopher Andrew Dobson (Figure 7.1) notes, intergenerational equity raises questions for the all-affected principle: people who are very young or not yet born have no voice in decision making about activities now taking place (Dobson, 2010).

Figure 7.1  Political philosopher Andrew Dobson has argued that the all-affected principle should be expanded to apply to young children, future generations and all species that will be affected by anthropogenic environmental change

Dobson makes a second point. At the heart of much environmental thought and practice is the intuition that it is not only humans who are 'affected' by harmful environmental changes and conditions (Dobson, 2010, p. 754). Non-human species, ecosystems and other aspects of the natural world are also affected. But how can those non-human life forms have a 'say' in environmental issues and the activities that trigger them?

# 3 Environmental goods and the commons

Before turning to the question of whether, and if so how, nature should have a 'voice' in decision making, it is important first to obtain a sense of how difficult it is to apply the all-affected principle to those human beings who have lost things they value through environmental change.

Speaking of the aftermath of the Deepwater Horizon spill, environmental lawyer Melissa Daigle recounts: 'Two of the questions I hear most often when I talk to coastal residents are: How much is a pelican worth? And, when do I get my check for not being able to fish (recreationally) this summer?' (Daigle, 2011, p. 266). While there may be an element of humour in these enquiries, they hint at how people may value both nature and their own livelihoods, believing that they deserve compensation when the actions of others negatively affect their welfare. In some cases, such compensation could be matter of economic and even physical survival for a family or community.

Many people affected by the Deepwater Horizon spill have claimed damages from BP under the US Oil Pollution Act of 1990. This act allows 'the United States, a state, an Indian tribe, or a foreign government' to recover for '[d]amages for injury to, destruction of, loss of, or loss of use of, natural resources, including the reasonable costs of assessing the damage' (quoted in Daigle, 2011, p. 255). This legislation was a response to the *Exxon Valdez* oil spill of 1989 and its impacts on Alaskan communities. These communities formed organisations to fight for compensation and to ensure that their local knowledge of coastal life was brought to bear on settlements for natural damage (Gordon et al., 2011).

But putting a monetary value on ecosystem damage is a complex process, and a branch of economics – environmental economics – has emerged to deal with the pricing of environmental goods (Burgess, 2003, p. 261). Note that the term 'good' is used here to include what are often referred to as services as well as tangible goods (Box 7.1).

**Private good**

A good that is rival and excludable.

**Public good**

A good that is non-rival and non-excludable.

## Box 7.1   Private and public goods

Some environmental goods – private goods – can be traded on markets. A **private good** is 'rival' and 'excludable'. A good is *rival* when consumption by one person reduces what is left for others. So the consumption, of, say, fish or timber means less is left for other consumers. A good is *excludable* when the owner of a good can legally prevent others from enjoying the benefit of the good. Those who buy fish and timber acquire legal rights to the good, and can prevent others from using it. A **public good**, on the other hand, is *non-rival* (consumption by one person does not reduce the amount available for others) and *non-excludable* (no one can be prevented from enjoying the benefits of a public good). Public goods can be provided by nature (e.g. the atmosphere and the oceans) or by human agency (e.g. roads, schools, hospitals and street lighting).

Figure 7.2   The consumption of environmental private goods can proceed without much thought to the consequences, in the process destroying what we value (Source: Eales, 1991)

But the situation becomes more complex when we consider the extraction of private goods from public goods and how this may lead to the degradation of the latter (Figure 7.2). So while the oceans are non-rival and non-excludable, private goods such as fish may be extracted from the oceans. Fish stocks are rival: the more fish I extract the fewer fish are left for others. So if too many fish are extracted from the seas, fish stocks may collapse and marine biodiversity may suffer. Similarly, pollution may kill off fish stocks. In each case, the decline of fish stocks may be seen as a *negative externality* generated, respectively, by those who overfish and those who pollute (Chapter 6, Section 2.2). The oceans are often referred to as a *global common* and in this respect the degradation of the oceans and marine life is often called a *tragedy of the commons* (Chapter 2, Section 4). Another example of the global commons is the atmosphere.

---

## Activity 7.3   Preventing the tragedy of the global commons

You have seen that the atmosphere and the oceans may be considered environmental public goods as well as global commons. Using the example of the oceans, can you propose any solutions to the tragedy of the global commons? You may find the work of Hardin and Pigou helpful here (Chapters 2 and 6).

### Comment

There is no easy answer to this question. However, three possibilities offer themselves from our work so far. Two are suggested by Pigou. The first is to tax or fine those who create negative externalities. So polluters can be fined, as can fisherfolk who overfish (which would require a legally enforceable definition of 'overfishing'). Second, those who create positive externalities can be subsidised by government. So those actors who clean up oil pollution or work to conserve fish stocks can receive payments from the state. A third solution is to restrict or regulate access to the global commons. Hardin argued that restricting access to common land or regulating grazing rights could prevent the tragedy of overgrazing local commons. Similarly, measures could be taken to regulate the access of fishing vessels to the seas, or to regulate their catches. International agreements have been reached on the long-term conservation of fish stocks (United Nations, 1995) and on limiting marine pollution from ships (International Maritime Organisation, 1997), although these agreements are weak and enforcing them is difficult.

---

Because environmental public goods and the **ecosystem services** they provide are non-excludable in the sense that everyone can enjoy them, they are difficult to price. It is therefore difficult to account for them in market prices.

**Ecosystem service**
A benefit that people obtain from an ecological system.

Calculating the costs of any harm done by humans to an ecosystem requires taking into account the diversity of species in the ecosystem and the complex interconnectivity between them. It is also necessary to take into account the resilience of the ecosystem, namely the extent to which it will recover from a disturbance. Environmental economists Paulo Nunes and Jeroen van den Bergh argue that this becomes progressively more difficult the more significant the disturbance and the larger the area the ecosystem covers (Nunes and van den Bergh, 2001).

Economists distinguish between different categories of value. Let us take the case of a forest as an example.

**Use values**
Values that arise from the actual use of a particular environmental good.

**Use values** arise from the actual use of a particular environmental good. These can be subdivided into:

- *direct use values*: the enjoyment or satisfaction received directly from a forest, such as timber, fruits or nuts (private goods)
- *indirect use values*: such as the value of the forest in recreation and in providing watershed regulation and sequestering carbon, thus helping to mitigate climate change (public goods)
- *option use values*: the possible direct use values for the future which have not yet been exploited, or may not yet have been discovered. For example, in many forests plants grow that provide the chemical compounds used for medicines.

**Non-use values**
Values that do not arise from the use of an environmental good.

**Non-use values** are can be divided into two kinds:

- *existence values*: those values that an individual will assign to an environment even if they have not, and never will, use it. For example, many people derive satisfaction from knowing that the Amazon rainforest exists, along with its rich diversity of species. Existence value also encompasses the rights of species to flourish irrespective of what humans think.
- *bequest values*: represent the rights of future generations to experience and enjoy nature.

**Total economic value**
The sum total of the use and non-use values of an environment for present and future generations.

The sum total of the various use and non-use values for present and future generations together comprises **total economic value (TEV)** (Burgess, 2003). TEV contributes to both conservation and economic development (Figures 7.3 and 7.4).

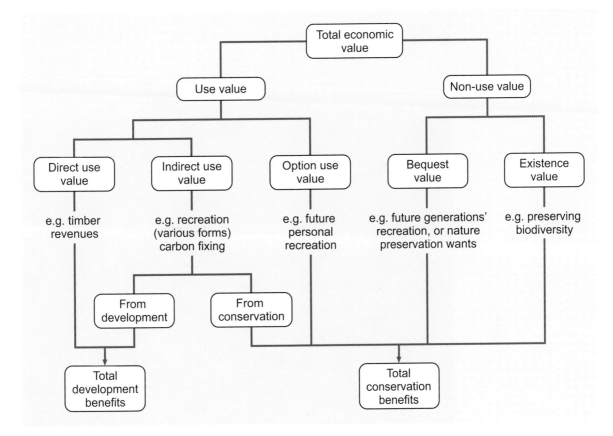

Figure 7.3  A total economic value (TEV) diagram illustrating the various elements comprising the value of a forest

Calculating TEV is an essential part of cost–benefit analysis (CBA) (Chapter 6, Section 2.2). But agreeing the various costs and benefits among different actors is not always easy. The economic values that comprise TEV themselves reflect commonly held ethical beliefs and personal values that provide the moral foundation for action. However, different people will favour different values over others. For example, someone who holds that all life is sacred will favour non-use values over and above use values. Fundamental value-driven beliefs on what is right and wrong are extremely difficult to accommodate in an economic framework (Hinchliffe and Belshaw, 2003). So even if one accepts the idea of total economic value, political disagreements over which individual values should count more than others are inevitable.

Figure 7.4    The Amazonian rainforest provides a vast array of economic values to many actors. But should all the values that make up the total economic value (TEV) of the Amazon be considered the same? Which values should count most in decision making?

# 4   Valuing environmental goods

## 4.1   The UK National Ecosystem Assessment

Despite these challenges a number of attempts have made to calculate the TEV of environmental goods. The Millennium Ecosystem Assessment (MEA) in 2005 attempted to calculate the value of the entirety of the Earth's ecosystems. At a more modest scale, the UK National Ecosystem Assessment, which involved over 500 scientists and economists, sought to put a value on the totality of environmental goods in the UK (UK NEA, 2011) (Figure 7.5). Its findings included:

- The benefits that inland wetlands bring to water quality are worth up to £1.5 billion per year to the UK.

- Pollinators (bees and other insects) are worth £430 million per year to UK agriculture (Figure 7.6).

- The benefits of living close to rivers, coasts and other wetlands are worth up to £1.3 billion per year.

- The health benefits of living with a view of a green space are worth up to £300 per person per year (DEFRA, 2011).

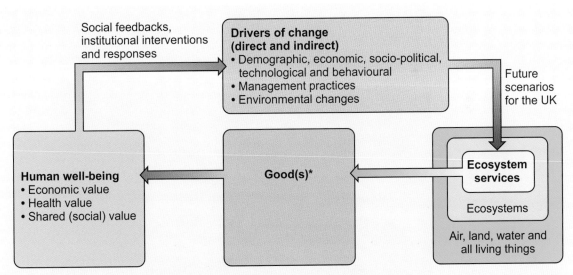

\* Note that the term good(s) includes all use and non-use, material and non-material benefits from ecosystems that have value for people

Figure 7.5   The full set of ecosystem processes, services, goods/benefits and values used in the UK National Ecosystem Assessment (NEA) (Source: UK, 2011, p. 15, Figure 9)

Figure 7.6   Pollination carried out by bees can significantly enhance agricultural production. But how can such services be priced in a market?

Figure 7.7   The Lake District National Park. What's its value?

The assessment argued that the biodiversity and ecosystems of the natural world are critically important to the UK's well-being and economic prosperity, but 'are consistently undervalued in conventional economic analyses and decision making' (UK NEA, 2011, p. 7). There was also acknowledgement that the full value of ecosystems cannot be valued in monetary terms (Figures 7.7 and 7.8).

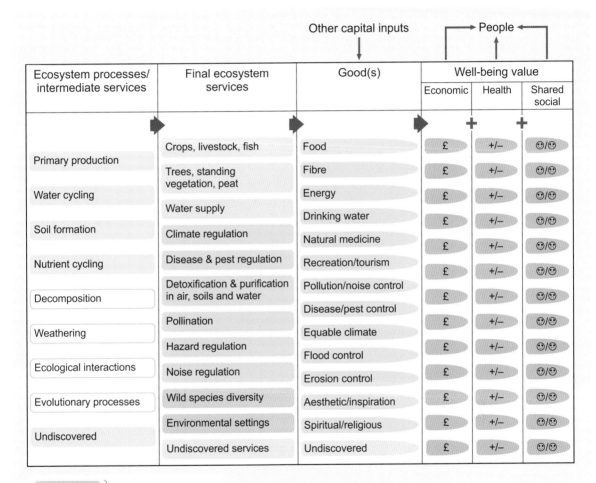

Figure 7.8   Conceptual framework for the UK National Ecosystem Assessment (NEA) showing the links between ecosystems, ecosystem services, good(s), valuation, human well-being, change processes and scenarios. Note that the term 'good(s)' includes all use and non-use, material and non-material benefits from ecosystems that have value for people. Cells with no colour are ecosystem services included in the UK NEA but not the Millennium Ecosystem Assessment (Source: UK NEA, 2011, p.16, Figure 10)

Activity 7.4    Health, happiness and the environment

The UK National Ecosystem Assessment noted that 'contact with nature gives pleasure, provides recreation and is known to have a positive impact on long-term health and happiness' (UK NEA, 2011, p. 7). Where should such values be placed in Figure 7.3 above?

Comment

This is an example of *indirect use value*.

The report found that maintaining the UK's parks, lakes, forest and wildlife is worth at least £30 billion a year to the economy. Bob Watson, co-author of the report, said that the assessment should be used to shape government policy at national and local level: 'Putting a value on these natural services enables them to be incorporated into policy … We can't persist in thinking of these things as free. We have to be better at managing our ecosystems' (quoted in Harvey, 2011, p. 15).

Box 7.2    UNEP's study on The Economics of Ecosystems and Biodiversity (TEEB)

A study for the United Nations Environment Programme (UNEP) on The Economics of Ecosystems and Biodiversity (TEEB) put the global damage done to the natural world by human activity at between $2 trillion and $4.5 trillion (TEEB, 2008). To put this in context, the lower estimate is roughly equivalent to the entire annual economic output of the UK for that year. The TEEB report also commented that the natural world's economic value, in terms of its provision of clean water, good quality soil, pollination and other services, was largely neglected by policy makers because it was 'invisible'. A series of reports published around the turn of the first decade of this century provided differing monetary valuations showing the uncertainty that, perhaps inevitably, characterises this type of valuation and calculation.

## 4.2 The pros and cons of economic valuation

Press reports at the time of the publication of the NEA in the UK tended to highlight headline figures; for example, 'Nature worth £19 billion to UK Economy'. But Ian Bateman, an economist and a leading academic author of the report, argued that putting a single value on nature was not sensible as 'without the environment we're all dead – so the total value is infinite' (Bateman, quoted in Black, 2011). This view that the total value of the environment is infinite has previously been expressed by environmental activists, including Larry Lohmann in *The Ecologist* magazine (Lohmann, 1991). In this view the value of the environment will extend to all generations indefinitely into the future. Any calculation of value is thus impossible, as if the value of infinity is fed into a mathematical calculation the calculation itself breaks down.

However, at a more modest scale, attempts to value ecosystem services economically allow those people who feel they have been negatively affected by the actions of others to claim redress. It offers a platform from which a public – a community of affected interests – can hold accountable those parties whom they consider responsible for harmful environmental change. So although the all-affected principle is far from being universally employed, it offers a general principle for public action.

We should not underestimate the moral significance of the idea of holding those who harm the environment economically accountable for their actions. But because putting an accurate and objective economic value on the harm to an ecosystem is fraught with methodological uncertainties, what might be more important is the political process by which this community assembles itself and convinces others that those parties responsible for causing environmental damage have a responsibility to pay for the damage caused, irrespective of where in the world such damage occurs (Figure 7.9).

However, three reasons may be offered against economic valuation of environmental goods. One is the difficulty – or rather inappropriateness – of converting indirect use values, such as spiritual or aesthetic values, into monetary figures. This, it can be claimed, involves putting a monetary value on the very recreational activities people resort to in order find respite from the pressure of monetary values.

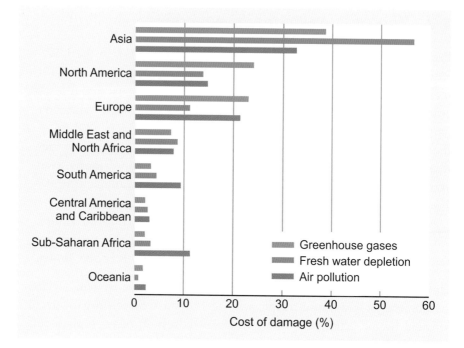

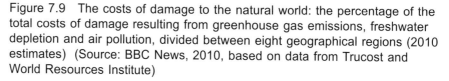

Figure 7.9   The costs of damage to the natural world: the percentage of the total costs of damage resulting from greenhouse gas emissions, freshwater depletion and air pollution, divided between eight geographical regions (2010 estimates)  (Source: BBC News, 2010, based on data from Trucost and World Resources Institute)

A second difficulty is the near impossibility of measuring the resilience of an ecosystem and thus the lasting economic harm done to it by human disturbance. Living things are constantly adapting in response to changes in their environment (Chapter 1), so what may be an appropriate measure of resilience at one point in time may cease to be so at another time. So, even if there was a broad agreement on the methods for calculating TEV, uncertainties on ecosystem resilience would mean that applying these methods with accuracy would be difficult.

This brings us to the third, and perhaps the most important, misgiving about calculating economic values for nature. Most of the components of TEV are economic values *for* human beings. This includes all direct use values, and many indirect values too. The criticism made is that nature is treated only in terms of **instrumental values**, as though it existed for human ends only (Burgess, 2003). But to many environmentalists a purely instrumental approach towards nature fails to account for the full value of nature. Such an approach ultimately

**Instrumental values**
Valuations of the environment for humans.

restricts the all-affected principle solely to *human* communities, thus excluding affected communities of other species.

# 5   The intrinsic value of life

For radical environmentalists, valuing nature instrumentally – as nothing more than a means to human ends – is part of the problem of environmental degradation, not the solution. What is needed, environmentalists Peter Bunyard and Fern Morgan-Grenville insist, is 'an ethic that recognizes the intrinsic value of all aspects of the non-human world' (Bunyard and Morgan-Grenville, 1987, p. 284). **Intrinsic value** may be defined as the value that nature has in and of itself, irrespective of any value that people assign to it (Figure 7.10).

Believing instrumental values to be just one aspect of the value of nature, some environmental theorists have sought to justify their position intellectually by establishing a philosophical basis for an alternative valuation of nature. This has resulted in various 'green' theories of value which, in the words of political scientist Robert Goodin, 'link the value of things to some naturally occurring properties of the objects themselves' (Goodin, 1992, p. 24).

As Andrew Dobson notes, seeking to revalue nature raises *practical* matters (Dobson, 2007). More than just a matter of asserting the duty to preserve natural values, decisions must be made about which dimensions of natural value *should* be preserved. If we follow Goodin in asserting 'the value of things created by natural processes rather than by artificial ones', just what might these things be? Individual animals? Species? Trees? Only living things? Or non-living things such as mountains and rivers too (Dobson, 2007)?

Given the inevitability of situations in the real world where difficult choices have to be made about which non-human things are protected, many environmental thinkers have been prompted to construct lists of priorities, or *hierarchies*, of valued entities. These hierarchies are usually arrived at by arguing that some entities have more value than others and should thereby weigh more heavily in the moral balance. For example, the environmental philosopher Lawrence Johnson bases his moral 'weighing up' on what he calls **well-being interest** (Johnson, 1991). This comprises those elements that contribute to a 'good life', such as basic material goods, freedom, health, good social relations, security and spiritual experience. Johnson argues that not all entities have the same kind of well-being interest. For example, humans are capable of a higher level of well-being than the smallpox organism.

**Intrinsic value**
The value that nature has in and of itself.

**Well-being interest**
Those elements that contribute to 'a good life'.

Complexity has also been invoked as a criterion around which to construct hierarchies of value for organisms. For example, the extent to which an organism shows complexity of relations in its 'capacity for richness of experience' is the criteria that philosopher Warwick Fox employs to compose his hierarchies of values. In this view, humans as complex beings have more value than a single-celled organism, although both have life. Fox maintains, therefore, that intrinsic value is not spread evenly across the biotic community and that 'his hierarchical conceptions of intrinsic value … provide a guide to action where values come into genuine conflict' (Fox, 1984, quoted in Dobson, 2007, p. 35). But this criterion of complexity is not unproblematic. A species of fungus or a small organism invisible to the naked eye may play more of a role in maintaining an ecosystem than other species that may enjoy a 'richness of experience', such as the pandas and tigers we see in documentary television programmes.

Figure 7.10 *Urtica dioica*, or the common stinging nettle, is widespread in the northern hemisphere. Often considered a weed, it is a food source for some butterflies and moths. It also has some medicinal uses for humans

What we call 'weeds', because they have no obvious instrumental value, may also play important roles in ecosystem functioning. The idea of a weed is a cultural category rather than a scientific one. In 1878, Ralph Waldo Emerson wrote that a weed is simply 'a plant whose virtues have not yet been discovered' (Emerson, 1878) (Figure 7.10). For example, many weeds bind the soil. The naturalist Richard Mabey notes that in the Mediterranean region weeds prevent soils and soil nutrients being blown away on desert winds (Mabey, 2010). Had it not been for the soil-binding function of weeds modern agriculture might never have had a chance to evolve.

## 5.1   Intrinsic values and rights for nature

A challenge for proponents of the intrinsic valuation of nature is to translate such values into policy. One approach is to assign rights to nature. A landmark text here is Christopher Stone's 1972 paper 'Should trees have standing?'. Stone (1972) argued that rights should not be solely anthropocentric and that natural things should enjoy legal rights of protection similar to those enjoyed by humans. For Stone, it is not a valid argument to say that trees should have no legal rights because they cannot speak; humans can speak for them. He does not argue that trees should never be felled, but does argue that humans should take into account the rights of a species to continue to exist when making policy.

Nearly 20 years later, in the early 1990s, conservationists and environmental scientists in the USA went to court to impose logging restrictions in forests in the US Pacific Northwest that are habitats for the endangered northern spotted owl (*Strix occidentalis*), arguing that the owl could not survive if logging continued. The logging industry responded that the restrictions would put loggers' jobs at risk. A slogan in logging communities at the time was 'Save a logger, eat an owl'. After a succession of court cases, logging restrictions were upheld, leading some commentators to suggest that the northern spotted owl had rights that trumped those of people (Yaffee, 1995) (Figure 7.11).

There is now a growing political movement to acknowledge legally the rights of nature, which is particularly strong in South America. In 2008 Ecuador became the first country in the world to recognise rights for nature in its constitution, which states that nature 'has the right to exist, persist, maintain and regenerate its vital cycles, structure, functions and its processes in evolution' (Ecuador Constitution 2008, Article 71, quoted in Stober, 2010, p. 235). The following year, the president of Bolivia, Evo Morales, made his proposal to the UN General Assembly on International Mother Earth Day (Chapter 5, Section 3), arguing that 60 years after the UN had adopted the Universal Declaration of Human

Rights it was time to recognise a new generation of rights, the rights of the Earth.

Figure 7.11   The northern spotted owl is an endangered species in North America

If we think in terms of the all-affected principle, there are opportunities for communities of affected interests to include among their number both humans and non-humans harmed by the actions of others. We can see the possibilities for such an inclusive notion of an affected community in the 2008 Ecuadorian constitution, which states: 'Every person, community, town (village) or nationality will be able to demand to the public authority the compliance of the rights of Nature' (quoted in Stober, 2010, p. 235). This provides an opening for human communities to act as a voice for the harm brought to non-humans, while at the same time acknowledging that harm to non-humans may be experienced as a loss for humans.

The recognition of legal rights for the Earth, nature and natural objects is an embryonic jurisprudence that is by no means accepted uncritically by legal scholars. However, were such a jurisprudence to develop it could lead to successful legal challenges in the courts against development activities that degrade the integrity of ecosystems. Under such a legal system certain activities, such as logging and fishing and even fossil fuel burning, could be considered illegal, or at least be viewed more seriously than they currently are.

The idea of nature having intrinsic value is not necessarily opposed to the notion of instrumental value. Individuals and communities are quite capable of holding different values, and shifting between them. Ultimately humans, like every other living thing, depend on environmental goods for their survival, which implies an instrumental orientation. However, many human cultures or traditions have afforded special status – spiritually or symbolically – to those living creatures on which they were most dependent.

For example, the awe-inspiring ancient cave art of Lascaux in France or Altamira in Spain (Figure 7.12) has been taken as an evidence of an early expression of deep symbolic bonds between humans and the animals they hunted: 'a mysterious relation – a relation of interest, of conspiracy, of complicity, and even of friendship – between the human hunters and the flourishing of the animal kingdom' (Blanchot, 1997, p. 3). Similar bonds have been noted in many hunter-gather societies, while the indigenous Andean spiritual view of nature plays an important part in the Bolivian view of rights of nature that President Morales took before the UN General Assembly (Vidal, 2011).

(a)                                                    (b)

Figure 7.12   Images of wildlife from (a) the Lascaux caves,  France; (b) the Altamira caves, Spain

# 6   What do values do for us?

At this point it is worth pausing and asking: what is the significance of values in the shaping of environmental issues? When we look closely at environmental thought and practice, this is far from clear. Often it appears that environmental values are assumed to be deep-seated and enduring. In this view, values are bound up in culture and tradition; different individuals or groups are imbued with a system of values and they apply these values whenever they encounter a new challenge, such as environmental change.

At other times, however, environmentalists tend to speak of values as though they were wide open to change, even a matter of choice. According to this view, individuals or groups are always open to having their values transformed: especially when someone reveals a 'better' set of values.

Indeed, a lot of radical environmental thought has presumed that a certain set of modern Western values – self-serving, materialist, instrumental – are at the root of environmental issues and that a necessary first step in solving these issues is a wholesale change in values (Goldsmith, 1992). Environmental researchers have sought evidence that social values are in the process of being radically transformed, and have found many positive signs that such a change is underway. Individuals are increasingly concerned about environmental change and prepared to take action (Catton and Dunlap, 1980), although many people continue to experience conflict when acting for the good of the environment negatively affects their personal situation (Corraliza and Berenguer, 2000).

The idea that values are a matter of choice assumes that values are 'out there', set apart from the messy entanglements and struggles of worldly existence. This view is by no means restricted to academics. In fact, when it comes to environmental challenges, 'value change' or 'attitude change' is often a top priority of government strategists and policy makers. As sociologist Elizabeth Shove argues, the notion that individuals have a choice of values or attitudes about the environment is the default setting in policy documents in the UK and other Western societies (Shove, 2010). Here, it tends to be bound up with the idea that if people can be encouraged or incentivised to select a new, more environmentally friendly, set of values, our societies will be better able to solve environmental issues.

But, as Shove would have it, this is a rather simplistic view of values. Viewing values and attitudes as matters of choice – as if we could reach out and select new values 'off the shelf' – underestimates the way that the values we live by tend to be embedded in the stuff of everyday life. Values and attitudes, Shove suggests, cannot be easily disentangled from daily social practices, and the institutions and infrastructures which make these practices possible (Barnett, 2010; Shove, 2010). They are mixed up with – and integral to – the mundane things we do, such as travelling to work, buying food, and accessing electricity or water supplies. Shove suggests that values are more tangled up in worldly processes and events than many environmental thinkers have assumed. In this view, values are continually formed and shaped through the process of issue formation and the emergence of communities of affected interests that contest real-world predicaments (Hinchliffe, 2007).

## 6.1   Being affected by non-humans

So far, we have considered communities of affected people largely in terms of the direct effects of a harmful environmental change. But the term 'affected' also conveys the capacity to be moved, influenced or perturbed by what others are experiencing. So 'a community of the affected' might also include those who are impacted on less directly by a predicament, but who feel inspired to join others in a political struggle. Indeed, the main intention of 'publicising' a predicament is to expand the community of affected people to bring in 'outsiders', so that an issue gains strength and momentum (Barnett, 2008). But this capacity to be affected by the plight of others, it would appear, is not restricted just to the fate of people. A significant aspect of being affected is to be moved, disturbed or surprised by the consequences for non-humans.

For example, before the Deepwater Horizon crisis many people were not aware that there were microorganisms capable of thriving on oil. For some, this was a rather astounding revelation. This was, in many senses, a novel encounter: one that engendered new scientific research and gave rise to a new understanding on the part of scientists and laypeople alike. In a similar way, coming across multitudes of deformed species, such as clawless crabs and eyeless shrimps, was a new and disturbing experience for fisherfolk, as in the case of the earlier discovery of the disappearance of marine life from the Gulf's hypoxic 'dead zone'.

It is precisely the appearance of aspects of nature which do not fit into familiar patterns and expectations that sets people thinking in new ways. In this way, we begin to see why it is important to think about the value of non-human life not only in terms of what it has in common with humans, but in terms of the ways in which its differences can impress themselves on us. Or, to return to the quote from Hirokawa with which we opened the chapter: such occurrences compel us 'to revise our perceptions on the value of nature and natural processes' (Hirokawa, 2011, p. 547).

It is through this sense of being able to affect humans in some significant way – emotionally or rationally – that we might think about non-humans as affected things or as beings that have a 'voice'. While it may not be a voice or expression we can clearly understand, non-humans can make us aware of their own predicament in many different ways: their behaviour can seem strange, their form or appearance can change, they can disappear or turn up in numbers we were not expecting. These ways of manifesting their affectedness are rarely entirely clear and unambiguous. But what we can do is to learn to look out for, or sense the significant changes in, the non-human beings with which we share our environments (Hinchliffe, 2007). And, in different ways, this is what farmers and fisherfolk, birdwatchers and scientific researchers, artists and poets, and many other ordinary people all do: they learn, over time, to be affected by those aspects of nature with which they interact (Bingham, 2006; Latour, 2004).

## 6.2   Making an issue out of non-human life

These experiences of being affected by non-human life can also inform the shaping of environmental issues and the convening of publics. The process of political deliberation by which an environmental predicament becomes an 'issue' may entail new ways of bringing non-human life – and the harm being done to it – into visibility (Chapter 6). And this may lead to new ways of expressing what nature means to a community. In this way, groups of concerned people come together to 'make public' the values they perceive in living things or ecosystems, and the threats to these values. In this respect expressing values is also a kind of 'performance', a demonstration of the importance of these values. It is through publicly declaring our values that we justify our actions, as well as our indignation over the actions of others.

When it comes to demonstrating a sense that something valuable has been lost or harmed, there are many different ways a community of affected people can express their beliefs and feelings. Some engage in scientific research; others take photos, tell stories, write to newspapers, make postings to social media or take to the streets in protest. It is through these very acts of communication that values themselves are shaped and contested. In the process of being expressed, values can be deepened and extended, embellished and elaborated, modified and transformed. This does not mean that there are no preconceived values; that we start afresh with each new encounter or event. But it is to say that values themselves are a part of the activity of defining an environmental issue: they are tangled up in dialogue, negotiations, events and the process of making things public (Barnett, 2011).

# 7 Summary

How we value nature plays a major part in distinguishing between those environmental changes or conditions which are accepted and those which are resisted. Values, therefore, are key to the framing of environmental issues. We can sum up the treatment of environmental values in this chapter as follows.

Environmental goods may be classified into public goods and private goods. Overharvesting of environmental private goods (such as fish and timber) may lead to the degradation of public goods (such as ocean degradation or the loss of the carbon sink function of forests). Economists have developed a taxonomy for categorising environmental goods, dividing them into use values and non-use values. Although there are exceptions, direct use values broadly equate with private goods while non-use values broadly equate with public goods. However, even if one accepts the economic approach to environmental values – and we have considered arguments for and against this – different actors will assign different weightings to different values. In other words, there are different hierarchies of values, based, for example, on well-being and complexity.

Another approach maintains that, while values do, to some extent, exist prior to the formation of environmental issues, the very process of issue formation can lead to contestation over values. Focusing on the way that the values of nature are caught up in real-world environmental predicaments helps us to recognise that values themselves may shift and transform as environmental issues are shaped and expressed. We have seen that new ways of conceptualising environmental harm can lead to new ways of defining environmental issues. The all-affected principle holds that all people affected by harm to the environment should have some say in the actions that cause this harm, irrespective of the political space where these actions were generated. Claims of environmental affectedness are often presented in terms of a demand for redress over the lost economic value of environmental goods. However, putting monetary values on ecosystems and people's experiences of nature is extremely complex and attempts to do so can focus attention restrictively on the instrumental values of nature. A range of alternative ways of affirming intrinsic values of nature have been advocated by environmental thinkers, including attributing rights to nature, an idea that is now finding expression in South America.

# References

Barnett, C. (2008) 'Convening publics: the parasitical spaces of public action', in Cox, K. R., Low, M. and Robinson, J. (eds) *The SAGE Handbook of Political Geography*, London, Sage.

Barnett, C. (2010) 'The politics of behaviour change', *Environment and Planning A*, vol. 42, pp. 1881–6 [online], DOI: 10.1068/a43291 (Accessed 29 July 2012).

Barnett, C. (2011) 'Geography and ethics: justice unbound', *Progress in Human Geography*, vol. 35, no. 2, pp. 246–55.

Barnett, C. and Bridge, G. (2012) 'Geographies of radical democracy: agonistic pragmatism and the formation of affected interests', *Annals of the Association of American Geographers* [online], DOI: 10.1080/00045608.2012.660395 (Accessed 26 July 2012).

BBC News (2010) 'Nature's sting: the real cost of damaging "Planet Earth"', October [online], http://www.bbc.co.uk/news/business-11495812 (Accessed 26 July 2012).

Bingham, N. (2006) 'Bees, butterflies, and bacteria: biotechnology and the politics of nonhuman friendship', *Environment and Planning A*, vol. 38, pp. 483–98 [online], DOI: 10.1068/a38436 (Accessed 29 July 2012).

Black, R. (2011) 'Nature "is worth billions" to UK', *BBC News*, 2 June [online], http://www.bbc.co.uk/news/science-environment-13616543 (Accessed 26 July 2012).

Blanchot, M. (1997) *Friendship*, Stanford, CA, StanfordUniversity Press.

Bunyard, P. and Morgan-Grenville, F. (1987) *The Green Alternative: Guide to Good Living*, London, Methuen.

Burgess, J. (2003) 'Environmental values in environmental decision making', in Bingham, N., Blowers, A. and Belshaw, C. (eds) *Contested Environments*, Chichester, John Wiley/Milton Keynes, The Open University.

Catton, W. and Dunlap, R. (1980) 'A new ecological paradigm for post-exuberant sociology', *American Behavioral Scientist*, vol. 24, no. 1, pp. 15–47.

Corraliza, J. and Berenguer, J. (2000) 'Environmental values, beliefs and actions: a situational approach', *Environment and Behavior*, vol. 32, no. 6, pp. 832–48.

Daigle, M. T. (2011) 'The value of a pelican: an overview of the Natural Resource Damage Assessment under Federal and Louisiana Law', *Ocean and Coastal Law Journal*, vol. 16, no. 2, pp. 253–68.

Department for Environment, Food and Rural Affairs (DEFRA) (2011) 'Hidden value of nature revealed in ground-breaking study', DEFRA[online], http://www.defra.gov.uk/news/2011/06/02/hidden-value-of-nature-revealed/ (Accessed 26 July 2012).

Dobson, A. (2007) *Green Political Thought*, Abingdon, Routledge.

Dobson, A. (2010) 'Democracy and nature: speaking and listening', *Political Studies*, vol. 58, no. 4, pp. 752–68.

Eales, S. (1991) *Earthtoons: The First Book of Eco-humour*, New York, Warner Books Inc.

Emerson, R. W. (1878) *Fortune of the Republic,* Boston, MA, Houghton, Osgood and Company.

Fox, W. (1984) 'Deep ecology: a new philosophy of our time?', *The Ecologist*, vol. 14, nos 5/6, pp. 194–200.

Goldsmith, E. (1992) *The Way: An Ecological World-View*, London, Rider.

Goodin, R. E. (1992) *Green Political Theory*, Cambridge, Polity.

Gordon, K., Buchanan, J. and Singerman, P. with Madrid, J. and Busch, S. (2011) *Beyond Recovery: Moving the Gulf Coast Toward a Sustainable Future*, Boston, MA and Washington, DC, Oxfam [online], http://www.oxfamamerica.org/publications/beyond-recovery-moving-the-gulf-coast-toward-a-sustainable-future (Accessed 26 July 2012).

Harvey, F. (2011) 'UK green spaces "worth £30bn in health benefits"',*The Guardian*, 2 June, p. 15.

Hinchliffe, S. (2007) *Geographies of Nature: Societies, Environments, Ecologies*, London, Sage.

Hinchliffe, S. J. and Belshaw, C. D. (2003) 'Who cares? Values, power and action in environmental contests', in Hinchliffe, S. J., Blowers, A. T. and Freeland, J. R. (eds) *Understanding Environmental Issues*, Chichester, John Wiley/Milton Keynes, The Open University.

Hirokawa, K. H. (2011) 'Disasters and ecosystem deprivation: from Cuyahoga to the Deepwater Horizon', *Albany Law Review*, vol. 74, no. 1, pp. 543–61; also available online at http://www.albanylawreview.org/articles/14_HIROKAWA.pdf (Accessed 26 July 2012).

International Maritime Organisation (1997) *International Convention for the Prevention of Pollution from Ships (MARPOL),* amended by protocols of 1978 and 1997 [online], http://www.imo.org/about/conventions/listofconventions/pages/international-convention-for-the-prevention-of-pollution-from-ships-(marpol).aspx (Accessed 26 July 2012).

Johnson, L. (1991) *A Morally Deep World: An Essay on Moral Significance and Environmental Ethics*, Cambridge, Cambridge University Press.

Latour, B. (2004) 'How to talk about the body? The normative dimension of science studies', *Body and Society*, vol. 10, nos 2–3, pp. 205–29.

Lohmann, L. (1991) 'Dismal green science', *The Ecologist*, vol. 21, no. 5, pp. 194–5.

Mabey, R. (2010) *Weeds: How Vagabond Plants Gatecrashed Civilisation and Changed the Way We Think about Nature*, London, Profile Books.

Millennium Ecosystem Assessment (2005) *Ecosystems and Human Well-Being: Synthesis Report*, Washington, DC, Island Press.

Nunes, P. and van den Bergh, J. (2001) 'Economic valuation of biodiversity: sense or nonsense?', *Ecological Economics*, vol. 39, no. 2, pp. 203–22.

Shove, E. (2010) 'Beyond the ABC: climate change policy and theories of social change', *Environment and Planning A*, vol. 42, no. 6, pp. 1273–85 [online], DOI: 10.1068/a42282 (Accessed 29 July 2012).

Stober, S. (2010) 'Ecuador: Mother Nature's utopia', *International Journal of Environmental, Cultural, Economic and Social Sustainability*, vol. 6, no. 2, pp. 229–39.

Stone, C. D. (1972) 'Should trees have standing? Towards legal rights for natural objects', *Southern California Law Review*, vol. 45, no. 2, pp. 450–501.

TEEB (2008) *The Economics of Ecosystems and Biodiversity* [online], http://www.teebweb.org/Portals/25/TEEB%20Synthesis/TEEB_insert_A4_online_end.pdf (Accessed 29 July 2012).

Tully, J. (2008) *Public Philosophy in a New Key: Vol. 2: Imperialism and Civic Freedom*, Cambridge, Cambridge University Press.

UK National Ecosystem Assessment (UK NEA) (2011) *The UK National Ecosystem Assessment: Synthesis of the Key Findings*, Cambridge, UNEP-WCMC.

United Nations (1995) *Agreement for the Implementation of the Provisions of the United Nations Convention on the Law of the Sea of 10 December 1982 Relating to the Conservation and Management of Straddling Fish Stocks and Highly Migratory Fish Stocks*, 8 September, A/CONF.164/37 [online], http://www.un.org/Depts/los/convention_agreements/texts/fish_stocks_agreement/CONF164_37.htm (Accessed 26 July 2012).

Vidal, J. (2011) 'Bolivia enshrines natural worlds rights with equal status for Mother Earth', 10 April, *The Guardian* [online], http://www.guardian.co.uk/environment/2011/apr/10/bolivia-enshrines-natural-worlds-rights (Accessed 26 July 2011).

Yaffee, S. L. (1995) *The Wisdom of the Spotted Owl: Policy Lessons for a New Century*, Washington, DC, Island Press.

# Chapter 8   Biodiversity loss: a global issue?

Philip O'Sullivan

# Contents

# 1 Introduction

So far in this block, we have examined how an experience of being affected by an undesirable environmental state may become an environmental issue through political interactions, scientific research and media reporting. In this chapter, we now move from struggles situated at local levels to global environmental issues.

There is increasing, and increasingly strong, scientific evidence of human threats to the biological diversity of the oceans and terrestrial ecosystems on a planetary scale. The evidence that human activities are transforming global ecological processes draws attention to the self-regulating capacities of Earth systems, and the risk that they can be pushed into alternative states. But it also raises questions about human social processes, and the extent to which humankind is able to regulate its own activities on a global scale.

# 2   Global threats to the oceans

Although it was a major oil spill, Deepwater Horizon was still localised, impacting predominantly on human communities and ecosystems in the Gulf of Mexico. There is now growing concern among scientists and other experts that the oceans are threatened at a global scale. There are two reasons for this. First, activities that may pose a risk to the oceans, such as deliberate and unintended pollution and nutrient run-off from the land, now take place in numerous discrete sites across the globe. Second, because the oceans are interconnected a disturbance in one part of the oceans may eventually have consequences elsewhere (Box 8.1).

---

### Box 8.1   Plastic ducks: peril at sea

In January 1992 several containers slid from the cargo ship *Ever Laurel* into the Pacific Ocean. One of them, carrying nearly 30,000 bath toys, broke open. Since then thousands of plastic ducks and other toys have floated northwards in the Pacific Ocean. It is predicted that eventually the toys will pass through the Bering Strait, and cross the Arctic Ocean to the north of Canada before entering the Atlantic Ocean (Figure 8.1).

The idea of an armada of plastic ducks loose on the high seas, while amusing, represents an ecological risk in the making. Plastic is a polymer, a synthetic material consisting of millions of interlinked structural molecular units. Plastics are not biodegradable. However, they do break down in size. Through being washed ashore repeatedly on beaches, plastic is ground down into increasingly smaller particles, sometimes smaller than a grain of sand. These particles attract pollutants and when eaten by marine life represent poison. Because they cannot be broken down through digestion, plastic particles pass up the food chain before reaching the top predators, such as whales, sharks – and humans. There is already evidence that plastics have entered the food chain. Particles from the plastic ducks carried by the *Ever Laurel* will eventually pose a health risk to marine species and humans, and that risk will grow as the plastic is progressively ground down (Hohn, 2012).

---

(a)                                           (b)

Figure 8.1   (a) The container ship *Ever Laurel*; (b) A yellow plastic duck

The risks to the oceans of human activity are now better understood, with scientific research revealing more about the risks to the oceans (Independent World Commission on the Oceans, 1998; Roberts, 2012). These risks have dramatically increased since the mid twentieth century. As oceanographer Sylvia Earle puts it, the last five decades have witnessed 'more destruction to ocean systems than during all preceding history' (Earle, 2010, p. 18). Indeed, current human and technological capabilities are such that 'a few hours indiscriminate trawling are sufficient to destroy a million years of coral growth and the assets required to support marine tourism or to maintain the livelihoods of traditional fishing communities' (Independent World Commission on the Oceans, 1998, p. 26).

The major human impacts on the oceans over the last 60 years are summarised in Box 8.2.

---

Box 8.2   Recent human impacts threatening the oceans

- Since the mid twentieth century hundreds of millions of tonnes of ocean wildlife have been removed from the sea. Many once common fish have seen 90–95% declines. Industrial fishing techniques have destroyed habitats and accidentally killed millions of tonnes of animals ('by-catches') that are simply discarded (Figure 8.2).

- Half the shallow coral reefs have disappeared or seriously declined since the 1950s. Coral reefs thousands of years old are being destroyed by deep trawling techniques.

---

- More than 400 'dead zones' (low-oxygen areas) have formed in coastal areas in recent decades, reflecting changes in ocean chemistry.
- Global warming is affecting ocean systems and life: those impacts in turn influence the atmosphere and terrestrial ecosystems.

Source: adapted from Earle, 2010, pp. 18–20

Figure 8.2   One of the oldest species on Earth, green turtles have been hunted for centuries for their meat and eggs. They are now protected in many countries but are at risk from fishing

Marine geochemist Scott Doney argues that:

Climate change, rising atmospheric carbon dioxide, excess nutrient inputs, and pollution in its many forms are fundamentally altering the chemistry of the ocean, often on a global scale and, in some cases, at rates greatly exceeding those in the historical and recent geological record.

(Doney, 2010, p. 1512)

The major observed trends, he notes, include increased acidification of seawater, reduced subsurface oxygen in both coastal waters and the open ocean, rising coastal nitrogen levels, and widespread increase in mercury and **persistent organic pollutants (POPs)**. POPs are carbon-based substances toxic to humans and wildlife that remain intact and accumulate in the fatty tissue of living organisms. They remain intact for a long period of time. Most of the environmental perturbations linked to human fossil fuel combustion, fertiliser use and industrial activity are projected to grow in coming decades, resulting in increasing risks to marine resources and ocean life.

**Persistent organic pollutants (POPS)**
Toxic substances that, once released into the environment, remain intact for long periods of time.

## 2.1  Human impact and the non-recovery of ecosystems

Maintaining biodiversity is much simpler than restoring it as some damaged ecosystems are unlikely to return to their original states, with any loss, in effect, being permanent.

---

### Activity 8.1  Human activity and permanent ecosystem change

Can you recall an example of a possible permanent change in an ecosystem from earlier in this block?

### Comment

In Chapter 5 you saw that the increased availability of hydrocarbons from the Deepwater Horizon oil spill resulted in the dramatic increase in some bacteria at the expense of other microorganisms and macroorganisms in the oceanic food web. It was suggested that this could lead to permanent changes in the Gulf marine ecosystem. Another example is extinction. Extinction can occur because of natural changes, or from human disturbance.

---

Figure 8.3   *The Fishmarket* by the Dutch artist Frans Snyders (1579–1657). Although the composition of fish shown is fanciful, the fishes and their sizes are representative of those available to customers of the day. In the centre a huge wolfish gapes, lying across sturgeon and halibut. To the left are cod, ling and salmon steaks. Also shown is the common skate (now extremely rare despite its name) and pike

One example of permanent change in a marine ecosystem is the collapse of fish stocks. Overfishing has severely depleted fish stocks in the North Atlantic, with catches falling in terms of both the weight of fish caught and their size (Roberts, 2012) (Figures 8.3 and 8.4). One species affected is the Atlantic cod (*Gadus morhua*). For five centuries, the coastal waters off Newfoundland provided abundant supplies of cod (Kurlansky, 1999). When, at an international gathering on fisheries in 1883, fears were expressed that stocks might become exhausted, the botanist T. H. Huxley denied that overfishing would lead to permanent exhaustion (cited in Simpson and Sharples, 2012). Cod was more or less sustainably managed off Newfoundland until the late 1950s when super-trawlers were introduced. Catches trebled, but by the 1970s populations had started to decline. A moratorium on cod fishing was introduced by the Canadian government in 1990, and scientists and fisherfolk waited for stocks to recover. Since the early 1990s, cod populations have failed to recover and the species remains at risk (Figure 8.5). A plausible theory suggests that the marine ecosystem that supports cod fisheries has different alternative states: one with cod in abundance, another with very low cod numbers. If industrialised fishing has tipped cod beyond its capacity for resilience, cod populations may not recover in the foreseeable future.

Figure 8.4   Grimsby fish market, England, in the early twentieth century. The size of the catch is unusually large by today's standards, as is the size of the fish

To make sense of this situation, we may look at the food web based around cod (Figure 8.6). This shows the feeding interactions between cod and other species and the complexity of interactions between different species. The population size of one species will affect the populations of many others. To understand what caused the collapse in the cod population it is necessary to look in detail at part of the food web (Figure 8.7). Cod fry feed on plankton (small aquatic plants and animals that drift with water movements). Large adult cod feed on a range of species including small fish and invertebrates such as crabs and shrimps. One fish species preyed on by adult cod is capelin (*Mallotus villosus*). A large part of its food consists of cod fry, so when the adult cod feed on the capelin this, in turn, reduces predation by capelin on cod fry. The reduced adult cod population caused by overfishing reduced predation on the capelin. As a result the population of capelin increased which, in turn, increased predation by capelin on cod fry. The populations of other species the adult cod fed on, such as crabs and shrimps, also increased and now dominate the area. Cod may now be locked into long-term low abundance (Pauly et al., 2002).

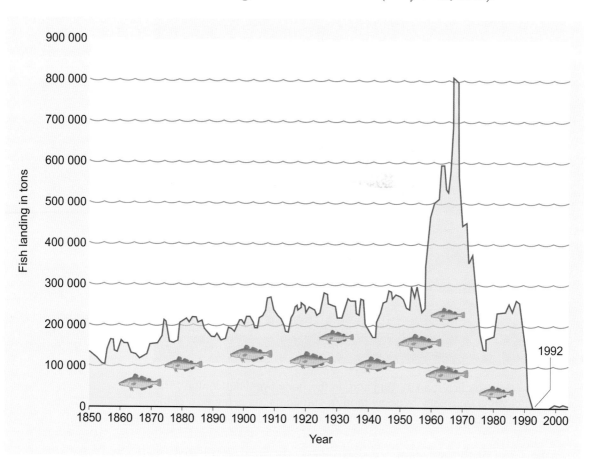

Figure 8.5 Amount of cod caught each year in the Newfoundland cod fishery from 1850 until 2000 (Source: Millennium Ecosystem Assessment, 2005, p. 12, Figure 11)

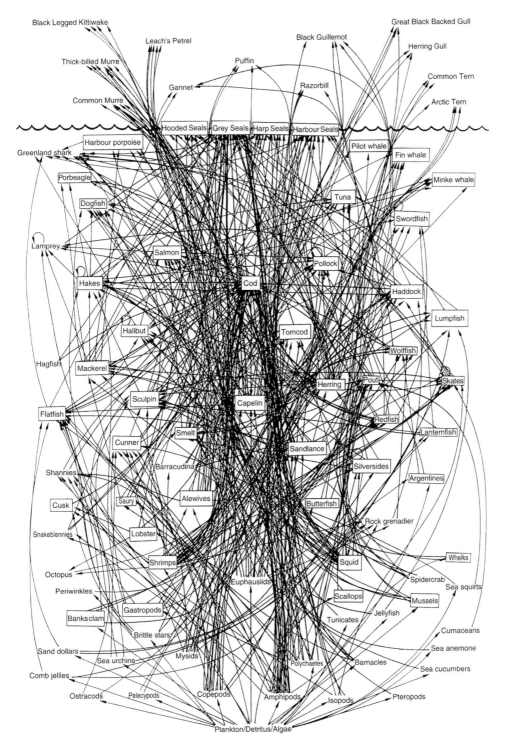

Figure 8.6 A partial food web for the Scotian Shelf in the Northwest Atlantic
(Source: Lavigne, 2003)

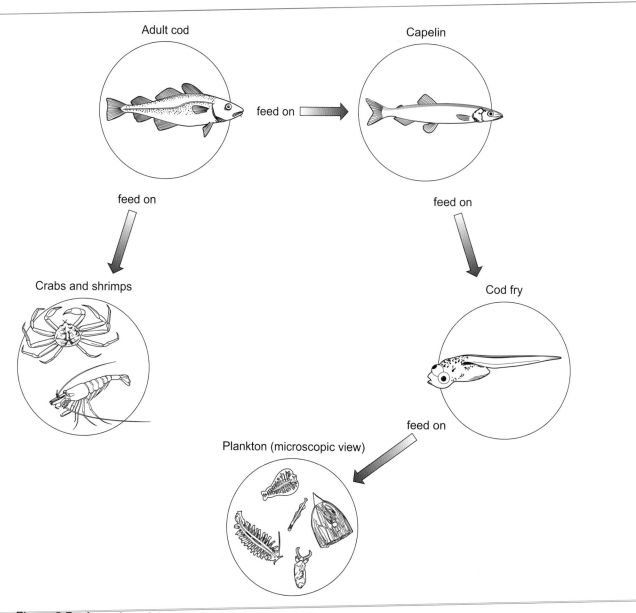

Figure 8.7    A section of the cod food web shown in Figure 8.6

# 3   From decline to extinction

The collapse of the North Atlantic cod population may be viewed as a classic tragedy of the commons – or what we might refer to more accurately as a tragedy of open access. The fate of cod is simply one among dozens of examples of severe impacts of overfishing on marine species.

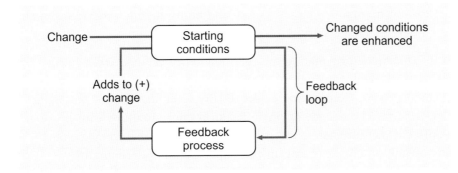

Figure 8.8   A positive feedback loop

The situation for many species is not simply declining numbers but the risk of extinction. Evidence suggests that both freshwater and marine vertebrate fish tend to be more at risk than their terrestrial vertebrate counterparts (Olden et al., 2007). Many different factors combine to determine a fish species risk of decline, recovery or extinction. Small populations are at greater risk of extinction than larger populations as they lack buffers in times of perturbation and natural fluctuation in numbers. Smaller populations are also likely to have a smaller range of genetic diversity than larger populations. This means that fewer individuals are likely to carry genes that provide resistance to diseases or tolerance to environmental stresses (Freeland, 2003). For a population that is suffering decline there is usually a point at which numbers become so small that it is difficult for animals to find mates and reproduce. The population decreases further so that it is more difficult for animals to reproduce, and so on. This is an example of a **positive feedback**, an interaction within a system that enhances change so that the change is more significant than would otherwise have been the case (Figure 8.8). Positive feedback may be imagined as a circular loop of effects that increases the likelihood of further change (Marten, 2001). In this case, if the positive feedbacks continue without interruption,

**Positive feedback**
Feedback that serves to enhance change, so that the change is greater than it would have been without the feedback.

population numbers will progressively fall until the species becomes extinct.

A major report from the International Programme on the State of the Ocean (IPSO) and the International Union for the Conservation of Nature (IUCN) suggests that the speed and magnitude of ocean degradation now exceed all previous predictions. The report claims that not only are we already experiencing severe declines in many species to the point of commercial extinction, but that within a generation we face the loss of numerous marine species and entire marine ecosystems such as coral reefs (Rogers and Laffoley, 2011).

A 2010 study led by marine biologist Daniel Boyce and colleagues, which tracked phytoplankton levels in the world's oceans over the last century, provides supporting evidence (Boyce et al., 2010). Combining satellite-derived evidence of phytoplankton concentrations with historical shipboard measurements, the study estimated that the average global phytoplankton concentration in the upper ocean is declining by approximately 1 per cent per year (Boyce et al., 2010). This has significant consequences, as phytoplankton accounts for around half the Earth's annual production of photosynthetic biomass, the basis for the marine food web (Schiermeier, 2010). The study estimates that, since 1950, phytoplankton biomass has decreased by around 40 per cent. As oceanographer Paul Falkowski comments: 'Clearly, 40% is a huge number. This implies that the entire ocean system is out of steady state, slowing down' (quoted in Schiermeier, 2010).

A steady decline in the oceanic phytoplankton concentration has serious implications for global fisheries and for the survival of marine life. Warming of the upper layers of the ocean is one of the main causes of phytoplankton loss (Boyce et al., 2010). The cumulative effects of multiple human impacts on the ocean is producing conditions of oceanic warming, low oxygen levels and acidification that are associated with previous extinction events in Earth's history. The IPSO/IUCN panel of experts concludes that there is now a 'high risk of entering a phase of extinction of marine species unprecedented in human history' (quoted in Harvey, 2011).

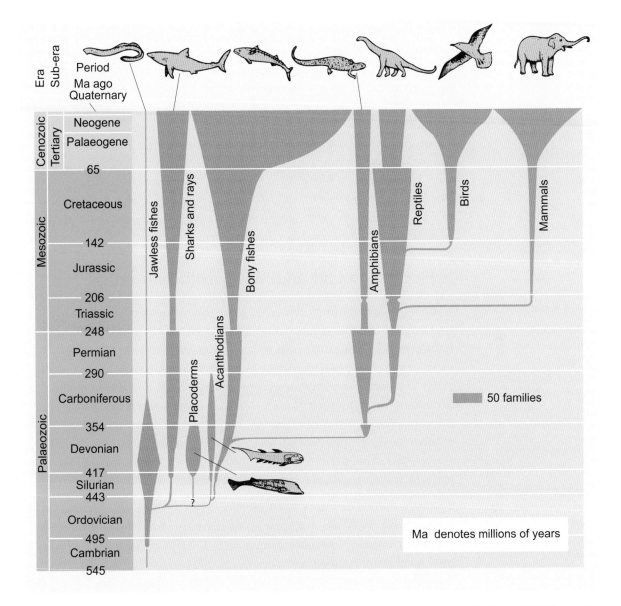

Figure 8.9   Geological time is divided into two intervals: the Cryptozoic Eon (4600 Ma to 545 Ma ago) and the Phanerozoic Eon (545 Ma to present). The Phanerozoic Eon is divided into eras, which are further subdivided into periods. This figure depicts the geological timescales of the Phanerozoic showing when various vertebrate groups were believed to have diversified

Extinction, it is important to note, is a natural process. The fossil record, as described by palaeontologists (scientists who study life from the geological past) represents more than 250,00 species, but these are believed to make up only a small fraction – possibly only 1 per cent – of all the species that have existed. Although most species have not been preserved in the fossil record, some conclusions can be drawn about changes in biodiversity over time. The earliest traces of life discovered by humans are in rocks that are around 3900 million years old. Approximately 545 million years ago (the beginning of the Phanerozoic Eon), a diversity of species appeared in the fossil record (Figure 8.9). However, the fossil record suggests that up to 99 per cent of species that once lived are now extinct.

## 3.1    Background and mass extinction rates

**Background extinction rate**
The average rate at which species extinction has occurred between mass extinctions.

Extinctions can be broadly placed into one of two categories: the background extinction rate and mass extinctions (Freeland, 2003). The **background extinction rate** refers to the average rate at which extinction has occurred between mass extinctions (see below), and this rate varies between different groups of organisms and different times, depending on numerous factors. While there is uncertainty owing to the incompleteness of the fossil record, it is estimated that an average of approximately 10 per cent of species have gone extinct every 1 million year period. This pattern of background extinction is estimated to account for up to 96 per cent of all extinctions to date (Raup, 1994).

**Mass extinction**
When a large number of species become extinct over a relatively short period of geological time.

The remaining 4 per cent is covered by mass extinctions. A **mass extinction** occurs when a large number of species – an estimated 75 per cent or more – become extinct over a relatively short period of geological time. At least five periods of mass extinction are discernible during the Phanerozoic Eon (Box 8.3). Mass extinctions are identifiable as periods of unusually high loss of biodiversity, well in excess of the background rate.

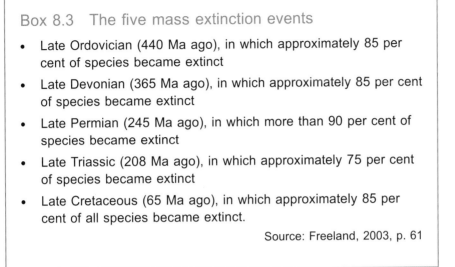

Box 8.3   The five mass extinction events

- Late Ordovician (440 Ma ago), in which approximately 85 per cent of species became extinct
- Late Devonian (365 Ma ago), in which approximately 85 per cent of species became extinct
- Late Permian (245 Ma ago), in which more than 90 per cent of species became extinct
- Late Triassic (208 Ma ago), in which approximately 75 per cent of species became extinct
- Late Cretaceous (65 Ma ago), in which approximately 85 per cent of all species became extinct.

Source: Freeland, 2003, p. 61

Activity 8.2   Mass extinctions

Look at Figure 8.9 and locate on it approximately when each of the five mass extinctions occurred.

While 'sudden' in geological time, each of these five extinction events lasted in the order of a million years. Although the beginning and end of each mass extinction event cannot be clearly differentiated from the background extinction rate, it appears that each took between 0.5 and 3 million years.

The most famous mass extinction is the one that ended the Cretaceous period 65 million years ago, when the dinosaurs became extinct (Figure 8.10). One prevailing theory is that a meteorite struck the Yucatan Peninsula in Mexico, generating a thick cloud of dust that enveloped the Earth, leading to sudden climate change. Earlier mass extinctions were probably caused by several factors, including climate change, reduced oxygen levels and changing sea level, although there is a high degree of uncertainty in the geological record on the full causes (Freeland, 2003).

Figure 8.10   Images of dinosaurs often capture our imagination. This figure is a representation of a river floodplain in North America during the Late Cretaceous. The diversity of plants includes conifers, ginkos, cycads and ferns. *Tyrannosaurus rex*, a large carnivorous dinosaur, emerges from the forest to attack the duck-billed dinosaur, *Edmontosaurus*. Overhead fly *Pteranodons*, winged reptiles with seven-metre wingspans

A key claim of the IPSO and IUCN report on the current state of the oceans is that the contemporary extinction of marine species is directly comparable with those of the five mass extinctions (Rogers and Laffoley, 2011). A significant difference, however, is that the current mass extinction is taking place over decades, compared with hundreds of thousands or millions of years in the case of earlier mass extinctions.

The evidence for a contemporary mass extinction is based on a comparison of the estimated current extinction rate with the background extinction rate. According to calculations by Robert May, made in 2001 when he was president of the Royal Society of London, the current extinction rate of birds and mammals is probably 100 to 1000 times higher than the background rate. May concluded that 'There is little doubt that we are standing on the breaking tip of the sixth great wave of extinction in the history of life on Earth' (quoted in Radford, 2001). The oceans appear to be the predominant site of the current extinction event (Rogers and Laffoley, 2011). However, terrestrial species are also threatened (Figure 8.11).

(a)

(b)

(c)

(d)

Figure 8.11   Examples of currently endangered terrestrial species: (a) Giant panda (*Ailuropoda melanoleuca*); (b) Whooping crane (*Grus americana*); (c) Purple cat's paw mussel (*Epioblasma obliquata obliquata*); (d) (female) Hazel pot beetle (*Cryptocephalus coryli*)

# 4   The Anthropocene: a new geological epoch?

The idea that the cumulative activity of humankind is generating a mass extinction event has led to the recognition that our species may now be the dominant force for planetary change. Some scientists argue that we are entering into a new geological epoch – the Anthropocene – from the Greek *anthropo* meaning human and *cene* meaning new. Popularised by atmospheric chemist Paul Crutzen (2002) (Figure 8.12), the term has attracted much support and popular attention. Since 2008, the question of whether or not the current geological epoch should be officially designated the Anthropocene has been under consideration by the Stratigraphy Commission of the Geological Society of London (Vince, 2011). Until such a designation is agreed we continue to live in the Holocene Epoch.

Figure 8.12   Paul Crutzen, an atmospheric scientist, is credited with popularising the term Anthropocene, a new geological epoch in which humans are the dominant force for planetary change

---

Activity 8.3   The Holocene

The present geological epoch, the Holocene, has lasted for about 11,500 years. Can you recall from Chapter 1 the geological event that marks the beginning of the Holocene?

Comment

The Holocene began with the onset of an interglacial stage – a period of comparatively warmer climate that lies within the much longer Quaternary Ice Age (see Box 1.1 in Chapter 1).

---

Although there is some debate about when the human species first significantly affected Earth processes at a planetary scale, most scientists agree that as the Earth entered the Holocene, humans were a relatively insignificant species in terms of environmental impacts. Geologists now predict that in the future the consequences of human agricultural and industrial activities will be visible in the geological record just as we now examine evidence in rock formations of previous epochs. The presence of the first human-produced chemicals and waste such as the plastic bag could leave their trace for millions of years (Vince, 2011). However, the full shift into the Anthropocene may be even more dramatic (Lövbrand et al., 2009).

In the light of accumulating evidence of the extent and speed of climatic fluctuation during much of the current Quaternary Ice Age, Earth scientists are reaching a new appreciation of the stability of the Earth's climate throughout the Holocene (Rockström et al., 2009). The rise of agriculture, urbanism and, much later, industrialism are all located within a period of unusual climatic stability. As anthropologist Brian Fagan puts it: 'Civilization rose during a remarkable long summer' (Fagan, 2004, p. 25). In this regard, there is growing consensus that the full arrival of the Anthropocene will be marked by a shift out of the 'Holocene stability domain' into an entirely new, and much less stable, planetary regime (Rockström et al., 2009, p. 33).

# 5   The role of life in regulating Earth systems

If we step back and view Earth systems over a longer temporal scale, it is once again stability which is notable. It is now widely accepted that life itself plays an important role in maintaining this stability. In the 1920s, the Russian mineralogist Vladimir Vernadsky (1863–1945) published his work *The Biosphere* (Vernadsky, 1998 [1926]), which explored the role of life in changing the mineral composition of the Earth's crust and in determining the composition of the atmosphere. The term **biosphere** is now used to denote that part of the Earth capable of supporting life. Half a century after Vernadsky's *The Biosphere* was published, there was a resurgence of interest in the role of life in the maintenance of the planetary system when scientist James Lovelock arrived at his own theory – Gaia theory – about the integral role of biological life in sustaining the Earth as an environment fit for living things (Lovelock, 1987).

**Biosphere**
That part of the Earth capable of supporting life.

Figure 8.13   James Lovelock's Gaia theory proposes that the various components of the Earth comprise a single interconnected system

Lovelock chose the name Gaia after the Greek goddess of the Earth (Figure 8.13). Gaia theory offers a holistic view of the Earth as a single interconnected system. The term **holism** is used to denote the view that the whole is more than the sum of its parts, and the parts cannot be understood without reference to the whole. In this view, to understand Earth processes we should not examine just the independent 'components', such as ecosystems and their material environments. Like any system, Lovelock argues, the Earth system has emergent properties that cannot be understood by examining the individual parts in isolation. An understanding of how they interact is also needed.

Lovelock proposed that the biosphere is *self-regulating* so that over geological time the Earth system will operate to ensure that the conditions for life are maintained. While extinctions may happen and some species die off, over time the Earth system will adjust to provide the conditions that enable new life forms to evolve and thrive. In this respect, Lovelock claims, the Earth exhibits a homeostatic effect (Watson and Lovelock, 1983). **Homeostasis** is the tendency of a life form to regulate its internal conditions to maintain health and stability in response to external changes. The human body, for example, seeks to maintain a temperature of around 37 °C. To maintain this temperature the body will sweat in warm conditions to cool down, and shiver in cold ones to generate heat. This is an example of a negative feedback and it is the basis of homeostasis. A **negative feedback** is an interaction that moderates change within a system, so that the change is less than it would have been without the feedback (Figure 8.14).

**Holism**
The view that the whole is more than the sum of its parts.

**Homeostasis**
The tendency of a life form to regulate its internal conditions to maintain health and stability in response to external changes.

**Negative feedback**
Feedback that serves to moderate change, so that the change is less than it would have been without the feedback.

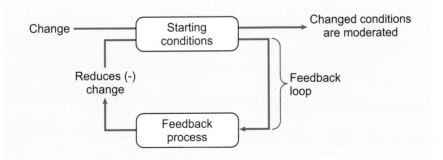

Figure 8.14   A negative feedback loop

To Lovelock, the Earth's homeostatic effect is maintained by numerous complex negative feedbacks that interact over time to maintain the conditions for life. These feedbacks include changes to maintain the atmospheric level of oxygen, surface temperature and ocean salinity within the parameters necessary for the continuation of life on Earth (Lovelock, 1987, 2006). Homeostasis comes about as a consequence of large numbers of local ecosystems mutually interacting to influence the functioning of physical systems at the planetary scale (Marten, 2001). Gaia theory has been greatly fortified by microbiologist Lynn Margulis's evidence about the role of microbial life in mediating major Earth processes to maintain the Earth in a continued state of homeostasis (Lovelock, 2006; Margulis, 1998).

Although Lovelock's depiction of the Earth system as a sort of 'super-organism' has ruffled some scientific sensibilities, there is now considerable support for the idea that the biosphere functions homeostatically in response to perturbations within the Earth system, as well as changes over time to incoming solar radiation (Bengtsson and Hammer, 2001; Smil, 2003).

# 6   Is social life self-regulating?

We have seen that complex feedback processes have kept Earth systems in a state amenable to life. However, growing evidence of the human impact on ecosystems raises questions about the capacity of modern human societies to regulate themselves in a way that supports the conditions for life.

The idea that human economic activity is fundamentally self-regulating is several centuries old, and still attracts strong support today. As we saw in Chapter 4, many traditional societies are capable of regulating their use of communal resources, a point that has been made in response to Hardin's original formulation of the tragedy of the commons. In social and economic theories of modern society, perhaps the most frequently invoked mechanism of social self-regulation has been the market. This view is often traced back to the Scottish philosopher Adam Smith (1723–1790). Smith's influential *The Wealth of Nations* (1982 [1776]) proposed the term *invisible hand* to describe the self-regulation of society by markets. The invisible hand, Smith suggested, is the totality of all the individual decisions taken by producers and consumers in markets, and it operates to achieve what is in the collective interests of society as a whole by ensuring that the goods and services produced are those that people most want (Taylor, 2003).

Smith's metaphor of an 'invisible' regulating force of the market operating through individual – and self-interested – economic agents has subsequently been taken up by economic theorists such as Milton Friedman to support 'free' or unregulated markets (Friedman, 1953, 2002). The application of free-market economics based on the work of Friedman has been especially popular since the 1980s and has been termed *neoliberalism* (Bakker, 2005; Harvey, 2007).

## Box 8.4   Markets

Markets were originally physical places where goods were exchanged (Figure 8.15). As a concept, the market has come to be seen as the process through which buyers and sellers of goods and services come together to engage in transactions. This can include the sale of 'labour': the capacity of one person to work for another.

Figure 8.15   The market is a place where buyers and sellers meet

Much economic theory is devoted to the study of markets and how they may (potentially) solve the problem of what to produce, and for whom. Repeated transactions between buyers and sellers – the relationship between supply and demand – is the process by which prices are established.

In the 'ideal' form of a market there is *perfect competition*, with many buyers and sellers who engage in transactions and who have full information on the prices being offered by other market players. The idea of perfect competition presupposes that all economic agents are primarily rational and motivated by self-interest. In the ideal scenario of the market, repeated transactions generate a condition of *equilibrium*; a balance between the supply of and demand for goods and services.

In most real-world markets there are many factors that compromise the ideal of perfect competition, such as the limiting or distorting of information available to buyers (such as biased advertising), power imbalances between buyers and sellers (for example, where one supplier has a monopoly in the market), and the effects of various forms of intervention by regulatory bodies. A *free market* is one in which there is a low level of regulatory intervention from government (e.g. imposing taxes, subsidies or price controls) in economic transactions.

---

## Activity 8.4   Markets and the environment

What sort of goods are markets best able to provide?

### Comment

Markets work best at providing private goods that can be traded between buyers and sellers. However, markets alone are not efficient at providing public goods which are non-rival and non-excludable, such as clean air and pollution-free oceans. This usually requires some form of intervention from government or intergovernmental organisations.

---

Markets may also be criticised on environmental grounds because they aim to provide market equilibrium (where the supply of a good equals its demand) rather than environmental sustainability. This argument has been made by environmental scientist Ralph Nadeau in his 2003 book *The Wealth of Nature* (Nadeau, 2003) (Figure 8.16). Nadeau argues that free-market economics generates huge negative externalities. There are no price signals that, for example, indicate to polluters that too much carbon dioxide is being emitted, or that indicate to government that people are going hungry because they have been evicted by a land grab, or that include the value a community attaches to a river or beautiful landscape. A free market, critics argue, responds to economic needs and wants rather than environmental needs (Elliott and Atkinson, 2008; Nadeau, 2003).

According to this view, while markets self-regulate society for economic ends, they do not provide the best model for organising relations between human beings and the rest of the natural world. Extending markets to the natural world reduces human relations with nature to use

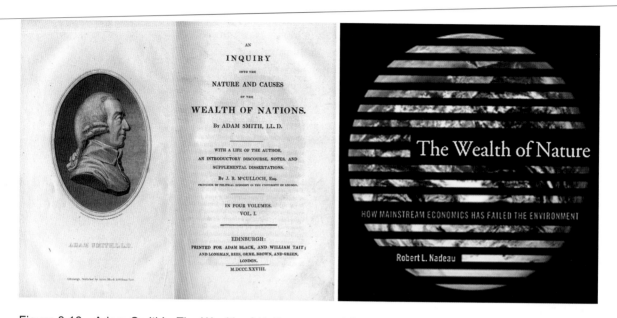

Figure 8.16   Adam Smith's *The Wealth of Nations* was published in 1776, while Ralph Nadeau's *The Wealth of Nature* followed 230 years later in 2006: two books with similar titles, but very different views on the virtues of free markets

values at the expense of non-use values, thus discouraging care of the environment (Bakker, 2005; Castree, 2003; Harvey, 1996; Smith, 1984).

If we wish to understand why the pressure of cumulative human activity now weighs so heavily on Earth systems, it is necessary to add a further level of analysis. We need to ask why the environmental impact of economic transactions carried out through markets has risen sharply over recent centuries. This requires that we examine the interwoven forces of capitalism and industrialism.

## 6.1   Capitalism and industrialism

Markets long pre-dated the rise of capitalism. The argument that will be made here is that it is not so much markets per se that generate environmental degradation, but markets under the conditions of modern industrial capitalism.

**Capitalism**

An economic system in which most of the factors of production used to produce goods and services are in private ownership.

**Capitalism** is an economic system in which most of the factors of production used to produce goods and services (including factories, machines, raw materials and information) are in private ownership. Those who do not own factors of production must work (or sell their labour) to support themselves. Capitalism has also been defined as 'the investment of money to make more money' (Fulcher, 2004, p. 18).

Competition between economic actors is the driving force of the capitalist system (Castree, 2003). The primary aim of production is to generate a profit for those who own – or have investments in – a business. For companies listed on a stock exchange, some profit is reinvested in order to generate further profits while some is distributed to shareholders as a dividend (Harvey, 2008). Stock exchanges function in a way that incentivises company growth. A company that does not generate what investors consider to be a sufficiently large profit will not be able to offer a large dividend and will suffer a fall in its share price as it becomes less attractive to investors. In this way, the general tendency of the capitalist system is towards expansion of the economy with profits being invested to generate more profits, notwithstanding occasional downturns or crises. (There is a view that crises occur in the capitalist system when limits arise in the opportunity to reinvest profits.)

The constant demand of an ever-expanding system for both raw materials and new sites of investment means that there is increasing pressure on the physical environment. As David Harvey, a geographer who is critical of capitalism, explains:

> Capitalists must also discover new means of production in general and natural resources in particular, which puts increasing pressure on the natural environment to yield up necessary raw materials and absorb the inevitable waste. They need to open up terrains for raw-material extraction.
>
> (Harvey, 2008, p. 24)

In this sense, there is a strong driving force that compels the capitalist system to regard the entire globe as its sphere of operations (Castree, 2003; Smith, 1984). Furthermore, the drive to increase profits leads many businesses to cut costs, including deliberately externalising environmental costs, in order to make the company more attractive to investors.

Those who support capitalism frequently invoke Smith's notion of the market to claim that capitalism is inherently orderly and self-regulating: that it contains its own internal checks and balances. However, the very process by which investment leads to growth and new investment in ever-expanding circles can be seen as intrinsically opposed to the idea of self-regulation and stability. Effectively, capitalism is a system with strong positive feedback mechanisms, with money invested to generate more money. For much of the last 250 years, this has resulted in increasing growth of profits for investors. In order to understand more fully how this drive for expansion has been realised and generated environmental problems, we need to understand the concept of industrialism.

Industrialism is related to, but should not be confused with, capitalism itself. Non-capitalist societies have promoted industrialism, most notably the Soviet-type system adopted by the USSR and its allies from the 1920s to the late 1980s. **Industrialism** involves the application of science and technology to the extraction of natural resources and to production processes. Applying new scientific insights and technological innovations to manufacturing has generated both new products and new production processes (Kumar, 1978; Reddish, 2003).

**Industrialism**
The application of science and technology to the extraction of natural resources and to production processes.

The continued growth of capitalist economies requires raw materials. Furthermore, one of the main objectives of industrial development is finding new sources of energy and new ways to exploit known energy reserves. In turn, the availability of expanded supplies of energy has pushed processes of industrialisation in new directions. Some of the earliest industrial development involved production processes powered by water, wind and biomass. But over most of the last two centuries, the key to industrialisation and capitalist growth has been the increasing use of fossil fuels. Tapping into reserves of fossil fuels laid down beneath the Earth's surface in the past has provided an energy source that has enabled a radical intensification of human interactions with nature (Reddish, 2003).

Capitalism and industrialism can each exist without the other. But in practice they have been closely entangled and mutually reinforcing (Giddens, 1990). Where capitalism provides the imperative for continual growth, industrialism provides the techniques and technologies which constantly transform production processes and the infrastructures on which production depends. This sets up a cycle in which growth requires increasing supplies of energy, while the search for new exploitable energy sources becomes one of the main aims of industrialism.

Whether industrial capitalism is viewed positively or critically, few would deny the enormous economic growth it has generated. Although some economies have specialised in particular forms of economic growth – such as the provision of financial services – which are not immediately dependent on growing energy supplies, the overall trajectory of industrial capitalism thus far has depended on finding new energy sources. The combination of the growth imperative of capitalism with the expanding technological capabilities of industrialism helps explain the ever-increasing pressure on the natural environment, and the resulting changes in Earth systems that the concept of the Anthropocene represents. As Andrew Dobson argues, this drive for growth suffers from the internal contradiction of undermining the very context in which it is possible, by unsustainably consuming a finite stock of resources in a world that does not have a limitless capacity to absorb the waste produced by the industrial process (Dobson, 2007).

## 6.2  Solving environmental issues: values and approaches

It must be stressed that not all environmental thinkers or practitioners share the account in Section 6.1 of the industrial capitalist system and the markets through which it operates. There is something of a fault line running through views on the relationship between industrial capitalism and the environment that can be summed up in two different value-based approaches. The first approach considers that environmental degradation is an accidental condition of industrial capitalism, and that, provided the necessary reforms are made, contemporary lifestyles and modes of production can be rendered more environmentally friendly. In this view, a sustainable capitalism is possible. Those who adhere to this approach may be called *light greens*.

The second approach holds that environmental degradation is an integral condition of industrial capitalism. In this view, modern forms of production and transport cannot be greened; they are inherently and unavoidably unsustainable and should be replaced with more environmentally friendly alternatives. The only solution, therefore, is systemic change. Those who adhere to this approach are referred to as *dark greens*. A key thinker representing this viewpoint is the Norwegian philosopher Arne Naess (1912–2009), who is credited with pioneering 'deep ecologism' (Naess, 1989). Dark greens are sceptical of the role of industrial technology, centralised state planning and global business corporations and argue for a slower pace of life and a reversion to more localised and eco-friendly forms of production and consumption (Table 8.1).

Table 8.1  Some indicative positions of light greens and dark greens

| Light greens | Dark greens |
| --- | --- |
| A belief in technological solutions to environmental problems | Technology is often the cause of, rather than the solution to, environmental problems |
| A commitment to more sustainable economic growth | There are ecological limits to economic growth |
| An emphasis on instrumental values; nature provides resources for the economy | An emphasis on intrinsic values: respect for nature |
| The state and business corporations have a role to play in solving environmental issues | Political and economic power should move from the state and big business to local communities |

Another fault line that divides environmental thinkers and activists concerns the strategies that should be adopted in order to achieve social change. Here again there are two dominant approaches. *Insiders* favour working with mainstream institutions such as legislatures, the state, business and international organisations, arguing that because these institutions hold political and economic power, changing them will generate broader change throughout the society. In the German Green Party (*die Grünen* or 'the Greens'), those who favour this approach are called Realos (realists). The second approach is taken by the *outsiders*, who favour more oppositional, and sometimes confrontational, approaches. Outsiders are referred to as Fundis (fundamentalists) by *die Grünen*. Approaches favoured by outsiders may include establishing networks of local, eco-friendly farm cooperatives, taking action to conserve local endangered species and disrupting flights at international airports (Table 8.2)

Light greens favour the reform of mainstream institutions and thus typically favour an insider approach. Note, however, that the distinction between insiders and outsiders is not a value-based one. For example, in *die Grünen* the Realos and the Fundis may, indeed often do, share similar values and long-term aims, although they disagree over the political approaches for achieving these aims. Today, the Realo view prevails in *die Grünen*, although the Fundi view still makes itself heard.

Table 8.2   Some indicative positions of insiders and outsiders (the Realo–Fundi divide)

| Insiders (Realos) | Outsiders (Fundis) |
| --- | --- |
| Support for a centralised Green Party structure that is active at the national level | Support for grassroots action as the most effective route for change |
| Radical change can be achieved through a piecemeal strategy via parliament | Radical change requires setting up alternatives outside mainstream politics |
| Achieving change requires compromise with other political parties and other actors | Rejection of coalitions with other parties and other actors |

Source: adapted from Carter, 2007, Box 5.2, p. 119

This account may have given the impression that environmental thinkers and activists can be neatly divided into different 'camps': light and dark; inside and outside. In fact, environmental thinking is far more complicated and 'messy' than such tidy dualisms suggest. The distinction between light and dark green values is not always clear in practice. And some groups consider that social change requires both insider and outsider approaches. Greenpeace, for example, lobbies business and parliamentarians, produces good quality research to support its campaigning, and has taken direct action to oppose whaling and nuclear tests in the South Pacific.

Even so, these are useful analytical distinctions. Disagreements over values and political approaches are two areas of controversy that help us to think through the question: what is an environmental issue?

# 7   Summary

So, is biodiversity loss a global issue?

We began this block by considering one event: an oil spill. Since then you have seen that this event, and biodiversity loss more generally, has global dimensions. Here we draw out three lines of thought explored in the block which suggest that biodiversity loss should be considered a global issue.

First, the Earth is an interconnected ecological system. What happens in one part of the Earth system may have consequences over space (elsewhere in the world) and time (in the future). The Earth, according to Lovelock, may be seen as a self-regulating entity that over geological time exhibits a homeostatic property that maintains the conditions for life. However, the case can be made that the disturbances that humans are causing to the Earth are so sudden and so severe that it is uncertain whether the self-regulating properties of the planet will be able to act in time to counter the damage humans are causing.

This leads to a second line of thought. While humans are capable of self-regulating social behaviour at a local scale to conserve resources, we presently seem unable to do so at a global scale. Some of the reasons for this concern markets: while they are self-regulating, markets aim to match supply with demand rather than promote environmental conservation. Markets are better suited to the provision of private rather than public goods; and negative externalities are not included in market prices. Other reasons concern industrialism and capitalism. The world is increasingly organised into a global economy with international trade in raw materials, services and manufactured products. Industrial capitalism has an inherent growth imperative that, far from ensuring stability and self-regulation, results in increasing pressure on natural environments.

Third, a global community of affected interests has arisen, not only around the Deepwater Horizon oil spill, but also around biodiversity loss in general. This community of interest includes not only those whose livelihoods are directly affected by biodiversity loss, such as fisherfolk and farmers, but also others who politically resist the loss of biodiversity, perhaps because they are emotionally affected by environmental damage or because they believe it to be wrong on principled grounds. This community of interest does not always agree, however, on the solutions. Different actors may have different value-based objectives; for example, between light green and dark green.

A shared experience of 'being affected' by undesired changes or conditions is at the core of public mobilisation around environmental issues. Issue formation, in this sense, depends on people joining others in acts of caring and responsibility. Those who are concerned about environmental degradation are always geographically situated; they live, work, and interact with other people and things in specific locations. However, a community of affected interests may come together in ways that span vast geographical distances. Globalisation and global forms of connectivity may put people at risk of distant actions, but they can also assist them in cooperating over vast geographical distances (Barnett, 2008). There is a gradual building up of a global politics which Bruno Latour suggests 'is constructed one step at a time' (Latour, 2004, p. 3). This is a process that has been gathering momentum for several decades.

# References

Bakker, K. (2005) 'Neoliberalizing nature? Market environmentalism in water supply in England and Wales', *Annals of the Association of American Geographers*, vol. 95, no. 3, pp. 542–65.

Barnett, C. (2008) 'Convening publics: the parasitical spaces of public action', in Cox, K. R., Low, M. and Robinson, J. (eds) *The SAGE Handbook of Political Geography*, London, Sage.

Bengtsson, L. and Hammer, C. (eds) (2001) *Geosphere-Biosphere Interactions and Climate*, Cambridge, Cambridge University Press.

Boyce, D., Lewis, M. and Worm, B. (2010) 'Global phytoplankton decline over the past century', *Nature*, vol. 466, no. 7306, pp. 591–6.

Carter, N. (2007) *The Politics of the Environment: Ideas, Activism, Policy* (2nd edn), Cambridge, Cambridge University Press.

Castree, N. (2003) 'Uneven development, globalization and environmental change', in Hinchliffe, S., Blowers, A. and Freeland, J. (eds) *Understanding Environmental Issues*, Chichester, John Wiley/Milton Keynes, The Open University.

Crutzen, P. J. (2002) 'Geology of mankind', *Nature*, vol. 415, no. 6867, p. 23.

Dobson, A. (2007) *Green Political Thought*, Abingdon, Routledge.

Doney, S.C. (2010) 'The growing human footprint on coastal and open-ocean biogeochemistry', *Science*, vol. 328, 18 June, pp. 1512–16 [online], DOI: 10.1126/science.1185198 (Accessed 27 July 2012).

Earle, S. A. (2010) *The World is Blue: How Our Fate and the Ocean's are One*, Washington, DC, National Geographic Society.

Elliott, L. and Atkinson, D. (2008) *The Gods that Failed: How Blind Faith in Markets Has Cost Us Our Future*, London, Bodley Head.

Fagan, B. (2004) *The Long Summer: How Climate Changed Civilization*, London, Granta.

Freeland, J. (2003) 'Are too many species going extinct? Environmental change in time and space', in Hinchliffe, S., Blowers, A. and Freeland, J. (eds) *Understanding Environmental Issues*, Chichester, John Wiley/Milton Keynes, The Open University.

Friedman, M. (1953) *Essays in Positive Economics*, Chicago, IL, University of Chicago Press.

Friedman, M. (2002) *Capitalism and Freedom*, Chicago, IL, University of Chicago Press.

Fulcher, J. (2004) *Capitalism: A Very Short Introduction*, Oxford, Oxford University Press.

Giddens, A. (1990) *The Consequences of Modernity*, Cambridge, Polity Press.

Harvey, D. (1996) *Justice, Nature and the Geography of Difference*, Cambridge, MA, Blackwell.

Harvey, D. (2007) *A Brief History of Neoliberalism*, Oxford, Oxford University Press.

Harvey, D. (2008) 'The right to the city', *New Left Review*, vol. 53, pp. 23–40.

Harvey, F. (2011) '"Shocking" state of seas threatens mass extinction, say marine experts', *The Guardian*, 20 June [online], http://www.guardian.co.uk/environment/2011/jun/20/marine-life-oceans-extinction-threat (Accessed 20 July 2012).

Hohn, D. (2012) *Moby Duck: The True Story of 28,800 Bath Toys Lost at Sea*, London, Union Books.

Independent World Commission on the Oceans (1998) *The Ocean Our Future*, Cambridge, Cambridge University Press.

Kumar, K. (1978) *Prophecy and Progress: The Sociology of Industrial and Post-Industrial Society*, Harmondsworth, Penguin.

Kurlansky, M. (1999) *Cod: A Biography of the Fish That Changed the World* London, Verso.

Latour, B. (2004) *Politics of Nature*, Cambridge, MA, Harvard University Press.

Lavigne, D. M. (2003) 'Marine mammals and fisheries: the role of science in the culling debate', in Gales, N., Hindell, M. and Kirkwood, R. (eds) *Marine Mammals: Fisheries, Tourism and Management Issues*, Melbourne, CSIRO Publishing.

Lövbrand, E., Stripple, J. and Wiman, B. (2009) 'Earth system governmentality: reflections on science in the Anthropocene', *Global Environmental Change*, vol. 19, no. 1, pp. 7–13.

Lovelock, J. (1987) *Gaia: A New Look at Life on Earth*, Oxford, Oxford University Press.

Lovelock, J. (2006) *The Revenge of Gaia*, London, Penguin.

Margulis, L. (1998) *The Symbiotic Planet: A New Look at Evolution*, London, Phoenix.

Marten, G. (2001) *Human Ecology: Basic Concepts for Sustainable Development*, London, Earthscan.

Millennium Ecosystem Assessment (2005) *Ecosystems and Human Well-being: Synthesis*, Washington, DC, Island Press; also available online at http://www.millenniumassessment.org/documents/document.356.aspx.pdf (Accessed 27 July 2012).

Nadeau, R. (2003) *The Wealth of Nature: How Mainstream Economics Has Failed the Environment*, New York, Columbia University Press.

Naess, A. (1989) *Ecology, Community and Lifestyle*, Cambridge, Cambridge University Press.

Olden, J. D., Hogan, Z. S. and Vander Zanden, M. J. (2007) 'Small fish, big fish, red fish, blue fish: size-biased extinction risk of the world's freshwater and marine fishes', *Global Ecology and Biogeography*, vol. 16, no. 6, pp. 694–701.

Pauly, D. J., Christensen, V., Guenette, S., Pitcher, T. J., Sumaila, U. R., Walters, C. J., Watson, R. and Zeller, D. (2002) 'Towards sustainability in world fisheries', *Nature*, vol. 418, no. 6898, pp. 689–95.

Radford, T. (2001) 'Scientist warns of sixth great extinction of wildlife', *The Guardian*, 29 November [online], http://www.guardian.co.uk/uk/2001/nov/29/highereducation.research (Accessed 27 July 2012).

Raup, D. M. (1994) 'The role of extinction in evolution', *Proceedings of the National Academy of Sciences of the United States of America*, vol. 91, no. 15, pp. 6758–63.

Reddish, A. (2003) 'Dynamic Earth: human impacts', in Morris, D., Freeland, J., Hinchliffe, S. and Smith, S. (eds) *Changing Environments*, Chichester, John Wiley/Milton Keynes, The Open University.

Roberts, C. (2012) *Ocean of Life: How Our Seas Are Changing*, London, Allen Lane.

Rockström, J., Steffen, W., Noone, K., Persson, Å., Chapin III, F. S, Lambin, E., Lenton, T. M., Scheffer, M., Folke, C., Schellnhuber, H., Nykvist, B., De Wit, C. A., Hughes, T., van der Leeuw, S., Rodhe, H., Sörlin, S., Snyder, P. K., Costanza, R., Svedin, U., Falkenmark, M., Karlberg, L., Corell, R. W., Fabry, V. J., Hansen, J., Walker, B., Liverman, D., Richardson, K., Crutzen, P. and Foley, J. (2009) 'Planetary boundaries: exploring the safe operating space for humanity', *Ecology and Society*, vol. 14, no. 2, Article 32 [online], http://www.ecologyandsociety.org/vol14/iss2/art32/ (Accessed 29 July 2012).

Rogers, A. D. and Laffoley, D. d'A. (2011) *International Earth System Expert Workshop on Ocean Stresses and Impacts: Summary Report*, IPSO, Oxford.

Schiermeier, Q. (2010) 'Ocean greenery under warming stress: a century of phytoplankton decline suggests that ocean ecosystems are in peril', *Nature*, 28 July [online], http://www.nature.com/news/2010/100728/full/news.2010.379.html (Accessed 29 July 2012).

Simpson, J. and Sharples, J. (2012) *Introduction to the Physical and Biological Oceanography of Shelf Seas*, Cambridge, Cambridge University Press.

Smil, V. (2003) *The Earth's Biosphere: Evolution, Dynamics, and Change*, Cambridge, MA, MIT Press.

Smith, A. (1982 [1776]) *The Wealth of Nations*, Harmondsworth, Penguin.

Smith, N. (1984) *Uneven Development: Nature, Capital and the Production of Space*, Oxford, Basil Blackwell.

Taylor, A. (2003) 'Trading with the environment', in Bingham, N., Blowers, A. and Belshaw, C. (eds) *Contested Environments*, Chichester, John Wiley/Milton Keynes, The Open University.

Turner, A. (2012) 'Moby-Duck's warning of a peril at sea', *Sunday Times*, *News Review*, 12 February, p. 8.

Vernadsky, V. (1998 [1926]) *The Biosphere*, New York, Copernicus.

Vince, G. (2011) 'Geologists press for recognition of Earth-changing "human epoch"', *The Guardian*, 3 June [online], http://www.guardian.co.uk/science/2011/jun/03/geologists-human-epoch-anthropocene (Accessed 29 July 2012).

Watson, A. and Lovelock, J. (1983) 'Biological homeostasis of the global environment: the parable of Daisyworld', *Tellus*, Series B, vol. 35, no. 4, pp. 284–9; also available online at http://www.tellusb.net/index.php/tellusb/article/view/14616 (Accessed 29 July 2012).

# Block 3  Water

# Chapter 9   Connections and complexity

Pam Furniss

# Contents

# 1 Introduction

All streams flow into the sea, yet the sea is never full. To the place the streams come from, there they return again.

(Ecclesiastes 1: 7)

Water is essential for life. Having enough water to survive is a challenge that has faced humans for millennia and it remains a daily priority for millions of people. Beyond basic survival, water is also critical for our ways of life as we use it for hygiene, agriculture, industry, fisheries, transport, leisure, amenity and waste disposal. As the global human population increases and ways of life change, the demand for water is rising, thus intensifying the pressure on water resources throughout the world. Water is equally essential for other living organisms and it plays a central role in shaping the environments of both humans and non-humans.

Unlike most of the resources on which living things depend, water flows. The fluid nature of water as a resource and the multiple, interconnected and growing demands made on water resources are the basis for the different kinds of controversy that arise around the issue of water use. Chapters 9 to 12 provide some of the background material to enable understanding of how and why such controversies occur and how they can be managed. These form part of the exploration of the block question *Why are environmental issues often controversial?*

In order to introduce some of the key aspects of water management and water use as a controversial issue, this chapter unpacks the notion of 'water security'. Water security is a term that has emerged from academic and policy engagements with the challenge of water provision and supply since the turn of the millennium. It has become a popular concept in water management from the global to the local level. Understanding its implications requires a thorough understanding of the functioning of the water cycle which is addressed later in the chapter.

## 2   Sharing a dynamic resource

Water moves. Hardly a startling or revelatory observation, you might think – self-evident, even – but the consequences of this movement are profound for environments and environmental issues. Water moves across the planet in streams, rivers, canals, lakes and oceans, sometimes in unpredictable ways, reminding us again that we live on a dynamic planet. Water is an ever-present force in forming and re-forming our landscapes. To a large degree the physical landscape around us was shaped – and continues to be shaped – by the movement of water. Whether as a flowing river, glacial ice, ocean waves or rain, moving water erodes rocks, transporting mineral particles which are deposited as sediments elsewhere. Water is the key agent in the formation of valleys, cliffs, deltas and other features of the land surface, from gentle slopes to magnificent canyons (Figure 9.1). The processes involved in the creation of these landforms occur over different temporalities, often slowly over millions of years. However, the erosion of the cliffs of Happisburgh, East Anglia reminds us that sometimes change can be sudden.

Figure 9.1   The most significant natural force in the shaping of the Grand Canyon is erosion, primarily from the movement of water over millions of years

If recognising the many different ways in which water moves is a first step to understanding the role it plays in environmental change, the second is recognising its variability. The distribution of water around the world varies both temporally and spatially owing to the variations in the climate and the unequal distribution of **precipitation**. The annual mean precipitation on Earth is around 1000 mm but there are large variations from this average in different places. Some areas receive less than 250 mm annually, such as the deserts of the Middle East, North Africa, northern Central Asia and central Australia (Figure 9.2). The annual precipitation in other areas can reach as much as 12,000 mm (for example, the Amazon Basin and parts of South and South East Asia). Precipitation may vary significantly over time, as well as spatially. In some regions rainfall is highly seasonal, as on the Indian subcontinent where the south-west monsoon brings intense rain for a few summer months (Figure 9.3).

**Precipitation**
The formation of rain, snow or hail through condensation of water vapour in the atmosphere.

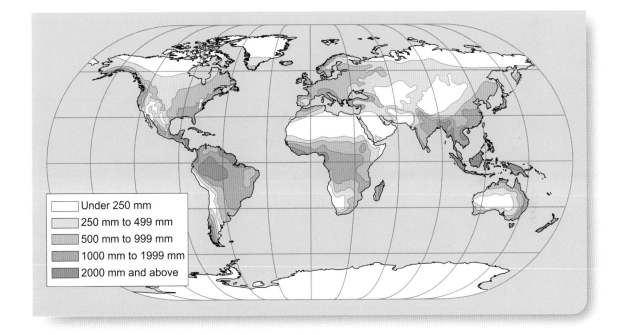

Figure 9.2  Average annual precipitation around the Earth

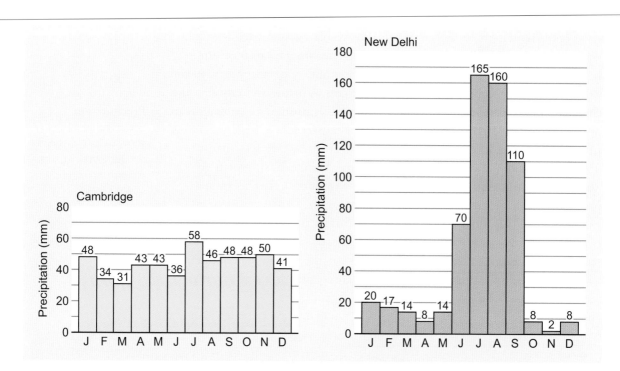

Figure 9.3   Average monthly precipitation for Cambridge, UK, and New Delhi, India

## Activity 9.1   Seasonal precipitation

The average annual precipitation for Cambridge and New Delhi is very similar, although markedly different in seasonal distribution (Figure 9.3). What are the minimum and maximum monthly precipitation figures for (a) Cambridge and (b) New Delhi?

### Comment

The monthly precipitation in (a) Cambridge varies from 31 to 58 mm, and in (b) New Delhi from 2 to 165 mm.

Seasonal variation in precipitation naturally translates into seasonal variation in river flow. For example, New Delhi is located on the banks of the Yamuna River, which carries 80 per cent of its annual flow in the monsoon months of July to September, with only 20 per cent in the remaining nine months of the year (Sharma and Kansal, 2011). Outside the monsoon season, some stretches of the river dry up completely.

Humans increasingly seek to manage how water flows, and when. Today, very few of the world's rivers are free from human intervention. Regulating rivers in order to reduce flooding and maintain steady water flow has long been part of human interaction with the environment. Building dams to regulate river flows is one example, and a cause of controversy that will be discussed later in this block.

Thinking about water highlights the usefulness of the concepts of time and space in thinking through environmental issues. Water does not stay still; it moves from place to place over time. Water thus varies in abundance in space and over time. Water resources are also subject to many different demands by people. People must share water – both with each other and with different species – but they can do so in different ways, some of which are more equitable than others.

How water should be shared is a profound challenge in different ways and at different scales. Before we explore what this means in more detail, however, we should establish what we mean by controversy. Following on from the definition of an environmental issue in Block 2, which emphasises that an environmental issue is one that involves actors engaging with one another publicly, we may define a **controversy** as a disagreement between actors over an issue, which is carried out in public.

**Controversy**
A disagreement between actors over an issue, which is carried out in public.

However, environmental issues are not always controversial. Disagreement is not a necessary dimension of an issue, although some form of dialogue or debate is. Some environmental issues can bring people together in more or less consensual contexts, striving towards a common goal. The issue in question may be resolved amicably and speedily, especially when the various actors work towards a shared understanding that takes into account the concerns of all.

But very often, however, environmental issues are controversial.

---

## Activity 9.2  Sources of controversy

From your work on the module to date, can you recall some things that can lead to environmental issues becoming controversial?

## Comment

There may be uncertainty on the precise causes of environmental change, and whether change (e.g. climate change or species extinction) is due primarily to natural factors or human agency. An environmental change that is considered unacceptable to one actor, perhaps because it is considered high risk, may be acceptable to another. Different actors may subscribe to different values. Even if actors share the same, or similar, values, they may favour very different political strategies for addressing the problem. Powerful actors may be better able to secure policies that favour themselves relative to less powerful groups.

In the case of water, there may, for example, be scientific controversy over predicting future rainfall patterns and their possible impacts on environmental change. Controversy over knowledge may lead to controversy over the risks and uncertainties of different courses of action. Water-related hazards such as flood and drought may compromise water supplies. There may be controversy over who should have the rights of access to an area of land or to a natural resource. And there may be controversy over who should take political action. For example, should problems of water scarcity be addressed by local communities, national government, the business sector or international organisations?

Controversy can be expressed in many different ways. For instance, a group of scientists may disagree at an academic conference on the methods they use for research. Communities may disagree on the values that underlie the use of a local resource. Dissenting opinions on water policy may be expressed in the media. There may be disagreement between two or more governments on the extraction of water from a shared lake or river. Throughout this block you will encounter different forms of controversy, ranging from situations where the gap between the positions of the various parties is hidden or latent, through competition and contest, to those controversies that are overtly conflictual (including armed conflict).

By now, the basis and reasons for water as a flowing, unequally distributed, essential resource that is often the subject of controversy should be starting to become more obvious. Water crosses boundaries of different properties, ecosystems and countries and thus connects communities in ways which other resources do not, with the consequence that the impacts of water use (in both their positive and negative aspects) are felt downstream. For example, imagine you are a landowner with a river running through your property. You may argue that this is your river and you can use the water as you wish to meet your needs. But the water in the river is moving. Your neighbours own the land further upstream. The river passes through their property first and they may claim ownership. The landowner further downstream may also have a strong sense of ownership. With competing views over ownership there is a controversy, and the potential for that controversy to lead to conflict between upstream and downstream users is clear. Controversy may arise if the downstream user believes the upstream user is taking more than their fair share of the resource, or if the upstream user pollutes the resource so that the downstream user cannot use it (Figure 9.4).

Figure 9.4   Upstream users usually have the advantage over downstream users

Attempts to solve this basic problem using market techniques may themselves be controversial (Chapter 12). As you saw in Block 2, markets work best with private goods. Private goods are excludable; the owner of a resource can prevent others from enjoying it. But exclusion is difficult to enforce with a fluid resource that crosses boundaries. As lawyer Joseph Dellapenna observes:

> The basic reason that markets do not work comes back to the most basic aspect of water as a resource – it moves. And as it moves it is used and re-used. Any transaction that would significantly alter when, where and how water is used, at least if the transaction is large, will have 'spill-over' effects on numerous other users.
>
> (Dellapenna, 2007, p. 401)

These spillover effects and the connections between use and reuse make sharing water a controversial issue.

# 3   Water security

The multiple dimensions of water use for people and the environment have been encapsulated by the concept of 'water security', a relatively recent, still evolving, but already widely used term in both academic and policy circles (Cook and Bakker, 2012; Grey and Sadoff, 2007; Lautze and Manthrithilake, 2012). A key early definition was provided by the Global Water Partnership (GWP) in 2000. According to GWP, water security is achieved when:

> every person has access to enough safe water at affordable cost to lead a clean, healthy and productive life, while ensuring that the environment is protected and enhanced.
>
> (GWP, 2000, p. 12)

Water security represents an overarching goal for dealing with the challenge of water provision. It aims to reconcile the different claims to water of different actors. As such, the GWP definition provides a useful summary of the essential aspects of global water management. But the definition is also a dense one, so let us now unpack it in order to set up some of the key themes of the block.

## 3.1   Population growth: 'every person'

If 'every person' in the world is to have access to enough safe water, both now and in the future, then one obvious variable is the number of people concerned. The graph in Figure 9.5 shows how rapidly the global population increased during the twentieth century. This increase is relevant to many environmental issues, especially those concerned with finite resources. Sir David Attenborough, patron of the UK charity Population Matters, has said 'all environmental problems become harder – and ultimately impossible – to solve with ever more people' (Population Matters, 2012). At a very simple level of analysis, more people means each receives a smaller share of a resource, with competition between them becoming ever more likely.

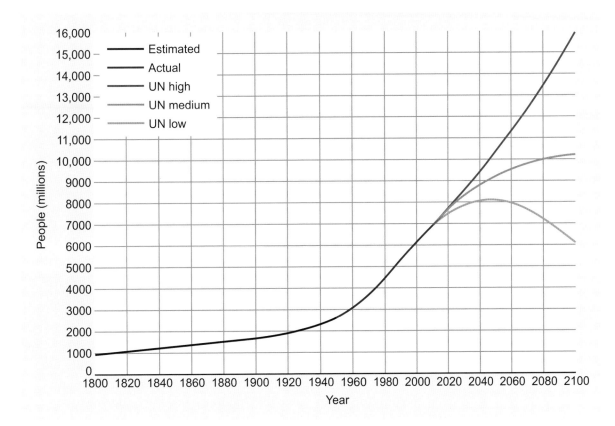

Figure 9.5  Changing global population from 1800 to 2100. Over the past 100 years, the global population has more than trebled in size. The United Nations' predictions of future trends vary with changing patterns of fertility and mortality, but the medium forecast is for the world's population to exceed 9 billion before 2050 and to rise to more than 10 billion by the end of the century (UN News Centre, 2011) (Source: based on World Population Review, 2012)

## Activity 9.3   Reading a graph – population growth

According to the data in Figure 9.5, what was the change in global population between 1960 and 2000? Give the answer in terms of both the number of people and the percentage change.

## Comment

The population increased from approximately 3 billion (3000 million) to 6 billion, an increase of 3 billion people, or a 100 per cent increase.

*Note:* From the graph, read off the population at the two dates given and subtract one from the other to get the increase in population. To calculate the percentage change, divide this number by the starting figure and multiply by 100. In this example, the increase (3 billion) and the starting figure (3 billion) are the same, therefore dividing one by the other equals 1, which multiplied by 100 gives 100 per cent.

The three possible future trajectories shown in Figure 9.5 reveal the uncertainties of predictions, ranging from a continuing steep increase to overall decline. In a 2004 report on world population, the United Nations acknowledged this uncertainty when it said: 'What will population trends be like beyond 2050? No one really knows. Any demographic projections, if they go 100, 200, or 300 years into the future, are little more than guesses' (United Nations, 2004, p. 3). This clearly makes long-term planning on water and other resources very difficult. Forecasters must also take into account the changing distribution of people in many parts of the world. Migration towards cities and increasing urban populations may exacerbate the resource allocation issues where density is high; for example, in slums.

Population change is an important variable in environmental change and in questions over resource distribution, but it is certainly not the only variable. Per capita consumption is also important: wealthier people tend to consume more water than poorer ones. Focusing solely on population numbers can lead to simplistic and frequently controversial discussions of the necessity for population control as a solution to resource scarcity. This raises complex moral and ethical questions with no easy resolution. Providing access to contraception is controversial in many cultures and access to abortion services even more so. Cultural, religious and social beliefs play a large part in the acceptability of birth control, while government-imposed measures, such as China's one-child policy, are particularly problematic. Less controversial approaches to population control include improving access to education for women and girls, which has been shown to be a key determinant of birth rate (McRary and Royer, 2006).

## 3.2   Quantity and quality: 'enough safe water'

Another phrase used in the GWP definition of water security is 'enough safe water'. This includes two key notions: 'enough' refers to quantity and 'safe' to quality. As noted above, the quantity of available water is related to the number of people, but the volume of water used by each person is also important. A broad range of economic, social and cultural factors interact to influence per capita water consumption. An important question in the concept of 'enough water' is, therefore: how much is enough? The requirement for basic human needs is estimated to be between 20 and 50 litres per person per day (Gleick, 2000; UNDP, 2006), but the actual domestic consumption varies enormously between different countries, as shown in Figure 9.6.

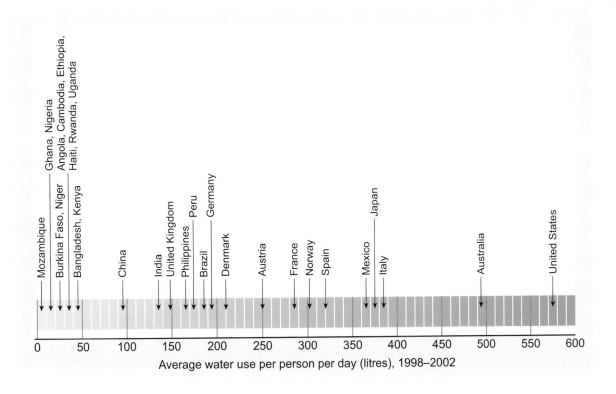

Figure 9.6   Average domestic water use per person per day for selected countries, 1998–2002 (Source: based on UNDP, 2006, p. 34, Figure 1.2)

Historically, the pattern of water consumption has been one of increasing per capita consumption over time. Growing affluence coupled with technological developments means that people tend to wash themselves and their clothes more frequently. Many people find it unacceptable to wash their body only once a week and not to have clean clothes every day, but this was the norm not so long ago. Take British showering habits as an example. Only a few decades ago, the weekly bath was part of the normal routine in many British households, but nowadays showering daily is quite common. Several different factors have contributed to this change in practice (Hand et al., 2005). Technological improvements include piped water supplies into bathrooms, access to instant hot water from modern heating systems and, more recently, the advent of power showers. These have been coupled with changes in social values concerning cleanliness and health, perceptions of body image and social pressures, not least from advertising and marketing campaigns for bathroom products. The speed, immediacy and perceived convenience of showers lead people to shower more frequently. So even though a shower may use less water than a bath, the overall water consumption can be higher.

In many industrialised countries the trend towards increasing domestic consumption has slowed through improving efficiency of water use. In England and Wales, the amount of water used for domestic purposes has levelled out at about 150 litres per person per day (Environment Agency, 2008). However, the pattern of increased use is present in many lower-income countries where people's aspirations and expectations are influenced by similar drivers for change to those noted above.

Increasing population and changing norms of water consumption are likely to mean not only increasing water use but also increasing impacts on water quality. Water quality is a general term describing the chemical, physical and biological condition of natural waters, but in the context of water security the emphasis is on safety. Safe water must be free of toxins and pathogenic (disease-causing) agents. In practice, this means free from contamination with human excrement because that is the cause of most waterborne diseases. Estimates vary but, globally, between 3000 and 5000 children under the age of 5 die every day from waterborne disease (UNICEF/WHO, 2009). Water pollution and the causes and consequences of waterborne disease are discussed further in Chapter 11.

## 3.3 Cost: 'at affordable cost'

There may be plenty of clean water available, but if it's priced so highly that people cannot afford it then water security will not be achievable. But how affordability should be measured may be a source of controversy. Should all people pay the same amount? Should rich people pay more? Is it right that people should pay for water at all, given that it is essential for survival? The complexities of water rights, pricing and markets are the subject of Chapter 12, so this introduction will be limited to just one or two ideas.

According to the Institute of Human Rights and Business (IHRB), an affordable water supply is one where the costs 'should not prevent a person from accessing safe drinking water and should not compromise his or her access to other basic services, including food, health and education' (IHRB, 2009, p. 17). Affordability includes more than having sufficient money to pay for the water, including the costs of connection such as pipes, taps and water meters. Another type of cost is opportunity cost. **Opportunity cost** is the value of the alternative option or activity that is foregone or sacrificed as the result of spending money on something else. So if I spend money on water, what am I giving up? If the answer is a luxury holiday, then the opportunity cost – giving up the holiday – would not prevent me from accessing safe drinking water. But if the opportunity cost of water was giving up food or medicine for a sick child, then many people would consider the cost to be too high and would forgo safe drinking water. In many developed countries, the opportunity cost relating to spending on mains water is generally fairly low in relation to the overall quality of life. But in other countries this is not the case; for example, when paying for water represents a large proportion of income. Note that opportunity cost need not necessarily be measured in money. A prohibitive opportunity cost would be a significant amount of time needed to collect water. In many parts of the world, women and children walk long distances each day to collect water with considerable opportunity cost (Figure 9.7). The time spent collecting water means less time for family life, education or productive employment. Assessing the affordability of water, therefore, should be based on both the financial costs and the opportunity costs.

**Opportunity cost**
The value of an alternative that is foregone or sacrificed.

Figure 9.7   Collecting water in Rajasthan, India. In many countries women and children can spend several hours a day walking to sources of drinking water

## 3.4   Ecosystems: 'ensuring that the environment is protected and enhanced'

The final phrase of the GWP water security definition reflects the importance of the environment. To achieve water security, the allocation of scarce water resources for human use should not be to the detriment of other species. Fresh water and wetlands provide some of the most important specialist habitats for wildlife and typically have high biodiversity. Freshwater ecosystems support 12 per cent of known species even though they cover only 1 per cent of the Earth's surface (Gleick, 2012). Rivers, ponds, lakes, marshes, bogs and swamps are among the richest habitats for many organisms, including aquatic plants, birds, amphibians, invertebrates and fish (Figure 9.8).

(a)   (b)   (c)   (d)

Figure 9.8   Examples of freshwater and wetland ecosystems: (a) river in Oregon, USA; (b) lake in Senegal, Africa; (c) peat bog in Scotland; (d) garden pond in Buckinghamshire, England

These habitats are becoming increasingly rare. Many wetlands have been drained to create land for agriculture or development, or damaged by pollution and neglect. Fortunately, the value of some important wetland sites has been recognised and they have been designated under national and international environmental protection schemes (Box 9.1).

---

**Box 9.1   Selected environmental protection designations**

*Ramsar sites*: *Wetlands of International Importance.* The Ramsar Convention (named after the Iranian city where the convention was agreed in 1971) is an international treaty for the protection of wetland ecosystems. There are nearly 2000 Ramsar sites worldwide with approximately 150 in the UK, including the Blackwater Estuary, Wicken Fen and Loch Lomond.

*World Heritage Site.* Designated by UNESCO, World Heritage Sites are places of cultural or physical significance and can include both natural phenomena such as forests, mountains and lakes (e.g. Djoudj National Bird Sanctuary in Senegal and the Giant's Causeway in Northern Ireland), and structures built by humans, (e.g. the Taj Mahal, the Pyramids at Giza, and Stonehenge).

*Special Protection Area (SPA) and Special Area of Conservation (SAC).* These are designated under European Union directives. SPAs are designated by the Directive on the Conservation of Wild Birds and SACs by the Habitats Directive. SACs and SPAs together comprise a network of protected areas across the European Union called Natura 2000.

*Site of Special Scientific Interest (SSSI).* This is a UK conservation designation applied to areas with biological or geological interest. There are more than 7000 SSSIs in the UK.

---

Wetlands designated under one of these schemes are protected for their biodiversity, as important habitats for wildlife, and possibly also for the visual and aesthetic pleasure they provide. Most of these aquatic environments are extremely vulnerable to change, particularly to variation in the quantity and quality of water. Their protected status means they have some safeguards against the potential damage caused by human use – and possible abuse – of these sites as a resource. However, these designated sites are the special cases and the vast majority of wetlands, lakes and rivers are unprotected and thus vulnerable to environmental degradation.

## 3.5   Water security: an evolving and contested concept

The definition of water security is still evolving. Definitions subsequent to the GWP one unpacked above sometimes include additional elements such as disaster and risk in recognition of the negative aspects of water that need to be considered alongside the positive aspects (Figure 9.9). Water can be an agent of damage and destruction. Excess water causes floods and lack of water causes droughts; surface run-off causes soil erosion; polluted water causes waterborne disease and harms the environment. These negative impacts of water have been taken into account by David Grey and Claudia Sadoff and led them to a slightly modified definition of water security as:

> The availability of an acceptable quantity and quality of water for health, livelihoods, ecosystems and production, coupled with an acceptable level of water-related risks to people, the environment and economies.

(Grey and Sadoff, 2007, p. 548)

| Water: both productive and destructive | | Water security | |
|---|---|---|---|
| A source of production, health, growth and cooperation, and... | a source of destruction, poverty and dispute. | Availability of acceptable quantity and quality of water for health, livelihoods, ecosystems and production, and... | acceptable level of water-related risks to people, environments and economies. |

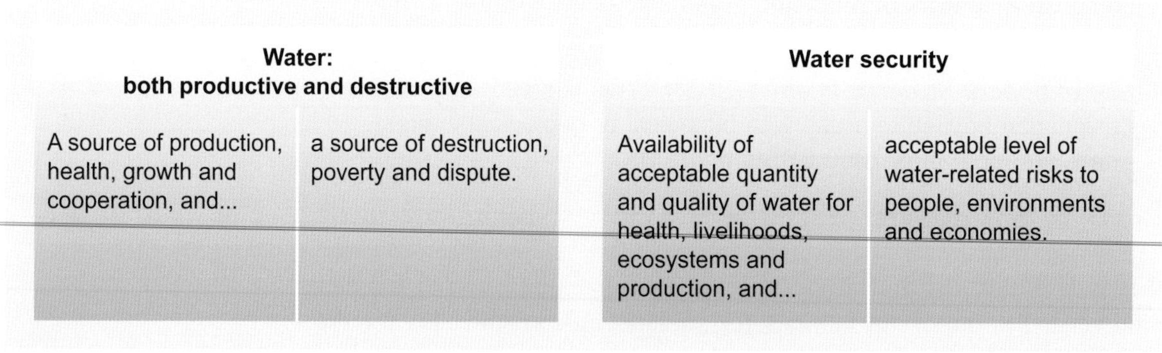

Figure 9.9   Defining water security: water as a source of production and destruction (Source: based on Grey and Sadoff, 2007, p. 548, Figure 1)

Grey and Sadoff (2007) go on to identify the factors that determine the scale of the challenge of achieving and sustaining water security, singling out three factors as being particularly important:

- *the hydrologic environment*: the level of water resource availability and its variations over time and space

- *the socio-economic environment*: the structure of the economy and the behaviour of its actors

- *the future environment*: including the effects of climate change.

It is worth noting that the concept of water security is not accepted by everyone as the best way to address the challenge of safe and affordable water provision. The concept has been criticised for being a theoretical ideal that lacks a clear quantified definition. Ethiopian lawyer Dereje Zekele Mekonnen, for example, writes of 'the non-legal, destructively elastic, and indeterminate concept of "water security"' (Mekonnen, 2010, p. 422). Jonathan Lautze and Herath Manthrithilake have attempted to address the problem by devising a method for quantifying the concept that breaks it down into its constituent elements in order to arrive at an overall water security index (Lautze and Manthrithilake, 2012). However, they too call into question the value of devising a new label, concluding that 'there may be confusion, scepticism and even fatigue associated with the introduction of another new term that is not concretely defined yet which is supposed to comprise a panacea for water managers' (Lautze and Manthrithilake, 2012, p. 85).

The debate over water security as an organising concept suggests that how an environmental issue is 'framed' (in other words, the vocabularies that are used in its expression) matters. Different framings may reflect some values and interests, but not others. The way an issue is framed can be a key basis for controversy around that issue. So if someone does not accept the assumptions packed into the notion of water security, then they may dispute the actions taken in the name of water security. Keep an eye out for this sort of controversy in relation to other issues as you progress through the module.

# 4   The water cycle and ecosystem services

Central to the hydrologic environment is the water cycle (Table 9.1, Figure 9.10). The **water (or hydrological) cycle** is the set of processes that moves water around the Earth and provides us with a constantly replenishing source of fresh water. All uses of water by people and the environment are dependent on the action of the water cycle. Indeed, humans increasingly interfere in the water cycle; for example, by building dams, using water for agriculture and piping it to homes for domestic use.

Driven by the energy of the Sun, water **evaporates** from oceans and surface water on land and forms water vapour in the atmosphere. The air is moved by wind and, as it cools (for example, as it rises over a mountain), the water vapour **condenses** into droplets, which form clouds. As you have seen (in Section 2), precipitation is the formation of rain, snow or hail through condensation in the atmosphere. Precipitation falling on the land follows several possible paths. Some **infiltrates** into the ground where it may remain near the surface as soil moisture or, depending on the geology, may move into the rocks below as **groundwater**. Some will remain on the surface of the land, forming streams and rivers, collectively known as surface **run-off**, eventually flowing downhill and discharging into the ocean.

Water is also transferred into the atmosphere by **transpiration** by plants. Plants draw water from the soil through their roots, and transfer it to the leaves from where it evaporates into the atmosphere. Transpiration can transfer significant amounts of water to the atmosphere. For example, a large oak tree transpires about 400 litres a day in the summer (about five bathfulls). The combined process of evaporation and transpiration that return water to the atmosphere is called **evapotranspiration**.

These transfer processes constantly renew and replenish the water reservoirs and provide us with the fresh water we need. This is why water is generally described as a **renewable resource**. It is renewable in the sense that the water cycle constantly makes water available for us to use. But water is also a **finite resource**, one that is not limitless.

Table 9.1   Water cycle terms

| | |
|---|---|
| **Water (hydrological) cycle** | The circulation of water around the Earth; the combined set of reservoirs (oceans, atmosphere, rivers, lakes, etc.) and processes (evaporation, air movement, precipitation, water flow, etc.). |
| **Evaporation** | The change of state from liquid to gas. |
| **Condensation** | The change of state from gas to liquid. |
| **Infiltration** | The downward flow of water through land surface into sub-surface layers. |
| **Groundwater** | Water stored in the pores and voids of rocks in the saturated zone below the water table. |
| **Run-off** | Water that 'runs off' the land (i.e. flows over the land surface under the influence of gravity). |
| **Transpiration** | The transfer of water to the atmosphere from the surfaces of leaves and other parts of plants. |
| **Evapotranspiration** | The combined processes of evaporation and transpiration, both of which entail the transfer of water from the Earth's surface into the atmosphere. |
| **Renewable resources** | Materials or energy sources that are naturally and continually replenished over a relatively short timescale. |
| **Finite resource** | One that is not limitless. |

The volume of water that exists on Earth today is the same as that present millions of years ago; there has been no net gain or loss. The hydrological cycle renews water but does not create it. In this sense, water differs from other renewable resources such as wind and solar energy. They are not finite but are truly renewable because there is a continuous 'supply' of wind and energy from the sun. The same could be said for water power in hydroelectric power plants and water mills that use the energy from the movement of water. But there are limits to the renewability of water as a resource for consumptive use.

Human needs for a supply of water are met principally by tapping into the water cycle at two stages: surface water and groundwater. Water is taken from rivers, lakes and underground sources for domestic supplies, for irrigation and for industrial use. The volume withdrawn is actually small relative to the total and is estimated as less than 10 per cent of the maximum available renewable freshwater resources in the world (Oki and Kanae, 2006). However, and as noted above, problems arise because of the variability of water resource availability over time and space. For example, the Amazon River, the largest in the world in terms of volume, accounts for 15 per cent of total global run-off but approximately 95 per cent of this is inaccessible for human use (Postel et al., 1996). Some parts of Asia receive almost 90 per cent of their annual rainfall in less than 100 hours, with a consequent risk of cycles of flooding and drought (UNDP, 2006). Availability depends on being able to store the water to even out the variable distribution. Some studies of global water availability take account of the human interventions in the natural water cycle in terms of both withdrawals and the regulation of surface flow (Alcamo et al., 2003). Oki and Kanae (2006, p. 1069) comment: 'In the … Anthropocene, where human impacts on natural processes are large and widespread, it no longer makes sense to study only natural hydrological cycles.' The effects of human activities on the water cycle illustrate the linkages and interwoven influences within our environment. Intervention at one point generally has impacts elsewhere. These impacts and unintended consequences from human activities are often the source of environmental controversies.

Our use of water extends beyond the direct use for drinking, fisheries, transport and recreation. There are other, less direct, ecosystem services that we also rely on. As you saw in Block 2, Chapter 7, an ecosystem service may be defined as a benefit that people obtain from an ecological system. Forests, for example, provide a range of ecosystem services, including private goods with direct use values (foods such as fruits and nuts) as well as those with indirect use values, including a long-term water supply. Much of the evapotranspiration from tropical forests ultimately returns to the forests as rain, replenishing streams and lakes and providing water for local people. The inclusion of protection and enhancement of the environment in definitions of water security is not, therefore, solely an altruistic endeavour; ecosystem services have added value that we depend on. These services have been categorised into four groups (Millennium Ecosystem Assessment, 2003):

- *provisioning services*: the products obtained from ecosystems, such as food, fresh water and fuel wood
- *regulating services*: the benefits obtained from the regulation of ecosystem processes, such as climate and disease regulation

- *cultural services*: the non-material benefits people obtain from ecosystems, including recreation and education, spiritual and religious significance, and aesthetic experiences
- *supporting services*: underpin these three categories and include soil formation, nutrient cycling and primary production that are necessary for all other ecosystem services.

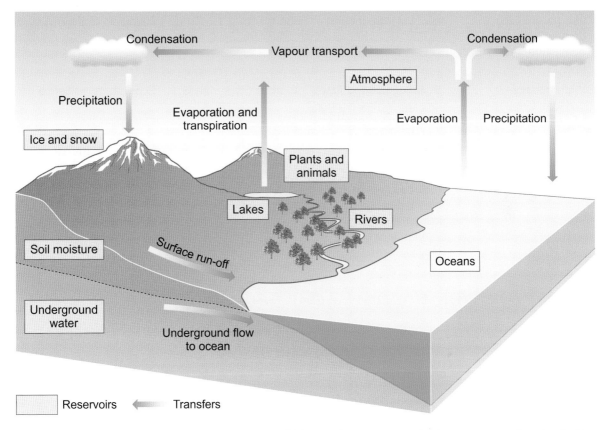

Figure 9.10   The water cycle (note that 'reservoir' is used to mean any body or reserve of water, both natural features and those that humans have created)

Table 9.2 lists the ecosystem services provided by fresh water and the water cycle under these four headings.

Table 9.2   Ecosystem services provided by fresh water and the hydrological cycle

| Provisioning services | Regulating services | Cultural services | Supporting services |
| --- | --- | --- | --- |
| Water quantity and quality for consumptive use (for drinking, domestic use, agriculture and industrial use) | Maintenance of water quality (natural filtration and water treatment) | Recreation (river rafting, etc., and fishing as a sport) | Nutrient cycling (role in maintenance of floodplain fertility) |
| Water for non-consumptive use (for generating power and transport/navigation) | Buffering of flood flows, erosion control through water–land interactions and flood control infrastructure | Tourism (river viewing) | Ecosystem resilience |
| Aquatic organisms for food and medicines | Climate regulation (source and sink for greenhouse gases, and influence on temperature and precipitation) | Existence values (personal satisfaction from free-flowing rivers) | Mitigation of climate change (floodplains providing physical buffering) |

Source: Mayers et al., 2009, p. 12, Table 2; adapted from Aylward et al., 2005

## Activity 9.4   Ecosystem services

Look at the services listed in Table 9.1 and think about them in relation to your own life. Do you personally benefit from these ecosystem services? If so, in what way?

### Comment

You will have your own individual response to this question, but this is mine. I benefit from provisioning services in the form of a clean, piped water supply to my house and also indirectly from other consumptive and non-consumptive uses. I can relate to 'aquatic organisms for food' because I like eating fish and shellfish. I find it difficult to make a personal link to most of the regulating and supporting services. I know I benefit from climate regulation and nutrient cycling, for example, but I cannot pinpoint specific examples. The category I can identify with most easily is cultural services. I've used water for recreation as a former member of the local sailing club. As a tourist I'm always attracted to water and will seek it out whenever I can, from taking walks along rivers to making a major diversion on a US holiday to see the Niagara Falls. When considering the different types of cultural service, I thought initially that tourism services blended with existence values; I made that tourist visit to Niagara because I valued the existence of the falls. But, in terms of the use/non-use distinction discussed in Block 2, note that by the act of visiting I was ascribing a use value to the falls in addition to the non-use existence value. (You may find it helpful to return to Chapter 7, which discussed the different types of value associated with the environment.)

# 5   Water and climate change

All discussions of water security and water availability have to be considered in the context of climate change. Although there is uncertainty over the scale and extent of climate change in the future, it is clear that it will affect the distribution and availability of water because of the likely alterations to patterns of precipitation and the effects of increasing temperature. The Intergovernmental Panel on Climate Change (IPCC) models indicate that a future warmer climate will cause a 'general intensification of the global hydrological cycle' (IPCC, 2007, Chapter 10, p. 750). Predictions suggest that, in many parts of the world, dry seasons will be drier, wet seasons will be wetter and there will be an increase in the frequency and intensity of extreme rainfall events. Even in areas where mean precipitation is expected to decrease, which includes most subtropical and mid-latitude regions, projections are for increased intensity of precipitation (even though there would be longer periods between rainfall events (IPCC, 2007)). In mid-continental areas, the IPCC predicts a greater risk of drought in summer.

Table 9.3   Possible impacts on water from global temperature increase

| Mean temperature rise (°C) | Impacts forecast |
| --- | --- |
| 1 °C | Small glaciers in the Andes disappear completely, threatening water supplies for 50 million people |
| 2 °C | Potentially 20–30% decrease in water availability in some vulnerable regions, e.g. southern Africa and Mediterranean |
| 3 °C | In southern Europe, serious droughts occur once every 10 years, 1–4 billion more people suffer water shortages worldwide, while 1–5 billion gain water, which may increase flood risk |
| 4 °C | Potentially 30–50 per cent decrease in water availability in southern Africa and Mediterranean |
| 5 °C | Possible disappearance of large glaciers in the Himalayas, affecting one quarter of China's population and hundreds of millions in India |

Source: adapted from HM Treasury, 2006, p. 57, Table 3.1

The Stern Review on the economics of climate change, published by the UK government in 2006, catalogued the possible impacts of different degrees of global warming (HM Treasury, 2006). Table 9.3 shows the forecast effects on the water cycle. The increasing severity of the impacts makes the potential hazards of climate change very clear. It also reminds us that the activities of people in certain parts of the world (generally the global North) will have profound consequences for people in other parts of the world (generally the global South).

# 6  Summary

The ideas that have been touched on in this chapter are developed in the remainder of the block, so you should check at this point that you have a good sense of the following points.

*The challenge of water provision and supply.* This was set up at the start of the chapter. You saw that, while water is essential to life both in the biological sense and for our ways of life in the wider social sense, the fact that it moves and is unevenly distributed means that it is often difficult to manage. This difficulty is currently being exacerbated at the global scale by growing population, changing ways of life and climate change.

*Water as the basis of controversy.* The fact that water is both essential and finite means that it is a resource that has to be shared. Disputes about exactly how that sharing is organised from the local to the global scale mean that water (like other environmental issues) is often the subject of controversy, which can take a variety of forms from contested assumptions to outright conflict.

*The concept of water security.* You saw how the concept of water security has emerged as a way of framing the challenge of water provision at a variety of scales. Unpacking this key definition provides a good sense of some of the many issues involved in managing water.

*The complexity of the water cycle.* Understanding the myriad connections and processes that together constitute the water cycle is key to any interdisciplinary exploration of the challenge of water. In particular, it is important to appreciate the precise sense in which water is both a renewable and a finite resource and the implications of this for the ecosystem services that water provides.

# References

Alcamo, J., Doll, P., Henrichs, T., Kaspar, F., Lehner, B., Rosch, T. and Siebert S. (2003) 'Global estimates of water withdrawals and availability under current and future "business-as-usual" conditions', *Hydrological Sciences Journal*, vol. 48, no. 3, pp. 339–48 [online]. Available at http://dx.doi.org/10.1623/hysj.48.3.339.45278 (Accessed 8 August 2012).

Aylward, B., Bandyopadhyay, J. and Belausteguigotia, J-C. (2005) 'Freshwater ecosystem services', in *Ecosystems and Human Well-Being: Policy Responses, Volume 3*, Millennium Ecosystem Assessment, Washington, DC, Island Press.

Cook, C. and Bakker, K. (2012) 'Water security: debating an emerging paradigm', *Global Environmental Change*, vol. 22, no. 1, pp. 94–102.

Dellapenna, J. W. (2007) 'Transboundary water sharing and the need for public management', *Journal of Water Resources Planning and Management*, Sep/Oct, vol. 133, no. 5, pp. 397–404.

Environment Agency (2008) *Water Resources in England and Wales – CurrentState and Future Pressures*, Bristol, Environment Agency.

Gleick, P. H. (2000) *The World's Water 2000–2001*, Washington, DC, Island Press.

Gleick, P. H. (2012) *The World's Water, Volume 7: The Biennial Report on Freshwater Resources*, Washington, DC, Island Press.

Global Water Partnership (GWP) (2000) *Towards Water Security: A Framework for Action*, GWP, Stockholm and London; also available online at http://www.gwptoolbox.org/index2.php?option=com_reference&reference_id=75&pop=1 (Accessed 7 August 2012).

Grey, D. and Sadoff, C. W. (2007) 'Sink or swim? Water security for growth and development', *Water Policy*, vol. 9, no. 6, pp. 545–71.

Hand, M., Shove, E. and Southerton, D. (2005) 'Explaining showering: a discussion of the material, conventional and temporal dimensions of practice', *Sociological Research Online*, vol. 10, no. 2 [online], http://www.socresonline.org.uk/10/2/hand.html (Accessed 8 August 2012).

HM Treasury (2006) *Stern Review: The Economics of Climate Change*, London, HM Treasury [online] http://www.hm-treasury.gov.uk/stern_review_climate_change.htm (Accessed 8 August 2012).

Institute of Human Rights and Business (IHRB) (2009) *Business, Human Rights and the Right to Water: Challenges, Dilemmas and Opportunities*, Roundtable Consultative Report, January [online]. Available at http://www.ihrb.org/pdf/Draft_Report-Business_Human_Rights_and_Water.pdf (Accessed 8 August 2012).

Intergovernmental Panel on Climate Change (IPCC) (2007) *Contribution of Working Group I to the Fourth Assessment Report of the Intergovernmental Panel on*

*Climate Change, 2007*, Cambridge and New York, Cambridge University Press; also available online at http://www.ipcc.ch/publications_and_data/ar4/wg1/en/contents.html (Accessed 8 August 2012).

Lautze, J. and Manthrithilake, H. (2012) 'Water security: old concepts, new package, what value?', *Natural Resources Forum*, vol. 36, no. 2, pp. 76–87.

Mayers, J., Batchelor, C., Bond, I., Hope, R. A., Morrison, E. and Wheeler, B. (2009) *Water Ecosystem Services and Poverty Under Climate Change: Key Issues and Research Priorities*, London, International Institute for Environment and Development, Natural Resource Issues No. 17 [online]. Available at http://pubs.iied.org/pdfs/13549IIED.pdf (Accessed 8 August 2012).

McRary, J. and Royer, H. (2006) *The Effect of Female Education on Fertility and Infant Health*, National Bureau of Economic Research, Working paper 12329, Cambridge, MA [online]. Available at http://www.nber.org/papers/w12329.pdf (Accessed 3 April 2012).

Mekonnen, D. Z. (2010) 'The Nile Basin Cooperative Framework Agreement negotiations and the adoption of a "water security" paradigm: flight into obscurity or a logical cul-de-sac?', *European Journal of International Law*, vol. 21, no. 2, pp. 421–38.

Millennium Ecosystem Assessment (MEA) (2003) *Ecosystems and Human Wellbeing: A Framework for Assessment*, Washington, DC, Island Press [online]. Available at http://www.maweb.org/en/Framework.aspx (Accessed 8 August 2012).

Oki, T. and Kanae, S. (2006) 'Global hydrological cycles and world water resources', *Science*, vol. 313, no. 5790, pp. 1068–72.

Population Matters (2012) 'New Report: "Population Growth Drives Water Shortage"', 31 January [online], http://www.populationmatters.org/2012/population-matters-news/report-population-growth-drives-water-shortage/ (Accessed 8 August 2012).

Postel, S. L., Daily, G. C. and Ehrlich, P. J. (1996) 'Human appropriation of renewable fresh water', *Science*, vol. 271, no. 5250, pp. 785–8.

Sharma, D. and Kansal, A. (2011) 'Current conditions of the Yamuna River – an overview of flow, pollution load and human use', TERIUniversity [online], http://fore.research.yale.edu/information/Yamuna/Current_Condition_of_Yamuna_River.pdf (Accessed 8 August 2012).

UNICEF/WHO (2009) *Diarrhoea: Why Children Are Still Dying and What Can Be Done* [online], http://whqlibdoc.who.int/publications/2009/9789241598415_eng.pdf (Accessed 16 August 2012).

United Nations (2004) *World Population to 2300*, ST/ESA/SER.A/236, New York, UN Department of Economic and Social Affairs.

United Nations Development Programme (UNDP) (2006) *Human Development Report 2006: Beyond Scarcity: Power, Poverty and the Global Water Crisis*, Basingstoke and New York, Palgrave Macmillan [online]. Available at http://hdr.undp.org/en/media/HDR06-complete.pdf (Accessed 8 August 2012).

UN News Centre (2011) 'Global population to pass 10 billion by 2100, UN projections indicate' [online], http://www.un.org/apps/news/story.asp?NewsID=38253 (Accessed 14 August 2012).

World Population Review (2012) 'World population 2012' [online], http://worldpopulationreview.com/world-population-2012/ (Accessed 8 August 2012).

# Chapter 10   Use and supply

Pam Furniss

# Contents

# 1  Introduction

Thousands have lived without love, not one without water.

('First Things First', W. H. Auden)

Unlike other resources on which we depend such as food, energy and building materials, there is no substitute for water. A reliable supply is essential and has been one of the key factors determining the location of human settlements for millennia. Even the grandest of cities may fail due to lack of water. The lavish city complex of Fatehpur Sikri in Uttar Pradesh, India was built in the sixteenth century as the capital of the Mughal Empire (Figure 10.1). The emperor and his court took up residence in 1571 but just 14 years later the city was abandoned. The need for a dependable water supply had not been taken into account and the city became unsustainable.

Figure 10.1   Fatehpur Sikri, Uttar Pradesh, India. Abandoned in the sixteenth century, the city is now a tourist attraction

This chapter examines the main sources and uses of water and considers variations in water use around the world. It also discusses water scarcity and how the concepts of virtual water and water scarcity aid understanding of the unequal distribution and use of water.

# 2   Sources of water

Human needs for water are met primarily from surface water and groundwater (Chapter 9). Surface water is drawn directly from springs, rivers and lakes. Groundwater is held in pores (tiny spaces) within the rock structure and is accessed via wells and boreholes. A rock that is sufficiently porous to store water and allow water to flow through it is called an **aquifer** (Figure 10.2). In soil or rock near the surface, pores are usually partially filled with air but at greater depths, below the **water table**, the pores are completely filled with water. The level of the water table varies depending on the rate of **recharge** and the quantity of water withdrawn through wells.

Whether a water source will reliably provide water over time (through the seasons and over many years) is determined primarily by the processes of the water cycle.

**Aquifer**
An underground layer of porous rock filled with water.

**Water table**
The level below which soil or rock is saturated with water.

**Recharge**
The downward movement of water from the surface that replenishes groundwater reserves.

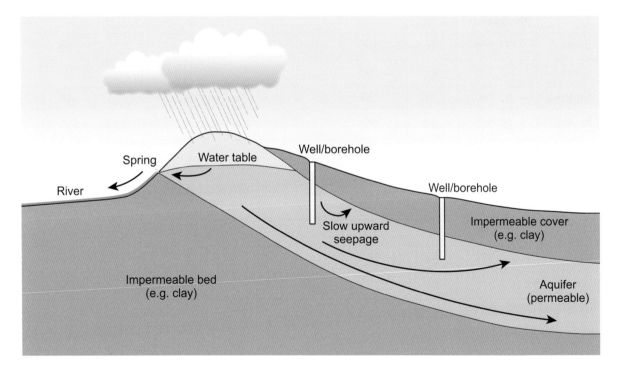

Figure 10.2   Groundwater can be accessed by sinking a borehole into an aquifer or a spring may form where groundwater meets the surface

## Activity 10.1   Renewing water resources

Which specific processes of the water cycle replenish surface and groundwater sources?

### Comment

Precipitation on land is the key process. Run-off feeds water into surface sources such as rivers and streams. Infiltration of water through the soil into the rocks below recharges groundwater reservoirs. However, all the processes of the cycle contribute to some extent.

Table 10.1   Drinking water sources for urban and rural populations in selected countries, 2010

| Country | Population | | Urban % | | Rural % | | Total % | |
|---|---|---|---|---|---|---|---|---|
| | Total (thousands) | Urban % | Improved | Unimproved | Improved | Unimproved | Improved | Unimproved |
| Brazil | 194 946 | 87 | 100 | 0 | 85 | 15 | 98 | 2 |
| China | 1 341 335 | 47 | 98 | 2 | 85 | 15 | 91 | 9 |
| Ethiopia | 82 950 | 17 | 97 | 3 | 34 | 66 | 44 | 56 |
| France | 62 787 | 85 | 100 | 0 | 100 | 0 | 100 | 0 |
| India | 1 224 614 | 30 | 97 | 3 | 90 | 10 | 92 | 8 |
| Ireland | 4470 | 62 | 100 | 0 | 98 | 2 | 99 | 1 |
| Senegal | 12 434 | 42 | 93 | 7 | 56 | 44 | 72 | 28 |
| UK | 62 036 | 80 | 100 | 0 | 100 | 0 | 100 | 0 |
| USA | 310 384 | 82 | 100 | 0 | 94 | 6 | 99 | 1 |
| World | 6 872 619 | 51 | 96 | 4 | 81 | 19 | 89 | 11 |

Source: WHO/UNICEF, 2012, 'Statistical tables', p. 39

Whether water is clean and safe to drink (i.e. free from disease-causing agents and contaminants) depends principally on the source. Water sources are classified as improved or unimproved. *Improved sources* are safe to drink and include household connections to a mains water supply, public standpipes, and protected wells and springs. *Unimproved sources* are surface waters such as rivers and lakes, and wells and springs

2 Sources of water

without structures to protect them from contamination. For example, a protected spring in a rural area would have a fence to keep animals away, be located away from human waste disposal sites and have a concrete surround to divert surface flow away from the spring head. Table 10.1 shows the proportion of people in selected countries living in urban and rural areas with access to improved and unimproved sources of drinking water. Figures for the world are included for comparison.

---

## Activity 10.2   Comparing urban and rural water access

What is the main difference in water access between urban and rural populations for the countries shown in Table 10.1? What are the possible reasons?

### Comment

For all countries, at least 93 per cent of urban dwellers have access to improved water sources. For all countries except the UK and France, the figure for rural populations is lower, in some cases significantly so. Towns and cities are more likely to have a piped supply system for water which is often, although not necessarily, safer to drink.

---

## Activity 10.3   Working with numerical data

Based on the data in Table 10.1, how many people living in rural Ethiopia do not have access to an improved water source?

### Comment

The total population of Ethiopia is 82,950,000. First we need to find out the rural population. The table indicates that the percentage of people living in urban areas is 17%, so the percentage living in rural areas is 83% (100 minus 17). The rural population is therefore 83% of 82,950,000:

$$\frac{83}{100} \times 82,950,000 = 68,848,500$$

The percentage of the rural population without access to improved sources is 66%. The relevant population figure is therefore 66% of 68,848,500:

$$\frac{66}{100} \times 68,848,500 = 45,440,010$$

The answer could be rounded up to 45.5 million.

---

It is worth thinking critically about data like that included in Table 10.1 and considering how accurate it is, how it was collected, and what assumptions it may reflect. For example, are there regional variations that are not presented in these country-based figures? Did all countries adopt the same investigation methods? Was every household surveyed, or were a limited number selected and data extrapolated from that sample? It could also be worth considering the details of the various categories: does the definition of 'urban' and 'rural' vary between countries, and which type of 'improved source' is referred to? An improved source might mean a non-stop piped supply of safe water, or it could be a public standpipe that is functioning for a few hours a day. Questioning how data is gathered and defined is not to imply that it lacks validity, only that when using data its possible limitations should be recognised.

Improving access to safe drinking water was one of the Millennium Development Goals (MDGs) set in 2000 (Box 10.1). Goal 7 includes the target to 'halve, by 2015, the number of people without sustainable access to safe drinking water'. In March 2012, it was announced that this goal had been reached ahead of schedule (WHO/UNICEF, 2012). This achievement was rightly applauded but the claim also caused some controversy due to doubts about the data, similar to the questions raised above. Even if the goal has been achieved there will still be more than 500 million people without access to safe drinking water.

> ## Box 10.1   Millennium Development Goals
>
> The Millennium Development Goals are eight goals for international development that formed part of the United Nations Millennium Declaration issued in September 2000. They are:
>
> Goal 1: Eradicate extreme hunger and poverty.
>
> Goal 2: Achieve universal primary education.
>
> Goal 3: Promote gender equality and empower women.
>
> Goal 4: Reduce child mortality.
>
> Goal 5: Improve maternal health.

Goal 6: Combat HIV/AIDS, malaria and other diseases.

Goal 7: Ensure environmental sustainability.

Goal 8: Develop a global partnership for development.

Each goal has a set of quantified or time-bounded targets. For each target there are measurable indicators that are used to assess progress towards meeting the goals. For Goal 7 on environmental sustainability the targets are:

- Integrate the principles of sustainable development into country policies and programmes and reverse the loss of environmental resources.

- Reduce biodiversity loss, achieving, by 2010, a significant reduction in the rate of loss.

- Halve, by 2015, the proportion of people without sustainable access to safe drinking water and basic sanitation.

- Achieve by 2020 a significant improvement in the lives of at least 100 million slum dwellers.

Source: adapted from UN Millennium Project, 2006

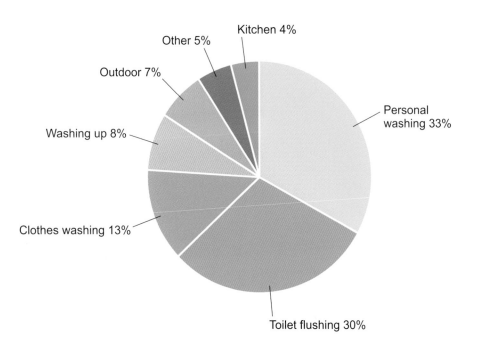

Figure 10.3   Average household water use by activity, for England and Wales (Source: based on WWF, 2009, p. 4)

**Infrastructure**

A network of fixed capital equipment.

The classification of water sources as improved or unimproved, although determined initially by the source of the water, also depends on any treatment that takes place between source and user. The UK, for example, has 100 per cent improved water because the water treatment and distribution infrastructure is in place to ensure clean, safe water is distributed to homes, offices and factories. An **infrastructure** is a network of fixed capital equipment. Infrastructures include roads, transport, communication systems and power plants. In the UK the water supply infrastructure includes water purification plants, pipelines, pumping stations, storage reservoirs, and so on. Large-scale water infrastructures are costly, resource-intensive facilities needing capital outlay, regular maintenance and skilled personnel. UK water users can generally be confident in the safety of the water supply for all everyday purposes including drinking. However, it is notable that about 30 per cent of this safe water used in homes in the UK is flushed down the toilet (Figure 10.3).

# 3   Uses of water

At this point, it would be helpful to clarify the difference between water abstraction, or withdrawal, and water consumption. Not all water withdrawn from a source is necessarily consumed; it may be withdrawn, used and then returned to the original source. There may be some changes in quality but it is essentially available to be used again. Water consumption, on the other hand, means the water is used so that it is not available for immediate reuse, because it has evaporated, been contaminated, or been incorporated into a crop or other product. For example, much of the water for the electricity supply sector is used for cooling in power stations (Figure 10.4). Some is consumed as it evaporates into the atmosphere as plumes of steam but most is ultimately returned directly to the river or sea and can be reused.

Figure 10.4   Cooling towers of the 2 GW Cottam coal-fired power station, Nottinghamshire, UK. This uses water from the River Trent, recycling most of it, except for that evaporated in the plumes of water vapour above the cooling towers

The direct use of water by people falls into three main categories:

* *domestic uses*, including drinking, washing and cooking

* *agricultural uses*, principally irrigation

* *industrial uses*, including power generation.

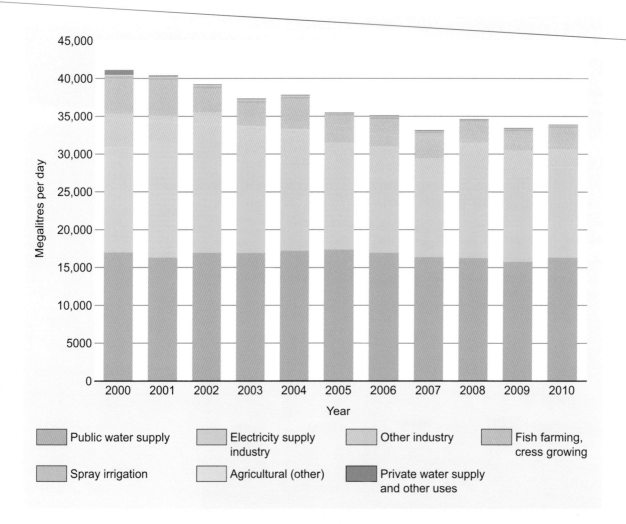

Figure 10.5   Abstractions from non-tidal surface water and groundwater by use: England and Wales, 2000–10 (Source: Defra, 2012a)

Figure 10.5 shows the volumes of water abstracted for different purposes in England and Wales from 2000 to 2010. The total volume abstracted has fallen slightly over this period but the volume used for public water supply has remained much the same at around 16–17 thousand megalitres per day, despite the increasing population. (According to WHO/UNICEF (2012) the population of the UK increased from nearly 59 million in 2000 to just over 62 million in 2010.) This suggests that technology to improve water-use efficiency – such as domestic appliances that use less water, and dual flush toilets – and changes in personal behaviour, such as turning the tap off when brushing teeth, may be having an effect.

Another reason for the steady state of public supply volume in England and Wales is the reduction in leakage from water mains. Since the mid 1990s there has been considerable investment by the UK water industry to repair aged and leaking pipes and reduce the volume lost to leakage. However, in the majority of areas the Economic Level of Leakage (ELL) has now been reached, as indicated by the levelling off of water leakages since 2007 (Figure 10.6). ELL means the cost of further leakage reduction exceeds the cost of producing water from an alternative source (Defra, 2008).

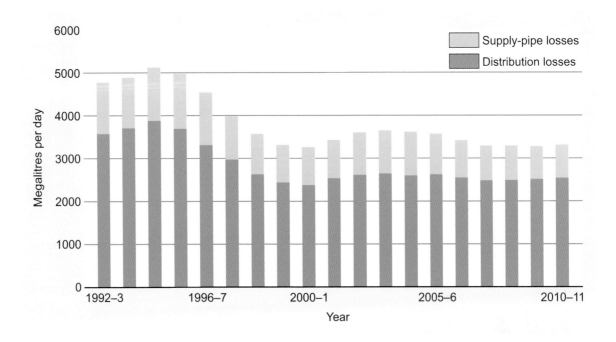

Figure 10.6   Water leakage in England and Wales, 1992–93 to 2010–11 (Source: Defra, 2012b)

## Activity 10.4   Leakage from public water supply

What happens to the water lost by leakage?

## Comment

Water leaking from underground pipes will soak into the ground where it may remain in the soil, be taken up by plants or infiltrate down into rock. In warmer climates, some will evaporate from the surface. One way or another it will be returned to the water cycle. In this way, it is not 'lost' as such. It will, however, have been treated, so there is an economic cost.

Guidance from Ofwat, the economic regulator of the water industry in England and Wales, says that ELL calculations should include the *externalities* of leakage repair that are borne directly by the water companies. (You were introduced to the concept of externalities in Chapter 6, Section 2.2.) In other words, the assessment of ELL needs to take account the costs that arise from the environmental and social impacts of leakage control activities. These externalities include, for example, the social costs of traffic disruption arising from leak repair and water mains replacement (Ofwat, 2007).

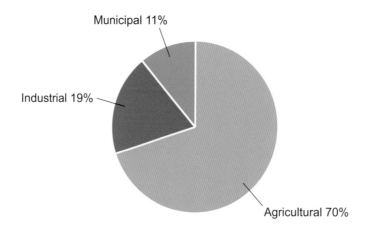

Figure 10.7   Global water withdrawal by sector (Source: based on FAO, 2012)

You can see from Figure 10.5 that in England and Wales the volume of water abstracted for agricultural purposes is very small, relative to other uses. The situation elsewhere in the world is very different. Globally, the proportion of water withdrawal for agriculture is about 70 per cent of the global total (Figure 10.7). However, around 50 per cent of the water withdrawn for agriculture is consumed through evapotranspiration (Aquastat, 2010). The relative significance of the three main categories of freshwater use is shown in Figure 10.8.

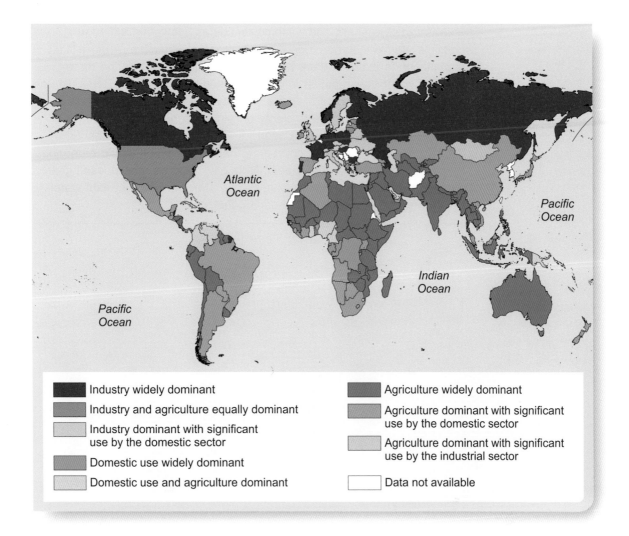

Figure 10.8   Freshwater use by sector at the beginning of the 2000s (Source: based on UNEP/GRID-Arendal, 2012a)

## Activity 10.5   Freshwater use

The map in Figure 10.8 shows that domestic use of water is the dominant sector in central Africa. Can you think of possible explanations for this?

## Comment

My approach to a question like this is to think of all possible explanations, however unlikely, before homing in on the more probable. One *possible* explanation of high domestic consumption is that people have many domestic appliances that use a lot of water, such as power showers, dishwashers and washing machines. However, although possible, in this instance it does not seem very plausible. A more likely explanation is that these are *relative* data: the map shows the three types of water consumption in comparison with each other. Domestic use may be dominant in central Africa because there is little large-scale industry, or because there is plenty of rain for agriculture (as shown in Figure 9.2) and therefore little need for irrigation. These are only theoretical explanations, of course; further investigation would be needed to confirm, or disprove, the theory. Note also that the map doesn't give any information about actual volumes of water, nor does it relate water use to the size of population of each country.

# 4   Water scarcity

Scarcity arises when the needs and wants of people for a resource exceed its availability. Water scarcity occurs when the demand for water cannot be met from available sources. This is partly influenced by geographical and seasonal variations in the distribution of water (Chapter 9). However, water scarcity is not an absolute measure of the amount of water: it is a relative concept reflecting an imbalance between availability and demand. This means that dry areas are not necessarily water scarce and water scarce areas are not necessarily dry. If demand is high, for example owing to high population, then even wet regions with a good water supply may be water scarce.

There are two broad types of water scarcity: physical water scarcity and economic water scarcity (Figure 10.9). **Physical water scarcity** is, as the name suggests, an actual shortage of water relative to demand and occurs when available resources are insufficient to meet all demands, including minimum environmental flow requirements. Although more likely in arid regions, physical scarcity can be created artificially if too much water is allocated to meet specific human and environmental needs. For example, over-abstraction from rivers for agricultural irrigation can cause physical water scarcity (IWMI, 2006). However, in many countries the problem is not physical scarcity but economic scarcity. **Economic water scarcity** means that, even though there is plenty of water available, the region lacks the human, institutional and financial resources to use it. Here the problem is not lack of water but lack of infrastructure and investment. This reframes the concept of water scarcity as something that is not necessarily natural and unavoidable, determined by climate and geography, but a phenomenon that is often caused or exacerbated by socio-political factors including inequality of access, power, poverty, and institutional and policy failures (Mehta et al., 2007). In the words of the United Nations Development Programme's (UNDP's) *Human Development Report*, 'much of what passes for scarcity is a policy-induced consequence of mismanaging water resources' (UNDP, 2006, p. 133).

**Physical water scarcity**
A shortage of water relative to demand that occurs when available resources are insufficient to meet all demands, including minimum environmental flow requirements.

**Economic water scarcity**
A lack of the human, institutional and financial resources required to use an available water supply.

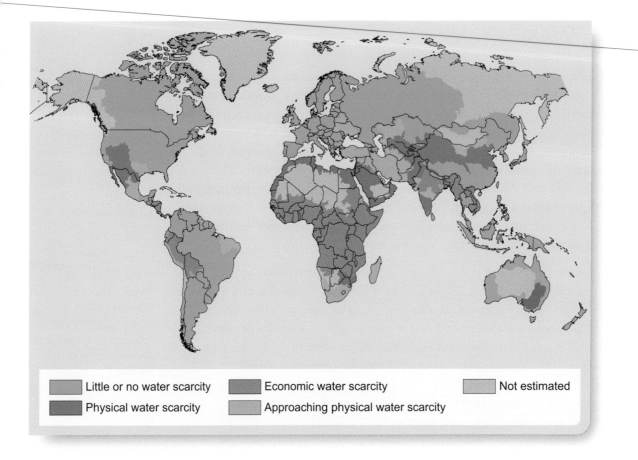

Figure 10.9   Areas of physical and economic water scarcity, 2008 (Source: based on UNEP/GRID-Arendal, 2012b)

Water scarcity, whether physical or economic, has clear links to the concept of water security. The provision of an acceptable quantity and quality of water is clearly more difficult if water is scarce. Where supplies are limited, the demands of people – for health, livelihoods and production – are likely to dominate over ecosystem needs, with over-abstraction a likely result. Even in countries not classified as water scarce, the environmental effects of over-abstraction can be significant. In England and Wales, although the volume of abstracted water varies over time, 15 per cent of rivers were classed as over-abstracted in 2008 (Environment Agency, 2008). Reduced volumes mean rivers flow more slowly, which affects aquatic ecosystems including the plants, invertebrates and fish, as well as birds and mammals. The lack of water also means that incoming wastewater, such as treated sewage, is not sufficiently diluted. Globally, many major rivers suffer from over-abstraction, including the Colorado, Ganges, Jordan, Nile and Tigris-Euphrates.

As well as over-abstraction from rivers, over-abstraction of groundwater is also a worldwide problem. Excessive pumping from aquifers means that water reserves are withdrawn faster than the rate of recharge. The result is a significant lowering of the water table, making it more difficult and expensive to reach the water that remains and reducing water levels in streams and rivers. An example is the Ogallala Aquifer in the US Midwest. This enormous aquifer extends beneath eight states and has been used intensively for irrigation since the 1940s. This has depleted the reserve such that the water level dropped by more than 18 metres between 1980 and 1999 (McGuire, 2001). Similarly, in Yemen, parts of India and northern China, the water table is falling by more than one metre a year (UNDP, 2006). In some places the removal of fresh water from aquifers causes infiltration by seawater which degrades the water, making it unsuitable for use. Saline intrusion is a widespread problem along the Mediterranean coastlines of Italy, Spain and Turkey, where seasonal increases in population from tourists contributes to the problem (EEA, 2008). In most cases, economic imperatives mean that exploitative abstraction continues despite its unsustainability. People are unwilling or unable to change their behaviour even when aware of the long-term consequences (Box 10.2).

## Box 10.2   The Aral Sea

The story of the Aral Sea is an infamous example of over-abstraction. Although called a 'sea', it is an inland lake on the border between Kazakhstan and Uzbekistan in the former Soviet Union. Once the fourth largest lake in the world, since the 1960s it has been steadily shrinking and now covers less than 10 per cent of its original area (Figure 10.10). During the 1960s, the Soviet authorities diverted the two rivers that fed the lake to provide irrigation water to what was desert with the aim of improving agricultural productivity. The goal was to secure self-sufficiency in cotton. The results have been devastating. With the shrinkage of the lake came destruction of a flourishing fishing industry, bringing economic hardship. The remaining highly polluted water and the dustbowl of the dried-up lake bed have led to widespread health problems. However, the contraction of the lake was predicted beforehand. The Soviet authorities decided that the benefits of agricultural production outweighed this drawback. The instrumental value of the water dominated their decision making and, in their view, the ends justified the means. Soviet Kazakhstan and Uzbekistan were in a similar position to that of colonies in relation to the Soviet central authorities dominated by Russia (Moore, 2001). As peripheral regions of the Soviet Union they were subject to resource exploitation. In recent years some efforts have been made to restore the flow, but these are limited to the northern residual fragment of the lake. There are small signs of recovery, but it is highly unlikely that the lake will recover significantly.

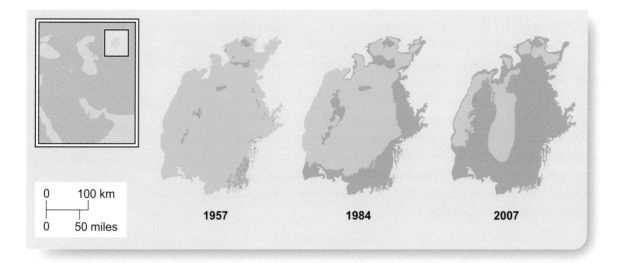

Figure 10.10   Aral Sea shrinkage. Brown areas signify areas of the lake lost to over-abstraction. By 2007, the surface area of the lake had declined to 10 per cent of its original size

# 5   Water transfer

If water is scarce in one location, then a solution could be to import it from somewhere with plentiful supplies. Water transfer, or catchment transfer, involves moving water from one river catchment to another. Using gravity to move water downhill is easy, but catchment transfer means it first has to be pumped up and over, or through, the dividing upland. Because water is heavy and large volumes are required, this is both technologically challenging and expensive. Transfer projects are only undertaken if the anticipated benefits exceed the likely costs (Box 10.3).

---

### Box 10.3   Cost–benefit analysis (CBA)

Cost–benefit analysis (CBA) is the process for valuing and comparing the anticipated costs and benefits of an economic activity (Chapter 6, Section 2.2). It is a tool for decision making that purports to calculate in purely monetary terms the costs and benefits associated with a particular decision. It is used to assess the economic viability of development and construction projects. The key stages of CBA are:

- *Project definition*. Identify the project and its objectives.

- *Identify all costs*. These include capital costs such as manufacturing and building, operation and maintenance costs including salaries, pollution clean-up costs, non-market costs (such as the effects on health and loss of amenity) and opportunity costs.

- *Identify all benefits*. These include direct profits/income, indirect benefits such as time savings, reduction of noise nuisance, beneficial changes in the landscape and enhanced protection for endangered species.

- *Quantify the costs and benefits*. Calculating the value of costs and benefits is one key area where controversy may arise, especially for less tangible items with intrinsic rather than instrumental value.

- *Present each item in a common and comparable format*. Usually a single figure is used to encapsulate the value of each item. Because costs and benefits are likely to occur at different points in the future, it is necessary to account for changes in value over time.

---

- *Sensitivity analysis*. Assesses the possible impact of uncertainty by posing 'what if?' questions. For example, what would happen if some or all of the data were incorrect? A sensitivity analysis highlights the critical factors that may affect the project's viability.

Inherent in CBA is the need to make significant assumptions in order to arrive at final values, including assumptions about the diverse interests of stakeholders. Defining the boundaries of CBA – the values that are included and excluded – is invariably controversial. Items may be excluded because of lack of knowledge, because powerful actors influence the values to be encompassed by a CBA or because some intrinsic environmental values do not lend themselves to monetary valuation.

Source: adapted from The Open University, 2006, and Asafu-Adjaye, 2005

In the UK, it has been suggested that a national 'water grid', similar to the gas and electricity grids, could alleviate drought problems in the south and east of England. This is a highly controversial proposal for several reasons (Water UK, 2012). The engineering works required for the pipework and pumping stations to achieve catchment transfers would be hugely expensive (with costs borne by the customer or taxpayer) and would also use large amounts of energy for pumping between catchments. Furthermore, the uncertainty of the UK climate and how it may change in the future makes it difficult to know where the connections should be made. Highly expensive infrastructure built to move water from A to B is not easily adjusted to move water from B to A should climatic conditions change. There is, therefore, the economic risk that expensive infrastructure could be constructed but not fully used. Also, there is an environmental risk that moving large volumes of water from one catchment to another may have damaging ecological effects. For example, transferring large volumes could affect the aquatic ecology because of variations in the chemical composition of water in different regions.

The objections to a national water grid have not prevented smaller-scale transfer schemes. The earliest of these in the UK was Llyn Llawddyn reservoir in Wales which was built in the 1880s to supply water to Birmingham. This was the first of several controversial schemes to divert Welsh water to supply growing urban populations in the Midlands and north of England. Opposition to these schemes grew during the twentieth century and culminated in a campaign in the 1950s to protect the village of Capel Celyn and surrounding farmland in the Tryweryn valley, which was to be flooded under a reservoir built to supply Liverpool, some 70 kilometres away. The scheme was opposed by local people and the local authority but decision-making power lay with the national parliament at Westminster. Despite protests and a nine-year campaign, the local community was powerless (Figure 10.11). Eventually the dam was built and the valley flooded, causing 70 people to leave their homes. Lake Celyn was opened in October 1965.

Figure 10.11   Protesters at a Save Tryweryn valley rally in Bala, September 1956

Nowadays, large-scale dam building projects are usually subject to an **Environmental Impact Assessment (EIA)** (Box 10.4). An EIA is as 'a procedure for predicting, analysing and evaluating the impacts of a proposed action on the environment and ensuring that information regarding these impacts is taken into account in decision-making' (Roberts, 1995, p. 120). EIAs were conceived, in part, to overcome some of the criticisms of CBA: namely, that attempting to reduce all elements to a monetary value does not adequately incorporate the less tangible environmental impacts.

**Environmental Impact Assessment** A procedure predicting, analysing and evaluating the impacts of a proposed action on the environment

---

### Box 10.4   Environmental Impact Assessment (EIA)

EIAs became part of European Union law in 1985 and were widely adopted as standard practice elsewhere by the end of the twentieth century. EIA processes vary but most comprise four main stages:

- *Starting up and scoping.* This stage investigates whether an EIA is needed for the project, what impacts and issues should be considered, and what alternatives exist.

- *Impact prediction, evaluation and mitigation.* The likely environmental impacts are predicted, their potential seriousness evaluated, and possible measures to reduce or remove environmental impacts investigated.

- *Participation, presentation and review.* This stage includes public consultation, which feeds into the preparation of an environmental impact statement, which is then reviewed and considered during the decision-making process.

- *Monitoring and auditing.* After the decision is taken the consequences and effects are tracked and assessed.

---

Although EIAs are in some respects an improvement on CBAs, they are subject to criticism and can thus be controversial. Even within the framework outlined in Box 10.4, there is room for different interpretations and selective inclusion. Like CBA, the scope and extent of EIAs are dependent on decisions taken by the assessors on what is and is not included. Many EIAs are criticised because they consider a single solution rather than a range of options. Public consultation may be minimal or non-existent. What constitutes the 'environment' may vary between different EIAs. The displacement of local people may not be included on the basis that displacement is a social, rather than an environmental, impact. The independence of the assessors may be called into question, depending on their relationship with the developing authority. The quality and robustness of EIAs depend ultimately on the assessing team, their independence, the assumptions they make and the values that underlie these assumptions.

On a completely different scale to the Tryweryn transfer scheme is China's highly controversial South–North Water Transfer scheme. This vast, long-term project was first proposed in the 1950s by Communist Party leader Mao Zedong, who suggested the north of the country could obtain some water from the south. The project aims to transfer water from the Yangtze River in the wetter south to the Yellow and Hai Rivers in the drier industrialised north. As Figure 10.12 shows, the project includes three south-to-north water diversions, some sections of which are now complete while others are still at planning stage.

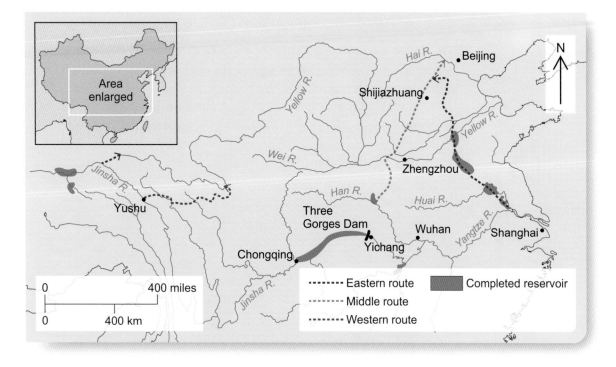

Figure 10.12   China's South–North Water Transfer project

There is no doubt that more water is needed in the north of the country. The Yellow River frequently runs out of water in the dry season and the aquifers in the north are becoming depleted. But there are many objections to the scheme (Stone et al., 2006). The project's infrastructure requirements are huge, with many dams and tunnels and three major canals. Critics say the costs of the scheme will make the water unaffordable for many people. People will be displaced by the reservoirs, which will put pressure on surrounding land as displaced people seek space to live and make a livelihood. There is the risk that pollution in the water from the south will contaminate northern rivers. There are also concerns that, although it has more water relative to the north, loss of water from the Yangtze will have major environmental and social impacts. Ironically, the scheme may not be needed over the long term; some climate change forecasts suggest that northern China could become wetter as temperatures rise, which calls the need for the transfer scheme into question. Opponents argue that there are alternative solutions. Stone et al. (2006) quote Ye Qian, a climatologist, as saying: 'If you have the right water management, you can save the same amount that they intend to transfer. Why are they doing this now? Because they have the money and people need jobs. But they need to think more about the consequences' (Stone et al., 2006, p. 1034).

This reflects a recurring theme of the role of values in decision making on development projects with significant environmental impacts. The rationale of governments and the funding organisations that hold decision-making power is usually based more on forecasts of jobs and economic benefits than on the social and environmental consequences.

# 6   Virtual water and water footprints

When assessing water consumption at the national level, it has been estimated that few countries are aware of how much water they use because, on average, 95 per cent of the water used is virtual water (POST, 2011). The term **virtual water**, also known as embedded water, was coined by Tony Allan in the early 1990s to denote the total volume of water required to produce a commodity, taking into account every stage in the production process. Originally applied only to food items, it is now also used for clothing and services. Some figures for virtual water content are remarkably high. For example, 1300 litres of water are used in the production of one kilogram of wheat and 15,500 litres for one kilogram of beef (Chapagain and Hoekstra, 2004). However, global average figures like these conceal significant regional and local variations depending on factors such as climate and differences in agricultural practices in different parts of the world. In general, irrigated crops consume a lot more water than rain-fed crops owing to losses by evaporation. Consequently, although the volume of water actually incorporated in a grain of wheat will be much the same whether the crop obtains its moisture from the soil or from artificial irrigation, the total volume used in production, and therefore the virtual water content, can vary significantly. For example, while the world average for wheat is approximately 1300 litres of virtual water per kilogram, country figures range from 849 litres per kilogram in the USA, to 1616 in Brazil and 2375 in Russia (Chapagain and Hoekstra, 2004). Within these national figures are further regional variations.

**Virtual water**
The total volume of water required to produce a commodity.

---

## Activity 10.6   Virtual water

Can you explain why the virtual water content of beef is higher than that for wheat?

### Comment

Virtual water assessment includes water used in all production stages. Wheat, like other plants, needs water to grow, but little other water is used in its production. With beef cattle there are more steps in production than for wheat. Cattle gain their energy from primary producers, such as grass, which needs water to grow. Cattle also drink water themselves. Water may also be used in meat preparation. Beef production is therefore more water intensive than wheat, resulting in a much higher virtual water content.

The virtual water concept, then, provides a useful means to raise awareness of our true total water consumption. It also offers another way of recognising the global interdependencies of a dynamic planet, in the sense that international trade in food and other commodities effectively amounts to trade in water. For example, Jordan 'imports' around 5–7 billion cubic metres of virtual water per year via its trading links (Chapagain and Hoekstra, 2004). The same country's annual water withdrawal from domestic water sources is much lower (around 1 billion cubic metres), so one interpretation of these figures is that Jordan is compensating for its own water scarcity by bringing in goods with high virtual water content from outside its borders. It is in this context that certain commentators, including the originator of the concept (e.g. Allan, 2011), have suggested that virtual water should be used as a way of organising global trade to relieve water scarcity problems. However, in practice, this would be enormously problematic given that global trade is shaped by very different priorities. It is important to recognise that, however useful it may be in other ways, virtual water cannot offer an explanation of global trade exchanges and does not currently alleviate water scarcity. Indeed, virtual water frequently goes in the 'wrong' direction in water resource terms. This is the case in China, where the net movement of virtual water by internal trade is from the dry north to the wetter south. Ma et al. (2006) estimate that the quantity of virtual water moving in that direction is actually more than the total volume that will be transferred from south to north by the three combined routes of the South–North Transfer Scheme.

The concept of virtual water and its relationship to total water consumption has led to the development of the concept of a water footprint. The **water footprint** of an individual, a business or a country is a measure of the fresh water used in the production of goods and services, including direct and indirect uses. It can also take account of the different sources of water and how much pollution is generated. The water footprint concept was introduced by water policy analyst Arjen Hoekstra in 2002, building on the idea of ecological footprints (Box 10.5).

**Water footprint**
The total volume of fresh water that is used to produce the goods and services consumed by an individual, a business or a country.

Box 10.5   Ecological footprints

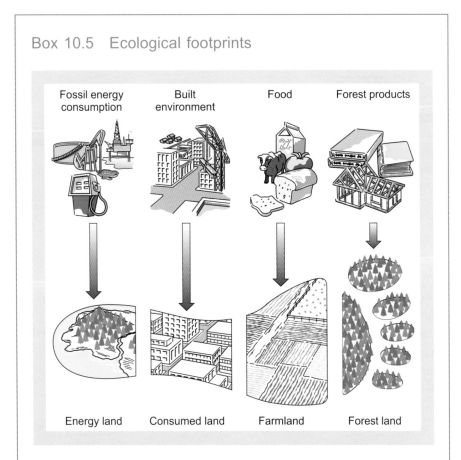

Figure 10.13   Converting consumption into equivalent areas of land (Source: based on Phil Testemale in Wackernagel and Rees, 1996, p. 67)

The concept of an ecological footprint is used to quantify the total human impact on an environment, using land area as the basic measure (Chapter 3, Section 3.2) (Wackernagel and Rees, 1996). The underlying concept is of a household, city, region or country that is imagined to be placed in the centre of a transparent dome which encloses an area of land. Wackernagel and Rees posed the question: how large would the dome have to be to enclose an area of the Earth's surface that could support the inhabitants at their current levels of consumption, assuming a continuous supply of fossil fuels and existing technologies? They devised a standardised method of calculating this 'footprint' area, based on four requirements for land:

•   land that is physically occupied by buildings, roads and infrastructure

- land needed to supply food and water for the inhabitants
- land to supply structural materials such as timber
- land needed to absorb the carbon dioxide produced by fossil fuel consumption.

One benefit of calculating ecological footprints is that it yields a measure of land area that can easily be understood and compared with other individuals, businesses and countries. But this simplicity is also a drawback; the technique has been criticised as an oversimplification of the complex ecological systems and processes involved in sustaining human populations.

Source: adapted from The Open University, 2006

At the national level, water use was usually assessed in terms of the withdrawal of surface and groundwater for domestic, agricultural and industrial purposes. The water footprint concept extended these data to include both the volume used from in-country sources and the virtual water used in other countries to produce imported goods. The water footprint of a country can be assessed by taking the use of domestic water resources, subtracting the virtual water flow that leaves the country, and adding the virtual water flow that enters the country (Chapagain and Hoekstra, 2004). Countries with large populations have large water footprints in absolute terms, although water footprints per capita vary significantly between countries. China's annual water footprint is a little over 1000 cubic metres per capita, whereas that for the USA is more than 2780 cubic metres per capita (Hoekstra and Mekonnen, 2012).

In a similar way to ecological footprinting, water footprint assessment has the attraction of yielding a single figure and is therefore a convenient means of raising awareness of the total volumes of water used. However, water footprinting is a complex process requiring the collection of multiple data sets and, although standard procedures have been proposed (Hoekstra et al., 2011), the term is not always used consistently and it has also been criticised for its over-simplification. Ridoutt and Huang (2012) argue that environmental relevance is the key to understanding water footprints and that the environmental consequences of water consumption will vary from place to place. They point out that water use in a region of water abundance does not have the same environmental impact as water use in a region of water stress. They also take issue with the claim that the water footprints of animal products are necessarily larger than those of crop products (Activity 10.6). If livestock are reared on non-arable land without irrigation they will have little impact on water resources, whereas to replace the animals with crops would create additional pressures on both land and water resources. In a policy statement, the Chartered Institution of Water and Environmental Management (CIWEM) has made similar comments, cautioning that, taken alone, water footprints do not measure environmental impact. It points out that matters of time and space are important because 'the use of a given volume of water has a different impact at one place compared to another, and at one time compared to another' (CIWEM, 2011). They call for a definition of water footprint that reflects these variations in environmental impact rather than the simple sum of virtual water used in production. The water footprint concept is perhaps most useful as a device to raise awareness of our water consumption habits and to recognise how our behaviour – individually, in organisations and as countries – can influence water resource availability.

# 7  Summary

This chapter has elaborated on the challenge of water provision that was introduced in the previous chapter and framed it as a matter of water security. Having explored issues of water usage and supply in more detail, you should now feel confident that (a) your knowledge of water as a global environmental issue has both broadened and deepened, (b) you have a working understanding of some key environmental policy terms and tools that have applicability beyond the topic of water (including CBA, EIA and ecological footprinting), and (c) you have progressed your understanding of the block question *Why are environmental issues often controversial?*

With regard to this last point, we focused on three areas. First, we examined how multiple and competing interests in, valuations of and demands on a finite and limited resource such as water are the very basis of environmental controversy. The Aral Sea story of the overuse of water showed how, at its most extreme, such differences can lead to ecological and social disaster. The same story also illustrated a second key point with respect to the block question, namely that inequalities of power often shape the interests, values, and demands which prevail with respect to the use (and abuse) of environmental resources. In this case that meant both the power of the centre over peripheries and the power to determine that economic arguments won out over environmental and social ones. (This crucial tension between economic gain and environmental impact in major infrastructure projects is returned to later in the block.) Similar forces were also shown to be at work with regard to water transfer schemes historically in north Wales, currently in China, and probably into the future in connection with virtual water. Finally, our unpacking of the process of CBAs and EIAs underlined that the very tools designed to establish the environmental impacts of resource usage can themselves be the basis of controversy, with what is included in such assessments, the quality of the data used, and the basic principle of calculating costs and benefits in monetary terms all likely to be contested by various parties.

# References

Allan, T. (2011) *Virtual Water: Tackling the Threat to Our Planet's Most Precious Resource*, London, I. B. Tauris.

Aquastat (2010) 'Disambiguation of water use statistics', 23 September [online], http://www.fao.org/docrep/013/al815e/al815e00.pdf (Accessed 11 August 2012).

Asafu-Adjaye, J. (2005) *Environmental Economics for Non-economists* (2nd edn), Singapore, World Scientific Publishing.

Auden, W. H. (2007) *W. H. Auden: Poems Selected by John Fuller*, New York, Random House Inc.

Chapagain, A. K. and Hoekstra, A. Y. (2004) *Water Footprints of Nations*, Delft, Netherlands, UNESCO-IHE [online], http://doc.utwente.nl/77203/1/Report16Vol1MainReport.pdf (Accessed 11 August 2012).

Chartered Institution of Water and Environment Management (CIWEM) (2011) 'Water footprinting' [online], http://www.ciwem.org/knowledge-networks/panels/water-resources/water-footprinting.aspx (Accessed 2012).

Department for Environment, Food and Rural Affairs (Defra) (2008) *Future Water: The Government's Water Strategy for England*, Cm 7319, London, The Stationery Office [online], http://archive.defra.gov.uk/environment/quality/water/strategy/pdf/future-water.pdf (Accessed 11 August 2012).

Department for Environment, Food and Rural Affairs (Defra) (2012a) 'Abstactions from non-tidal surface water and ground water' [online], http://www.defra.gov.uk/statistics/environment/inland-water/iwfg12-abstrac/ (Accessed 10 August 2012).

Department for Environment, Food and Rural Affairs (Defra) (2012b) 'Water leakage' [online], http://www.defra.gov.uk/statistics/environment/inland-water/iwfg13-leakage/ (Accessed 10 August 2012).

Environment Agency (2008) *Water Resources in England and Wales – Current State and Future Pressures*, Bristol, Environment Agency [online], http://publications.environment-agency.gov.uk/PDF/GEHO1208BPAS-E-E.pdf (Accessed 11 August 2012).

European Environment Agency (EEA) (2008) 'Impacts due to over-abstraction' [online], http://www.eea.europa.eu/themes/water/water-resources/impacts-due-to-over-abstraction (Accessed 11 August 2012).

Food and Agriculture Organization of the United Nations (FAO) (2012) 'Water use' [online], http://www.fao.org/nr/water/aquastat/water_use/index.stm (Accessed 10 August 2012).

Hoekstra, A. Y. and Mekonnen, M. M. (2012) 'The water footprint of humanity', *Proceedings of the National Academy of Sciences*, vol. 109, no. 9, pp. 3232–7 [online], http://www.pnas.org/content/109/9/3232.full.pdf+html?sid=b5bcb552-d47c-48de-882c-d1bbc08a25fb (Accessed 12 August 2012).

Hoekstra, A. Y., Chapagain, A. K., Aldaya, M. M. and Mekonnen, M. M. (2011) *The Water Footprint Assessment Manual: Setting the Global Standard*, London and Washington, DC, Earthscan.

IWMI (2006) *Insights from the Comprehensive Assessment of Water Management in Agriculture*, International Water Management Institute (IWMI), Colombo, Sri Lanka [online], http://news.bbc.co.uk/1/shared/bsp/hi/pdfs/21_08_06_world_water_week.pdf (Accessed 12 August 2012).

Ma, J., Hoekstra, A. Y., Wang, H., Chapagain, A. K. and Wang, D. (2006) 'Virtual versus real water transfers within China', *Philosophical Transactions of the Royal Society B*, vol. 361, no. 1469, pp. 835–42 [online], http://www.jstor.org.libezproxy.open.ac.uk/stable/20209684 (Accessed 12 August 2012).

McGuire, V. L. (2001) 'Water-level changes in the High Plains Aquifer, 1980-1999', US Geological Survey [online], http://pubs.usgs.gov/fs/2001/fs-029-01/pdf/FS-029-01.pdf (Accessed 12 August 2012).

Mehta, L., Marshall, F., Movik, S., Stirling, A., Shah, E., Smith, A. and Thompson, J. (2007) 'Liquid dynamics: challenges for sustainability in water and sanitation', STEPS Working Paper 6, Brighton, STEPS Centre.

Moore, D. C. (2001) 'Is the post- in postcolonial the post- in post-Soviet? Toward a global postcolonial critique', *PMLA*, vol. 116, no. 1, pp. 111–28.

Ofwat (2007) *Best Practice Guidance on the Inclusion of Externalities in the ELL Calculation*, Ofwat [online], http://www.ofwat.gov.uk/regulating/reporting/rpt_com_leakmethrev_bestpractice.pdf (Accessed 12 August 2012).

Parliamentary Office of Science and Technology (POST) (2011) 'Water in production and products', *Postnote*, no. 385, August [online], http://www.parliament.uk/documents/post/postpn_385-water-in-production-and-products.pdf (Accessed 12 August 2012).

Ridoutt, G. R. and Huang, J. (2012) 'Environmental relevance – the key to understanding water footprints', *Proceedings of the National Academy of Sciences*, vol. 109, no. 22, E1424 [online], http://www.pnas.org/content/109/22/E1424.full.pdf+html l (Accessed 12 August 2012).

Roberts, P. (1995) *Environmentally Sustainable Business: A Local and Regional Perspective*, London, Paul Chapman Publishing.

Stone, R., Jia, H. and Bagla, P. (2006) 'Going against the flow', *Science*, vol. 313, no. 5790, pp. 1034–7.

The Open University (2006) T863 *Environmental decision making: a systems approach*, *Techniques Book*, Milton Keynes, The Open University.

UNEP/GRID-Arendal (2012a) 'Freshwater use by sector at the beginning of the 2000s' [online], http://maps.grida.no/go/graphic/freshwater-use-by-sector-at-the-beginning-of-the-2000s (Accessed 10 August 2012).

UNEP/GRID-Arendal (2012b) 'Areas of physical and economic water scarcity' [online], http://www.grida.no/graphicslib/detail/areas-of-physical-and-economic-water-scarcity_1570 (Accessed 10 August 2012).

United Nations Development Programme (UNDP) (2006) *Human Development Report 2006: Beyond Scarcity: Power, Poverty and the Global Water Crisis*, Basingstoke and New York, Palgrave Macmillan [online], http://hdr.undp.org/en/media/HDR06-complete.pdf (Accessed 12 August 2012).

UN Millennium Project (2006) 'Millennium Development Goals: What they are' [online], http://www.unmillenniumproject.org/goals/index.htm (Accessed 10 August 2012).

Wackernagel, M. and Rees, W. (1996) *Our Ecological Footprint*, Gabriola Island, BC, New Society Publishers.

Water UK (2012) 'National water grid' [online], http://www.water.org.uk/home/policy/positions/national-water-grid (Accessed 12 August 2012).

World Health Organization (WHO)/ UNICEF (2012) *Progress on Drinking Water and Sanitation: 2012 Update*, Geneva and New York, WHO/ UNICEF [online], http://whqlibdoc.who.int/publications/2012/9789280646320_eng.pdf (Accessed 10 August 2012).

Worldwide Fund for Nature (WWF) (2009) *Rivers on the Edge* [online], http://assets.wwf.org.uk/downloads/rivers_on_the_edge.pdf (Accessed 10 August 2012).

# Chapter 11   Pollution and health

Pam Furniss

# Contents

# 1   Introduction

More people die from unsafe water than from all forms of violence, including war.

(Ban Ki-moon, UN Secretary-General, World Water Day message, 22 March 2010)

The previous chapter looked at the use and supply of water. But what happens to it after it has been used? Used water eventually ends up in rivers, the sea or groundwater and is very likely to have been changed by its use, and possibly contaminated. One of the principal sources of that contamination is our own bodies. Discharge of human excreta into the environment is one of the most significant causes of water pollution, with damaging consequences for aquatic ecosystems, and is a major cause of human disease and death. The connections of the water cycle and our use of surface waters to meet our need for drinking water inevitably pose dangers unless water is treated.

This chapter considers the main types of water pollutant but pays particular attention to human waste and sanitation, and the links between waste disposal, hygiene and human health. The chapter concludes with a discussion of opportunities to use human wastes as a resource.

# 2  Sanitation: an environmental issue

Globally, about 1.5 million children under the age of 5 die every year from diarrhoeal diseases (UNICEF/WHO, 2009). The great majority of these are preventable deaths attributable to inadequate sanitation, unsafe water supply and poor hygiene. Sanitation means the separation of human waste from human contact, for hygienic purposes and for disease prevention. Sanitation is therefore an important issue for human health, but is it an environmental issue? An environmental issue may be defined as an undesired change in the environment that prompts people to engage publicly (Chapter 6). How does sanitation fit with this definition? At the household level, sanitation means access to a toilet or latrine. If people have to defecate and urinate in the open, this causes an undesired change in the environment. The second aspect of the definition, public engagement, is more debatable. The topic of sanitation and the disposal of faeces and urine is not something that most people discuss in public. Shock tactics have been employed by campaigning groups in order to get the public's attention. The UK-based environmental pressure group Surfers Against Sewage has campaigned against the discharge of raw and inadequately treated sewage into the sea since 1990. In China, the Green Family Youth Association of Environmental Protection seeks to raise awareness of the dumping of raw sewage into rivers and streams. Figure 11.1 shows campaign posters from both organisations that are designed to raise awareness of sewage disposal.

Although people recognise the importance of sanitation, not least because of the impacts on their own health and well-being, the lack of political engagement on the problem may prevent it becoming a fully-fledged environmental issue. The two campaigns noted above seek to overcome distaste and unwillingness to consider sewage as a public issue. Furthermore, the lack of enthusiasm for the subject goes beyond the attitudes and engagement of the general public. Politicians and decision makers are just as likely to avoid the problem, with the result that sanitation is rarely high on political agendas for investment or development. Alternatives such as improving water supply or better health services are more appealing priorities for funding, even though they may be addressing problems caused by poor sanitation. According to the charity WaterAid, 'political neglect is the root cause of the lack of progress in the sanitation sector' (WaterAid, 2008). Faeces and latrines are just not going to produce the newspaper headlines that politicians want.

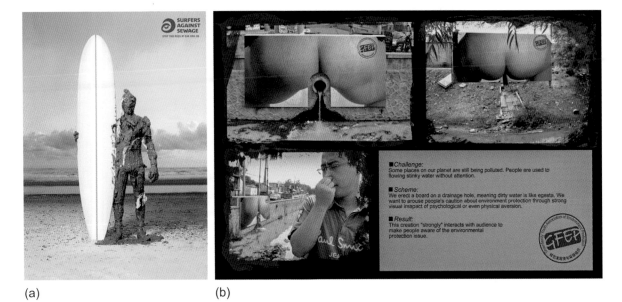

(a)                                          (b)

Figure 11.1   (a) Surfers Against Sewage poster showing a surfer covered in faeces; (b) Advertising campaign from China's Green Family Youth Association of Environmental Protection designed to raise awareness of the dumping of raw sewage into rivers and streams

The Millennium Development Goal (MDG) on environmental sustainability included the target to halve by 2015 the proportion of the population without access to sanitation (Chapter 10). But what does lack of sanitation mean in everyday life? In MDG terms, about 2.5 billion people in the world do not have access to improved sanitation, of which more than a billion have no access to a toilet at all (UNICEF/ WHO, 2012). For some people this means defecating in a bucket or in a plastic bag to be thrown out into the street. For many the only options are to defecate and urinate in a public space, such as a field, waste ground, the side of the road, a river bank or a railway track. No access to sanitation means no privacy, with hundreds or even thousands of other people having to do the same thing in the same place. This is degrading and dangerous, especially for women who may have to risk venturing into public places and making themselves vulnerable to attack. Women and girls frequently wait until the cover of darkness to perform the most basic and essential of bodily functions. Apart from the degrading effects on the people themselves, the environmental impacts are enormous. Human waste contaminates water supplies and has undesirable consequences for aquatic and wider ecosystems.

(a)

(b)

Figure 11.2 Sanitation in Ethiopia: (a) Improved sanitation – a pit latrine with slab. This one also has vent pipe, foot rests, lid (to cover the hole and reduce odours) and surrounding walls of branches and leaves; (b) Unimproved sanitation – an open latrine with no privacy for the user and an insecure cover of logs

Data collection for assessing progress towards meeting the MDGs is the responsibility of the World Health Organization/United Nations Children's Fund Joint Monitoring Programme (WHO/UNICEF JMP). It classifies sanitation facilities across the world as 'improved' or 'unimproved'. Only those people with access to improved services are deemed to have 'access to sanitation' as defined by the JMP. Improved sanitation includes flush toilets connected to a piped sewer system or septic tank, pit latrines as long as they have a slab that covers the pit (Figure 11.2a), and **ecological sanitation** systems (latrines that convert human waste into material that can be safely recycled, for example in soil, without damaging the environment or endangering human health). Unimproved sanitation means there is no effective barrier to human contact with human excreta. This includes pit latrines without a slab, open latrines (Figure 11.2b), buckets and bags, and open defecation in public places. Sanitation facilities that are shared among households are also classed as unimproved, according to the JMP system. The availability of different sanitation technologies shows marked regional variations across the world, as shown in Figure 11.3.

**Ecological sanitation** An approach to sanitation that aims to use human excreta as a resource, minimise environmental contamination, and prevent disease.

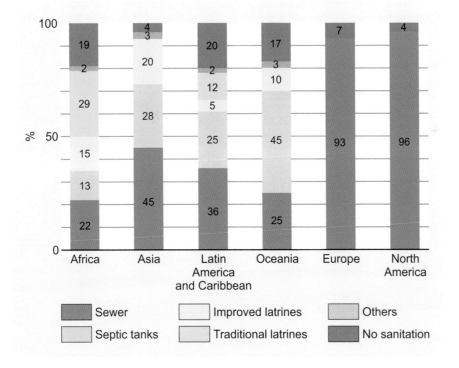

Figure 11.3  Distribution of sanitation technologies across the world (Source: based on Bahri, 2009, p. 16, Figure 1)

Considerable progress has been made towards achieving the MDG for sanitation but the pattern of change is different for urban and rural populations. According to JMP data, between 1990 and 2010, 724 million people in rural areas gained access to improved sanitation but the number of urban dwellers without access increased by 183 million (UNICEF/WHO, 2012). This disparity is principally caused by the rapid growth in urban populations. The rate of migration to cities is such that the provision of sanitation services often cannot keep pace. There are several contributory causes for this that have been evident at various times in the history of urban development in different parts of the world. In a comparative study of urban sanitation in nineteenth-century industrialised countries and the present day 'developing' world, Konteh (2009) identified several determinants of urban sanitation and health, which they categorised in four groups, as shown in Table 11.1. Different combinations of these causal factors and their interconnections create situations that do not have simple, easy solutions. As the global population rises and the shift to urban living continues, these factors have combined so that, although the *percentage* of the global population without access to improved sanitation has decreased from 51 per cent to 37 per cent since 1990, the total *number* of 2.5 billion has changed very little (UNICEF/WHO, 2012).

Table 11.1   Determinants of urban sanitation and health

| **Physical** | **Economic** | **Political** | **Social** |
| --- | --- | --- | --- |
| Housing | Wealth/poverty | Policies | Household size |
| Water | | Governance | Crowding |
| Sanitation | | Institutional arrangements | Hygiene practices |
| Waste disposal | | | Education |
| Drainage | | | Social capital |

Source: Konteh, 2009, p. 71, Table 2

**Appropriate technology**
A technology that is culturally acceptable and financially and environmentally sustainable.

Social attitudes to sanitation may vary. Those people who have routine access to flush toilets may consider dry latrines to be unpleasant, inferior or a health risk. But flush toilets use an enormous amount of water and they are inappropriate in many parts of the world, especially where water is scarce. The concept of **appropriate technology** is relevant here. An appropriate technology is one that is suitable for a particular purpose and context in terms of local cultural, social, economic and environmental circumstances. An appropriate technology must be effective and affordable, easily installed and maintained, and durable. These factors will vary in different locations; what is appropriate in one context may not be so in others. In places without piped water supply, dry latrines are the only appropriate sanitation technology. Even in countries with relatively high rainfall like the UK they can be the best option in some rural locations with irregular use, such as toilet facilities for remote beauty spots.

The pit latrine is one of the most basic dry sanitation technologies, consisting of a pit dug in the ground. To be considered as improved sanitation, pit latrines must have a cleanable cover slab in order to separate people from their wastes (Figure 11.4). Over time, the waste in the pit slowly breaks down naturally by the action of bacteria and other microorganisms. The location of pit latrines is important because they are potential causes of groundwater pollution and therefore must be located away from, and downhill of, water wells and springs so that the possible transmission of pathogens via groundwater movements is avoided. **Pathogens** are infectious biological agents, such as bacteria, viruses, protozoa or parasitic worms, that may cause disease to their host.

**Pathogen**
An infectious biological agent that may cause disease to its host.

Ecological sanitation, or ecosan, is a variation on the simple pit latrine. Ecosan is an approach to human waste management rather than a single method. In ecosan systems, human excreta is considered a resource, not waste. The principle is to make use of excreta by transforming it into an end product that can be used as a soil fertiliser. Ecological sanitation aims to decrease contamination of the environment and to prevent the transmission of disease. An additional benefit of using waste in this way is that the amount of artificial fertiliser used in cultivation of fields is decreased, which saves money for the farmer and protects lakes and other water bodies from pollution caused by run-off of these additional fertilisers.

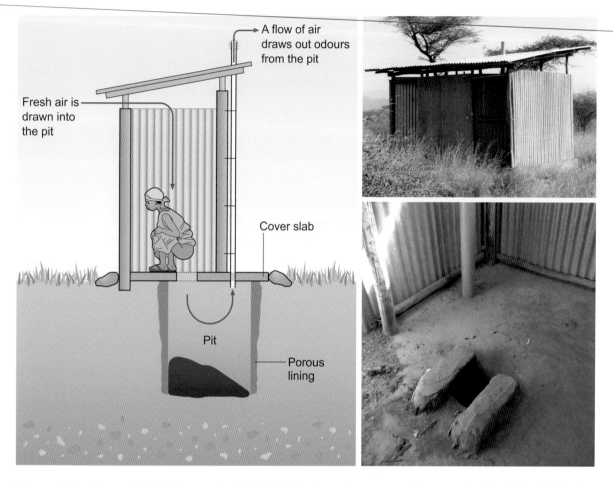

Figure 11.4   The ventilated improved pit (VIP) latrine is an improvement over a simple pit. Its distinctive feature is the vent pipe, which allows foul odour from the pit to escape and helps to control flies (Source: based on WHO and IRC, 2003, p. 105, Figure 8.2)

A simple form of ecological sanitation advocated for use by rural households in Africa is the Arborloo (Figure 11.5). It is used like a normal pit latrine but with the regular addition of soil, wood ash and leaves. When full, it is covered with leaves and soil and a small tree is planted on top to grow in the compost. (The tree gives the system its name: 'arbor' is Latin for 'tree'.) Another pit is dug nearby and the whole structure is relocated over the new pit. No handling of the waste is required. If a fruit tree is grown, there is the added benefit of food or income for the household.

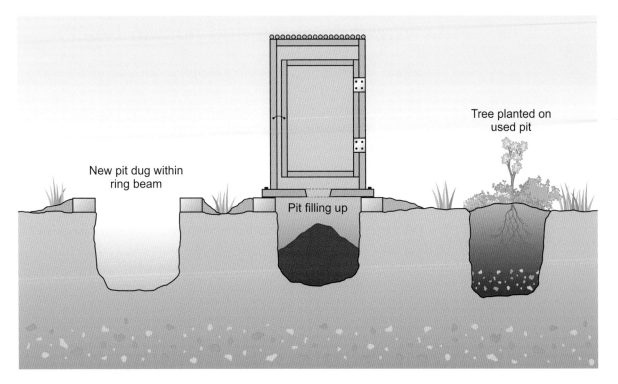

Figure 11.5   Arborloo – a single-pit ecosan system (Source: based on Stockholm Environment Institute, 2007, p. 3, Figure 2.1)

# 3    Water, hygiene and human health

The impact of having no access to sanitation goes far beyond the effect on human dignity and the social and cultural difficulties of open defecation. Waste that is not contained or disposed of hygienically can contaminate rivers, lakes and groundwater that are sources of water for drinking, cooking and washing. If the waste comes from infected people, then the people using the water are likely to become infected, leading to an iterative cycle of disease from people to water and back again.

The link between disease and contaminated water was first recognised by the English physician John Snow (see, for example, Davey Smith, 2002). In 1854, Snow famously traced the source of a cholera outbreak in London to a specific water pump and, despite scepticism and disbelief of his theory of cause and effect, he successfully campaigned for the pump to be closed (Figure 11.6). The health risks to which many people in developing countries today are exposed are not dissimilar to those that the urban poor faced in Europe until the development of water supply and sewerage infrastructures in the nineteenth and twentieth centuries.

**Faeco-oral transmission**
The passage of pathogens from faeces to mouth.

Cholera is transmitted by drinking water contaminated with the bacterium *Vibrio cholerae*. To become infected with cholera a person must ingest water or food that has been contaminated with faeces from people infected with the disease. This is the **faeco-oral transmission** route of disease. The faeco-oral route, as the name suggests, depends on transmission of pathogens from human faeces of an infected person to the mouth of someone free of disease, who then becomes infected. As well as cholera, faeco-oral transmission is the cause of many other diseases, including typhoid, dysentery, various types of viral gastroenteritis that are a common cause of diarrhoea in children, and many protozoan (single-celled) parasites such as *Giardia* and *Cryptosporidium* (Figure 11.7).

(a)

Figure 11.6   (a) John Snow;
(b) Deaths from cholera in the Soho
district of London, September 1854.
By recording the location of cholera
deaths, John Snow was able to
demonstrate that most of the deaths
occurred among people who
consumed water from the water
pump in Broad Street (now Broad-
wick Street)

(b)

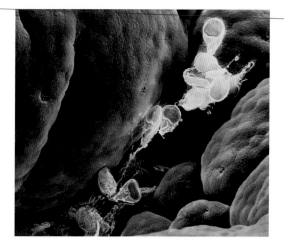

Figure 11.7   Scanning electron micrograph of *Giardia lamblia* in the human intestine. This single-celled protozoan, shown in green, causes the disease giardiasis, with symptoms of abdominal cramps, swelling, diarrhoea and nausea (magnification x 1100)

## Activity 11.1   Faeco-oral disease transmission

Diarrhoea can have a variety of causes but is usually transmitted faeco-orally. What possible pathways of faeco-oral transmission can you think of?

### Comment

People who have to obtain their water from unprotected sources such as a river may be drinking water contaminated with faeces. Food can easily be contaminated if handled by an infected person who hasn't washed their hands properly. In places without sanitation where open defecation is the only option, flies moving from faeces to uncovered food can carry bacteria with them. Without thorough and frequent hand washing, infection can also pass easily by direct person-to-person contact; for example, contact between a mother and child, and then from fingers to mouth.

All these transmission pathways contribute to the rapid spread of disease in disaster situations; for example, following major earthquakes or in refugee camps. Cholera is particularly dangerous in circumstances where people are close together with sanitation systems that are non-existent or broken, with limited or no available clean water for drinking and washing. When there is no safe water source, people have to risk using untreated water. In such situations it needs only one person to be carrying a disease, possibly without symptoms, to start an epidemic.

As well as clean water and effective sanitation, thorough hand washing is essential to break the faeco-oral transmission route. Research by Fewtrell et al. (2005) has shown that hand washing is actually more important than other factors for disease prevention. They concluded that diarrhoeal episodes are reduced by 45 per cent through hand washing compared with 25 per cent by improving water supply, 32 per cent by improving sanitation, and 39 per cent by household water treatment and safe storage. It is also worth noting that hand hygiene is not just an issue for countries with limited water supplies and inadequate sanitation, or in emergency situations. 'Now wash your hands please' is a familiar sign in many public lavatories, but not everyone follows the instruction. Curtis et al. (2011) reported the findings of three separate surveys into hygiene habits in the UK:

> In a motorway service station in the south of England, just 65% of women and 31% of men washed their hands with soap after using the toilet facilities (Judah et al., 2009) and a study in the north of England recorded that just 43% of mothers washed their hands with soap after changing a dirty nappy (Curtis et al., 2003). A survey by Judah and co-workers (Judah et al., 2010) reported that 28% of commuters in five UK cities had bacteria of faecal origin on their hands.
>
> (Curtis et al., 2011, pp. 314–15)

There are other diseases associated with water that are not transmitted faeco-orally. Insufficient water for washing can lead to poor personal hygiene, which is a contributory factor in the transmission of scabies (skin infection caused by a parasitic mite), typhus (bacterial infection carried by lice) and trachoma (bacterial eye infection that can lead to blindness). Another group of diseases have a close association with water because the parasites that cause them spend part of their lifecycle in freshwater habitats such as lakes, ponds, wet ditches and canals. Bilharzia (also known as schistosomiasis) is caused by a parasitic worm that spends part of its life in the body of particular species of water snail; people can become infected from swimming or wading in water where the snails are found. Human agency has a significant impact on the prevalence of schistosomiasis; water storage and distribution networks for irrigation can provide a habitat for the snails (Figure 11.8). Another example of a water-related disease is dracunculiasis or guinea worm, which is transmitted by drinking water contaminated with copepods (very small crustaceans) that contain the larvae of the worm. As an interesting aside, at the time of writing, dracunculiasis is set to become only the third disease in history to be eradicated from the Earth after smallpox and rinderpest (a disease of cattle). In 2011 there were just over 1000 cases confined to four African countries compared with 3.5 million cases in 1986 (CDC, 2012).

Figure 11.8    An irrigation channel near Ross Bethio, Senegal. Such channels make ideal habitats for the water snails that spread bilharzia

# 4   Water pollution

There are many ways in which human activities can pollute aquatic ecosystems. **Water pollution** can be defined as a change in water quality, due to human activity, that has an adverse effect on people or the environment. Water quality describes the physical, chemical and biological characteristics of fresh water. It is not an absolute measure – water that is 'good quality' for one purpose may not be acceptable for another. Under the terms of the European Union's Water Framework Directive (Box 11.1), river water quality is assessed by a classification system that uses more than 30 variables. These are grouped into measures of ecological status (e.g. fish, invertebrates, macrophytes), and of chemical status (e.g. heavy metals, pesticides, nutrients) (Environment Agency, 2011). These measures are used to assign an overall quality status on a scale of *high*, *good*, *moderate*, *poor* and *bad*. Similar assessment schemes cover estuaries, coastal waters, groundwater and lakes, as well as rivers. The Water Framework Directive requires that all inland and coastal waters should aim to achieve at least *good* ecological status. However, this is not measured in absolute terms because there are geographical variations in what 'good' quality could be expected to be. For this reason, quality status is assessed against locally determined standards of the biological community that would be expected in conditions of minimum anthropogenic impact.

**Water pollution**
A change in water quality, due to human activity, that has an adverse effect on people or the environment.

---

### Box 11.1   Water Framework Directive (2000/60/EC)

The Water Framework Directive (WFD) is a piece of European Union legislation designed to establish a legal framework to protect and restore clean water in sufficient quantity across Europe. It was adopted into UK law in 2003 and the various instruments it specifies are gradually being implemented.

The WFD requires that all inland and coastal waters within defined river basin districts must reach at least *good* status by 2015 and defines how this should be achieved through the establishment of environmental objectives and ecological targets for surface waters. It is a large and complex piece of legislation with several distinctive features. It takes a holistic approach to water management that recognises the interconnections between human and environmental needs and it encourages active public participation in decision-making processes.

---

In order to reach *good* status for each river basin district, the WFD specifies the requirement to:

- define what is meant by *good* status by setting environmental quality objectives for surface waters and groundwaters
- identify in detail the characteristics of the river basin district, including the environmental impact of human activity
- assess the present water quality in the river basin district
- undertake an analysis of the significant water quality management issues
- identify the pollution control measures required to achieve the environmental objectives
- consult with interested parties about pollution control measures, the costs involved and the benefits arising
- implement the agreed control measures, monitor the improvements in water quality and review progress and revise water management plans to achieve the quality objectives.

Source: adapted from Commission of the European Communities, 2007; Foundation for Water Research, 2010

Numerous pollutants may enter the water cycle from industrial and agricultural processes and other human activities. Their effects, once released into an aquatic environment, depend mostly on the type of pollutant; the main types are described in the following sections. Many pollutants are removed or their effects are reduced by natural processes of dilution, dispersion or deposition. Dilution reduces the concentration of soluble pollutants and may render them harmless if the dilution volume is sufficient. (This can be compared with dissolving a teaspoonful of sugar in a bucket or a cup. The volume of the bucket is greater than the cup, hence the sugar solution in the bucket is more dilute.) Insoluble pollutants will not dissolve but may be dispersed (i.e. spread out) or deposited (i.e. settle to the bottom). These processes depend on the type of particle and principally on the speed of water flow. In fast-flowing river water solid particles will be carried along in the flow and dispersed downstream, but in still water they are more likely to settle to the bottom.

## 4.1   Organic material

One of the most common pollutants of surface water is organic material which enters rivers and lakes as human waste, animal waste, other farm effluents, food-processing waste and some other industrial wastewaters. In a scientific context, the terms organic and inorganic have a specific meaning (Box 11.2).

---

### Box 11.2   Organic and inorganic

In the context of water pollution, organic material or organic matter means anything of animal or plant origin. The derivation of the word is from having organs or an organised physical structure, as found in living *organ*isms. Natural organic material in aquatic and terrestrial environments (e.g. animal wastes, leaf litter, dead organisms) is **biodegradable**, meaning it can be broken down by bacteria and other microorganisms into relatively harmless end products. Inorganic substances such as sand and silt, on the other hand, have a mineral, rather than biological, origin. Inorganic materials of this type are generally inert, meaning they do not react chemically or biologically and therefore do not degrade.

In chemistry, organic chemicals were originally limited to those substances found only in living organisms that contain carbon atoms linked with hydrogen (hydrocarbons), and their derivatives. Subsequently, many useful artificial hydrocarbon compounds have been developed that are also called organic because of their similar properties. Organic chemistry is the study of these hydrocarbon compounds and inorganic chemistry is the study of compounds that do not contain hydrocarbons.

**Biodegradability**
A property of a substance that can be broken down by biological processes.

---

### Activity 11.2   Biodegradability

'All organic substances are biodegradable.' Is this statement true or false?

### Comment

*False.* Most naturally occurring organic substances are biodegradable but some artificially produced organic substances are not. For example, the group known as persistent organic pollutants (POPs), which includes polychlorinated biphenyls (PCBs) and many pesticides, persist in the environment because they do not degrade. Plastics contain hydrocarbons and are thus organic, but most plastics are non-biodegradable (Chapter 8, Section 2, Box 8.1). Time is also an important factor. Those organic substances that are biodegradable may break down only slowly over time. For example, and as you saw in the case of Deepwater Horizon, oil is organic and ultimately biodegradable but the process may take many years.

**Aerobic**

An aerobic process or organism is one that requires a supply of oxygen.

Biodegradation in surface waters is principally an **aerobic** process, meaning it needs a supply of oxygen. Aerobic bacteria (oxygen-dependent bacteria) living in water feed on organic material and break it down into simpler, generally harmless, substances. In the process, the bacteria use oxygen dissolved in the water for respiration. Oxygen enters water from two sources: by mixing with air at the surface, and from photosynthesis by green aquatic plants. Dissolved oxygen is essential to maintain freshwater ecosystems. Fish, amphibians and many invertebrates depend on oxygen dissolved in the water to survive (Figure 11.9).

When organic matter is released into a river the result is an increase in the number of aerobic bacteria responsible for its breakdown. The increased bacteria population consume more oxygen from the water. If large amounts of organic materials are discharged into a body of water, the oxygen demands of the bacteria feeding on it can exceed the rate at which the oxygen can be replenished and so the dissolved oxygen concentration of the water falls. This brings about a reduction in aquatic life; many animals in the water will die as the oxygen concentration decreases, and few plants thrive when organic pollution is severe. If the quantity of organic pollution is very high, then all the oxygen from the water may be used, leading to **anaerobic** (without oxygen) conditions in which aerobic bacteria cannot live and a different set of bacteria, anaerobic bacteria, take over the breakdown of organic matter, giving rise to a different set of end products, including foul-smelling gases. This is unlikely in most rivers where the water is moving but can happen in lakes or slow-flowing channels.

**Anaerobic**

An anaerobic process or organism is one that does not require oxygen.

(a)

(b )

(c)

(d)

(e)

(f)

Figure 11.9   Many aquatic animals are dependent on unpolluted water: (a) nymph of Southern Hawker dragonfly (*Aeshna cyanea*); (b) adult Southern Hawker dragonfly; (c) common frog (*Rana temporaria*); (d) three-spined stickleback (*Gasterosteus aculeatus*); (e) Great Diving Beetle (*Dytiscus marginalis*); (f) white-clawed crayfish (*Austropotamobius pallipes*)

The oxygen demand exerted by the breakdown of organic matter is used to measure the degree of organic water pollution. The five-day Biochemical Oxygen Demand, or $BOD_5$, test is the standard technique for assessing contamination of water by organic substances. The test involves mixing a sample of river water or effluent with fully oxygenated water, measuring the dissolved oxygen content, waiting five days to allow the bacteria to break down the organic matter, and then measuring the dissolved oxygen content again. The reduction in oxygen content is proportional to the organic content of the original sample.

The ability of aerobic bacteria to break down organic matter into generally harmless substances is also the process at the heart of sewage treatment systems. Wastewater treatment plants are designed to create ideal conditions for the growth of aerobic bacteria so that the levels of organic matter in the incoming sewage are reduced to almost none in the outgoing treated effluent.

## 4.2    Living organisms

Some aquatic organisms are less desirable than others. As discussed in Section 3, several human diseases are caused or transmitted by pathogenic bacteria and also by specific types of protozoa (single-celled organisms), worms and snails. The most common route for these living pollutants to enter water supplies is by contamination with human faeces, either directly or by discharge of raw or partially treated sewage. They may also be picked up when water passes through soil that is polluted with human and animal wastes.

As well as the bacteria that break down organic matter, there are many other types that are commonly present in fresh water. One of these, *Escherichia coli (E. coli)* (Figure 11.10), has particular value as an indicator of microbiological contamination. The species *E. coli*, one of the large group of faecal coliform bacteria, has many different strains (variants). Most strains are harmless, in fact many are beneficial, but some are pathogenic. For example, the strain *E. coli* O157:H7 is a known cause of food poisoning. *E. coli* is useful as an indicator species because it is relatively easy to detect in freshwater samples. All humans and other warm-blooded animals have millions of *E. coli* in their intestines and, consequently, in their faeces. If laboratory analysis of river water detects the presence of *E. coli*, this indicates recent faecal pollution. Because most strains are harmless, the presence of *E. coli* is not in itself a problem but the presence of faecal pollution suggests that other, pathogenic, microorganisms could be present.

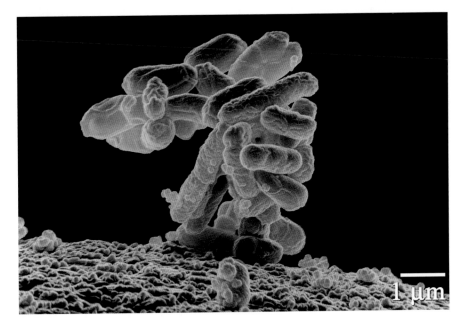

Figure 11.10   A magnified image of the *E. coli* bacterium (1 μm = 1 micrometre or 1 × 10$^{-6}$ metres)

## 4.3   Plant nutrients

Plant nutrients are inorganic substances, mainly nitrogen and phosphorus compounds, which are essential for normal plant growth. Nitrogen and phosphorus enter fresh water from human and animal wastes, detergents and fertilisers. **Eutrophication** is the process that occurs when bodies of water become enriched with nutrients, thus stimulating plant growth. Eutrophication can cause a sudden increase in the population of microscopic algae, a phenomenon known as an algal bloom. The main problem with algal blooms is that the increased population of aquatic plants can die off equally quickly if the supply of nutrients is exhausted. The subsequent decay of the plant material by bacteria can cause complete deoxygenation of the water, leading to anaerobic conditions. Plant nutrients can also lead to an increase in the growth of larger plants and may contribute to problems with invasive species (Figure 11.11).

**Eutrophication**
An accumulation of plant nutrients in fresh water leading to a rapid growth in plant life.

Figure 11.11    Water hyacinth (*Eichhornia crassipes*) spreading across the water surface of Lake Corpus Christi, Texas, USA. Native to South America, it is a classic example of an invasive species that has become a problem in many parts of Africa, North America and Asia

## Activity 11.3    Eutrophication

Why is eutrophication more likely to be a problem in lakes than in rivers?

### Comment

Flowing water in a river will disperse the nutrients whereas the nutrients will accumulate over time in the still water of a lake.

## 4.4   Pesticides and other toxic chemicals

Pesticides can be subdivided into insecticides, herbicides, fungicides, rodenticides, molluscicides, and so on, according to the organisms they are targeting. There are innumerable different pesticides in use, many of them possible causes of water pollution. Some well-known examples are DDT (dichlorodiphenyltrichloroethane), malathion and parathion. DDT has been used since the 1930s to control insects, especially mosquitoes which are the vector of malaria. Other toxic chemicals may be released into the environment in wastewater from industrial processes; for example, polychlorinated biphenyls (PCBs), a by-product of the plastics industry. DDT and PCBs are classic examples of persistent organic pollutants (POPs). These are stable compounds that are not biodegradable and therefore they can accumulate in water and in living organisms. Other non-biodegradable pollutants include the compounds of heavy metals such as mercury, cadmium, lead and chromium.

## 4.5   Sediments and suspended solids

Sediments can be organic or inorganic and include fine particles of soil, mud, silt or sand. When moving along in flowing water they are referred to as suspended solids. Suspended solids can be washed into a stream or river as a result of land cultivation, in run-off from roads and hard surfaces, and also from construction, demolition and mining operations. Solid particles from inorganic origins are inert, meaning they are unreactive and non-biodegradable. Large quantities of suspended solids may reduce light penetration into the water, which can affect the growth of plants. Sediments may smother organisms on the riverbed when they settle.

The types of water pollutant described in this section, with their sources and effects, are summarised in Table 11.2.

Table 11.2  Common water pollutants

| Pollutant | Common sources | Effects |
|---|---|---|
| *Organic material* (biodegradable material that is decomposed by aerobic bacteria using water-dissolved oxygen) | Human waste/domestic sewage, animal waste, food processing, road run-off | Small quantities are removed by natural processes but large amounts will reduce dissolved oxygen levels and may produce anaerobic conditions |
| *Living organisms* (pathogens such as bacteria, viruses, protozoa, parasitic worms) | Human waste, animal waste | Human diseases including cholera, typhoid, dysentery |
| *Plant nutrients* (mainly nitrogen and phosphorus compounds) | Domestic sewage, agriculture (especially from chemical fertilisers), some industrial wastes | Eutrophication, excessive plant growth: can cause physical blockage and oxygen depletion |
| *Pesticides and other toxic chemicals* (pesticides, industrial by-products, soluble metal compounds, acids) | Agriculture, industry, mining, road run-off | Toxic effects on fish and other animals |
| *Sediments and suspended solids* (particles of soil, sand, clay, etc. which may settle as sediment in still waters or be carried along in river flow) | Soil erosion by run-off, any land disturbance such as quarrying, road building | Can smother plants and any bottom-living organisms, reduces light penetration |

## Activity 11.4  Pollution from human waste

Look again at Table 11.2 and identify the pollutant groups listed there that originate from human waste.

### Comment

Organic material, pathogenic organisms and plant nutrients are all pollutants that can be released into the aquatic environment from human excreta.

# 5 Problem or resource?

The wastes produced by people, whether from their own bodies or as by-products of their activities, can create many environmental problems. Whether it's solid waste in the form of domestic refuse, carbon dioxide from fossil fuel burning, toxic wastes from industry, or water pollution from human excreta, waste lies at the heart of many environmental issues. To deal with the problem, many people argue that a general shift in thinking is needed – from waste as a problem to waste as a resource – which could then bring both environmental and economic benefits.

There are several options for making good use of human excreta and wastewater. They can be used to provide fertiliser or as an energy source, or recycled to meet some of the growing demand for water. The Arborloo and other ecological sanitation methods provide a good example of the advantages of using the fertilising properties of human waste. Using treated or partially treated wastewater for irrigation is another. It not only provides water for growing crops but also supplies plant nutrients. Wastewater typically contains organic matter, nitrogen, phosphorus and potassium, all of which improve soil fertility. Direct use of human-derived wastewater, with or without treatment, has been common practice in many places throughout the world for centuries. Box 11.3 describes an example from Mexico.

---

### Box 11.3 Using wastewater in Mexico

In the Mezquital Valley in Mexico, 85,000 hectares of land are irrigated with mostly untreated wastewater from Mexico City. This allows agricultural development in an area with only 550 mm of rainfall a year, and soils with low organic matter and nutrient content that would otherwise be of limited productive value.

After 80 years of irrigation, the levels of the plant nutrients potassium and nitrogen and of organic matter in the soil have increased significantly. However, there have also been some disadvantages, such as an increase in soil salinity in some places and some accumulation of heavy metals (a waste product of some industrial processes). An incidental side-effect has been the recharge of the underlying aquifer which, in some places, has raised the level of the water table to surface level, resulting in the

---

emergence of springs. These springs have become the only source of water for more than 500,000 people.

Source: adapted from Bahri, 2009, p. 25

Despite its advantages, some people have cultural or aesthetic objections to reusing wastewater, and there can also be health risks, especially if the wastewater is used for domestic purposes or in the production of food for direct consumption, such as vegetables. Table 11.3 summarises the main benefits and risks of reusing wastewater.

Table 11.3   Comparison between the economic value of wastewater and nutrients derived from wastewater, and the associated environmental and public health risks

| Economic value of wastewater and nutrients | Environmental and public health risks |
|---|---|
| Conserves water and reduces freshwater demand | Health risks for the irrigators and communities in contact with wastewater (increased incidence of diarrhoeal diseases) |
| Provides a reliable water supply to farmers | |
| | Health risks for the consumers of vegetables irrigated with wastewater |
| Acts as a low-cost method for disposal of municipal wastewater | |
| | Pathogens in wastewater can cause health problems for cattle |
| Reduces pollution of rivers, canals and other surface waters | |
| | Contamination of groundwater (including nitrates, trace organics and pathogens) |
| Recycles organic matter and nutrients to soils, thereby reducing the need for artificial fertilisers | |
| | Build-up of chemical pollutants in the soil (including salts and heavy metals) |
| Increases crop yields and therefore has direct positive income effect for farmers | |
| | Creation of habitats for disease vectors (mosquitoes) |

Source: adapted from Bahri, 2009, p. 22, Table 3

More typically, rather than being reused directly, wastewater is returned to a river to take advantage of the natural cleansing processes by aerobic bacteria. It can then be abstracted again further downstream and used again. But that stage is not necessary if appropriate treatment is in place to safeguard against the potential health risks. Supporters of the reuse of wastewater suggest it should be incorporated into the global water cycle as another transfer process that can replenish supply (Figure 11.12) and become an integral component of water resource management.

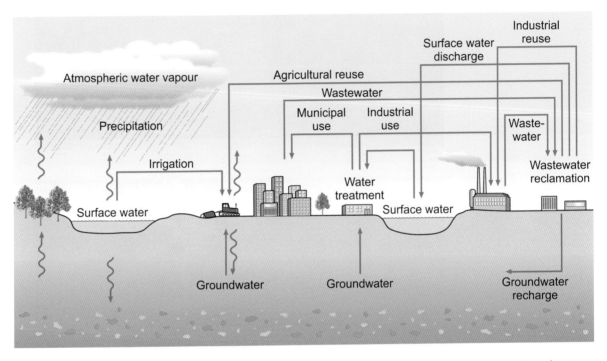

Figure 11.12   The role of engineered treatment, reclamation and reuse facilities in the cycling of water through the hydrologic cycle (Source: based on Asano and Levine, 1995)

Human excreta can also be a valuable source of energy. The process of **anaerobic digestion** converts organic wastes into sludge and **biogas**, mainly methane, inside a sealed container called an anaerobic biogas reactor or anaerobic digester. The organic waste is collected and stored in the container where it is a source of food for anaerobic bacteria. The bacteria digest the waste and produce biogas, which can be piped away and burned as a fuel to produce heat both at a small scale in the kitchen for use in cooking and also in larger-scale heating systems and for electricity generation. The digested sludge that remains at the end of the process can be spread on land where it acts as a soil conditioner and fertiliser.

**Anaerobic digestion**
The decomposition of waste under anaerobic conditions to produce biogas and a compost-like residue.

**Biogas**
Gas produced by anaerobic digestion consisting mostly of methane and carbon dioxide.

(a)

(b)

Figure 11.13   (a) Anaerobic digesters at Didcot Sewage Treatment Works, Oxfordshire, UK. Biogas from these digesters can be fed into the national gas grid system to meet domestic energy needs; (b) Anaerobic digester under construction in Ethiopia. Most of the chamber is below the ground surface. The opening at the top will be closed around an inlet for the incoming waste and an outlet pipe for biogas. An outlet pipe for digested sludge (not visible) is built into the side of the chamber (Source: WaterAid in Ethiopia)

The first biogas reactor is believed to have been developed in India in 1859, and the technology transferred to the UK in the late nineteenth century at a time of growing concern about urban sanitation. The development of a controlled process of heating and mixing in sealed tanks came in the 1920s and 1930s (Mihelcic et al., 2007). Since that time, anaerobic digestion has been used in municipal sewage treatment works in the UK and elsewhere to stabilise the sludge produced in sewage treatment (Figure 11.13a). Digesters may also be found in high-density pig and cattle production units. Small-scale digesters are increasingly common throughout Africa and Asia. By 2001, it was estimated there were 6 million community-based biogas plants in China and 2 million in India (Mihelcic et al., 2007). It is an affordable technology that is relatively simple to construct and maintain (Figure 11.13b). Neighbourhoods can join together to share a digester, or, if sufficient wastes are generated, individual households can each have one.

## Activity 11.5   Anaerobic digestion

Have another look at Figure 11.13a. Why does the digestion chamber need to be sealed?

### Comment

Anaerobic bacteria are responsible for the digestion. As anaerobic bacteria require an oxygen-free environment, air must be excluded from the digester.

Using human excreta as a resource requires an effective sanitation system to collect and control the waste, but the benefits of sanitation go far beyond the potential for resource use. Better management and financing of sanitation can produce usable effluent that will help to relieve water scarcity as well as reduce water pollution, but there are also wider financial gains derived from the impact of effective sanitation on individuals, communities and the public. The Water Supply and Sanitation Collaborative Council (WSSCC) (2011) sums up the benefits of investment in sanitation:

- *Dignity.* Greater human dignity, freedom and equality for women and men, boys and girls.

- *Health.* If everyone had access to adequate sanitation and water services, the world's health sectors would save around US$12 billion every year.

- *Productivity.* Meeting the MDG target on sanitation and water would free up 74 billion working days per year.

- *Education.* Meeting the MDG target on sanitation and water would result in 270 million additional days of school attendance worldwide each year.

- *Tourism.* The risk of poor sanitary conditions can deter tourists who bring significant income to many countries. For example, a study in Cambodia, Vietnam, Indonesia and the Philippines estimated that poor sanitation costs these four countries around US$350 million per year in lost tourism revenue.

- *Jobs.* Investing in sanitation can provide jobs in latrine construction, retail and marketing of sanitary products, and operation and maintenance services. It can also bring income from reuse of human waste for the production of biogas and as agricultural fertiliser.

Sanitation is therefore not only an environmental issue, as discussed in Section 2, but also clearly a social and economic issue. It is also a political one. Effective sanitation for the poor requires national level support from government and may also require support from private investors and international organisations (Box 11.4).

### Box 11.4   Sanitation programme for the urban poor in Dakar, Senegal

In Dakar, access to sanitation facilities reflects the distribution of power within society and was originally provided only for relatively affluent members of the population living in central parts of the city covered by the sewerage network. Extending sanitation provision beyond this privileged class has been politically controversial for three reasons. First, sanitation has had to compete with other, and electorally more attractive, priorities such as road building and improvements in Dakar. Second, decision making on sanitation has been characterised by a long-standing value preference for visible, large infrastructure investments in sanitation that demonstrate modernity and technological progress at the expense of appropriate technology. Third, the Senegalese government and private investors have had different approaches. Until the 1990s Senegalese policy makers treated the sanitation and water sectors as interconnected components in its development strategy, believing that this was technically and organisationally the most effective way of improving services and extending them to poorer areas. However, private investors wanted the more financially attractive water sector to be separated from the far less attractive sanitation sector.

At the beginning of the 2000s the importance of sanitation on the domestic political agenda increased when Dakar hosted the 2004 Global WASH Forum. (WASH stands for Water, Sanitation and Hygiene.) Subsequently, the World Bank and the Water and Sanitation Program (a multi-donor partnership) have been key funders for sanitation projects in Senegal, providing up to 90 per cent of funds. A politically more favourable climate and the ability of the sanitation sector to build on experiences and successes of the implementation of water projects provided an opportunity to shift attention to the sanitation needs of Dakar's poor. The Programme d'Assainissement des Quartiers Péri-Urbains de Dakar (PAQPUD; Sanitation Programme for Peri-Urban Communities of Dakar) was launched in 2002 as a way of targeting areas in Dakar outside the sewerage network. The goal to bring on-site sanitation to 60,000 households in poor peri-urban areas by 2006 was achieved. The programme offered technologically appropriate sanitation solutions, and households could choose from a range of different options in different price categories, most of which meet the criteria for 'improved' sanitation under the MDGs. However, despite these successes, there were significant drawbacks. The poorest households were unlikely to benefit. Subsidies were a one-off investment and were not intended to cover maintenance costs. Experience showed that there was a clear difference between the willingness to pay for sanitation and the ability to pay. As one community leader explained: 'Some of our neighbours don't have enough money for regular meals. How should they afford the expense of a latrine?'

Source: adapted from Water and Sanitation Programme and the World Bank, 2011

# 6   Summary

In this chapter you have learnt, through the example of sanitation, that not all environmental problems necessarily or easily become environmental issues in the sense that you were introduced to in Block 2 (i.e. an undesired change in the environment that prompts people to engage publicly). Sanitation has historically remained somewhat invisible compared with other comparable problems and it has required what may be termed 'shock tactics' on the part of environmental campaigners to bring it to wider attention.

The chapter has explored how, even when environmental issues make it on to political or policy agendas, the question of what sort of action should follow depends very much on whether and how that issue resonates with the priorities of decision-making bodies. In the case of sanitation, this has meant that actors struggle for the issue to be taken seriously in comparison with other issues and – when it is taken seriously – any investment often takes the form of high-profile infrastructural projects in situations where more targeted facilitating of appropriate technology would have generated better outcomes.

You have also been reminded why an interdisciplinary approach to environmental issues is so important. Both in terms of your own analysis and in terms of how the best and most integrated responses are informed, investigating sanitation, health and water pollution requires an understanding of various disciplinary perspectives, including on (a) the *science* of how waterborne diseases such as cholera are spread, (b) *technology*, in particular its appropriateness and effectiveness, and (c) the *social* factors – including income, gender and different framings of risk – that shape everything from what gets chosen as a response to an environmental issue, to its acceptability and practicability (and thus likely long-term success).

# References

Asano, T., and Levine, A. D. (1995) 'Wastewater reuse: a valuable link in water resources management', *Water Quality International*, no. 4, pp. 20–24.

Bahri, A. (2009) 'Managing the other side of the water cycle: making wastewater an asset', TEC Background Paper, no. 13, Global Water Partnership [online], http://www.gwptoolbox.org/images/stories/gwplibrary/background/tec_13_english.pdf (Accessed 15 August 2012).

Centers for Disease Control and Prevention (CDC) (2012) *Latest on Guinea Worm Eradication* [online], http://www.cdc.gov/parasites/guineaworm/ (Accessed 15 August 2012).

Commission of the European Communities (CEC) (2007) *Towards Sustainable Water Management in the European Union*, Commission Staff Working Document, SEC (2007)362.

Curtis, V., Biran, A., Deverell, K., Hughes, C., Bellamy, K. and Drasar, B. (2003) 'Hygiene in the home: relating bugs to behaviour', *Social Science and Medicine*, vol. 57, no. 4, pp. 657–72.

Curtis, V., Schmidt, W., Luby, S., Florez, R., Toure, O. and Biran, A. (2011) 'Hygiene: new hopes, new horizons', *The Lancet Infectious Diseases*, vol. 11, no. 4, pp. 312–21.

Davey Smith, G. (2002) 'Commentary: Behind the Broad Street pump: aetiology, epidemiology and prevention of cholera in mid-19th century Britain', *International Journal of Epidemiology*, vol. 31, pp. 920–32 [online] http://ije.oxfordjournals.org/content/31/5/920.full.pdf (Accessed 15 August 2012).

Environment Agency (2011) *Method Statement for the Classification of Surface Water Bodies v2.0*, July [online], http://publications.environment-agency.gov.uk/PDF/GEHO0911BUEO-E-E.pdf (Accessed 16 August 2012).

Fewtrell, L., Kaufmann, R. B., Kay, D., Enanoria, W., Haller, L. and Colford, J. M. Jr (2005) 'Water, sanitation and hygiene interventions to reduce diarrhoea in less developed countries: a systematic review and meta-analysis', *The Lancet Infectious Diseases*, vol. 5, no. 1, pp. 42–52.

Foundation for Water Research (FWR) (2010) *The Water Framework Directive* [online], http://www.euwfd.com/html/wfd_-_a_summary.html (Accessed 16 August 2012).

Judah, G., Aunger, R., Schmidt, W.P., Michie, S., Granger, S. and Curtis, V. (2009) 'Experimental pretesting of hand-washing interventions in a natural setting', *American Journal of Public Health*, vol. 99, no. S2, pp. S405–11.

Judah, G., Donachie, P., Cobb, E., Schmidt, W. P., Holland, M. and Curtis, V. (2010) 'Dirty hands: bacteria of faecal origin on commuter hands', *Epidemiology and Infection*, vol. 138, no. 3, pp. 409–14.

Konteh, F. H. (2009) 'Urban sanitation and health in the developing world: reminiscing the nineteenth century industrial nations', *Health and Place*, vol. 15, no. 1, pp. 69–78.

Mihelcic, J. R., Zimmerman, J. B. and Ramaswami, A. (2007) 'Integrating developed and developing world knowledge into global discussions and strategies for sustainability. 1 Science and technology', *Environmental Science and Technology*, vol. 41, no. 10, pp. 3415–21.

Stockholm Environment Institute (2007) *Toilets that Make Compost: Low-cost, Sanitary Toilets that Produce Valuable Compost for Crops in an African Context*, Stockholm, Stockholm Environment Institute [online], http://www.ecosanres. org/pdf_files/ToiletsThatMakeCompost.pdf (Accessed 16 August 2012).

UNICEF/WHO (2009) *Diarrhoea: Why Children Are Still Dying and What Can Be Done* [online], http://whqlibdoc.who.int/publications/2009/ 9789241598415_eng.pdf (Accessed 16 August 2012).

UNICEF/WHO (2012) *Progress on Drinking Water and Sanitation: 2012 Update* [online], http://whqlibdoc.who.int/publications/2012/9789280646320_eng.pdf (Accessed 16 August 2012).

WaterAid (2008) *Giving Sanitation the Green Light* [online], http://www.wateraid. org/documents/giving_sanitation_the_green_light.pdf (Accessed 16 August 2012).

Water and Sanitation Program (WSP) and the World Bank (2011) *The Political Economy of Sanitation: How Can We Increase Investment and Improve Service for the Poor? Operational Experiences from Case Studies in Brazil, India, Indonesia, and Senegal* [online], http://www.wsp.org/wsp/sites/wsp.org/files/publications/WSP-Political-Economy-of-Sanitation.pdf (Accessed 15 August 2012).

Water Supply and Sanitation Collaborative Council (WSSCC) (2011) GDP for GDP Brochure: *Don't Waste a Good Investment*, Water Supply and Sanitation Collaborative Council [online], http://www.wsscc.org/resources/resource-advocacy-materials/gdp-gdp-brochure-dont-waste-good-investment? rck=1956c16e5111f6cef1b928efe86238f7 (Accessed 16 August 2012).

WHO and IRC (2003) *Linking Technology Choice with Operation and Maintenance in the Context of Community Water Supply and Sanitation: A Reference Document for Planners and Project Staff*, Geneva, WHO and IRC Water and Sanitation Centre [online], http://whqlibdoc.who.int/publications/2003/9241562153.pdf (Accessed 15 August 2012).

# Chapter 12   Conflict and cooperation

Pam Furniss

# Contents

# 1   Introduction

> Fierce national competition over water resources has prompted
> fears that water issues contain the seeds of violent conflict. … If
> all the world's peoples work together, a secure and sustainable
> water future can be ours.
>
> (Kofi Annan, UN Secretary-General, World Water Day message,
> 22 March 2002)

Water has been a cause of conflict for several thousand years. A
chronological list of all incidents of water-related conflict from history,
prepared by Peter Gleick, is regularly updated with recent events (Gleick
and Heberger, 2012). The first entry dates from 3000 BC. So water
conflict is nothing new, although the nature of the disputes has changed
over the years. Gleick (2012) notes a recent and continuing trend
towards disputes over economic development, water allocation and
water equity. Contrary to Kofi Annan's fears, quoted above, of all the
incidents that could be described as water conflicts, most are within
rather than between countries and have more to do with political
struggles than trans-border disputes. Few are solely about water
resources, where water supplies or access to water are at the root of the
tensions. Some are development disputes where water resources are a
major source of contention in the context of economic and social
development. In many cases, water or water systems are used as military
or political tools by both state and non-state actors as a means to
achieve other goals. Despite the lengthy chronicle of water conflicts,
none of these has, as yet, developed into the sort of violent conflict
between countries over competition for water resources of which Kofi
Annan warned. However, there are opposing views on the likelihood of
future water wars. Some say that water scarcity, increasing demand and
climate change will inexorably lead to growing tension and ultimately to
armed conflict between states. Others argue that there is likely to be
more than one motive for starting a war, and that water is only one
among several issues, including ethnic antagonism, ideology, border
disputes and religion.

In this chapter we consider the systems of rights that underpin
international water relations and the questions of ownership,
management and control where rivers cross national borders. We look

at the river basin or catchment area as the logical unit of water management and at the importance of integrating water with other aspects of natural resource management. The chapter begins by asking whether water should be seen as commons or commodity and develops this by discussing the pricing of water. Throughout this chapter, the block question *Why are environmental issues often controversial?* comes to the fore as we consider questions of ownership, rights and power.

# 2   Commons or commodity?

Many people argue that fresh water should be considered a common resource, one that people enjoy and have the right to use but over which no individual can claim exclusive rights (Chapter 2). In this view, water resources should be managed in the interests of all. An alternative view is that if water has the status of a common resource, some people will treat it as free and use it carelessly and profligately, and that this could lead to a tragedy of the commons, in this case water scarcity. One proposed solution is to make people pay for the water they use. The logic here is that, if water is seen as a commodity that can be bought and sold, rather than a common, then people will value it more and therefore use less. The higher the price that people pay for the good the more incentive they have to conserve it.

---

## Activity 12.1   Public and private goods

The commons or commodity question echoes the idea of public and private goods introduced in Chapter 7. Can you recall how private goods are defined?

## Comment

In economic terms, the tests to be applied to decide if a good is private are whether it is rival and excludable. If water is supplied by pipe into a home then it is excludable because the homeowner can control access to it. Does it also meet the rivalry test? Taking the UK as an example, the people who have water piped to their homes are not limited in the amount they use by what other people use – but this only applies up to a point. The system would not be able to keep supplying water if everyone left all the taps on all the time – at which point water would become rival. From this it can be concluded that piped water has the characteristics of a private good.

---

However, the water systems in the Western world which effectively turn water into a private good are only one way that water is managed. The alternative idea that water is a public good also needs to be examined. Economist Alex Robson explains that a public good is not just 'good for the public' (Robson, 2007). If this were the definition then water (and a whole range of other environment-related elements) would fit the brief very well. A public good needs to fulfil the non-rival and non-excludable requirements. Thinking of water in the same way as food helps to answer these points. Food is necessary for human existence but is clearly a private good; what I consume you cannot. The same can be applied to water. If I drink a litre there is one litre less available for everyone else. This confirms the view that, if neoclassical economic rules are followed, water is a private good. Robson (2007, p. 40) states this categorically when he writes: 'water is a perfectly rivalrous, perfectly excludable, pure private good and is about as far from the definition of "public good" as we can get.'

Despite the economists' arguments, many people consider that water, far from being a private good, is a basic human right. This view was endorsed by the United Nations in July 2010 when the organisation formally recognised 'the right to safe and clean drinking water and sanitation as a human right that is essential for the full enjoyment of life and all human rights' (United Nations, 2010). But if all humans are entitled to water as a right, how does this square with the idea of water as a commodity to be bought and sold? There appear to be two directly opposing views: one that water is a commodity that can and should be bought and sold; the other that water is a human right that should be freely available to all. Robson (2007, p. 40) dismisses the 'ridiculous' human rights arguments, 'because supplying [water] to one person means that someone else has missed out on consuming that water. In turn, this means that if I have a 'human right' to consume water, someone else must have an obligation to supply it to me – at their own expense of course'. Other writers support the use of water markets, in which water is traded as an economic good between buyers and sellers, as a means to allocate water resources and alleviate problems of water scarcity. Anderson et al. (2012, p. 6) describe water markets as a 'too-little used tool'. They say that 'without markets and prices to provide incentives for both demanders and suppliers, water crises will persist'. Adler (2008) promotes water markets as a response to climate change because, he argues, they can create the flexibility needed to respond and adapt to the future uncertainties of climate change.

Supporters of the human rights position argue that the commodification of water promotes the interests of corporations and individuals rather than the equitable provision of water services and that it is in direct conflict with the traditions and practices of many peoples throughout the world. International water rights campaigner Maude Barlow outlines the two positions:

There are two competing narratives about the Earth's freshwater resources being played out in the 21st century. On one side is a powerful clique of decision-makers, heads of some powerful states, international trade and financial institutions and transnational corporations who do not view water as part of the global Commons or a public trust, but as a commodity, to be bought and sold on the open market. On the other is a global grassroots movement of local communities, the poor, the slum dwellers, women, indigenous peoples, peasants and small farmers working with environmentalists, human rights activists, progressive water managers and experts in both the global North and global South who see water as a Commons and seek to provide water for all of nature and all humans.

(Barlow, 2009, p. 1)

The renowned environmental activist Vandana Shiva (Figure 12.1) has described this as 'a clash between two cultures: a culture that sees water as sacred and treats its provision as a duty for the preservation of life and another that sees water as a commodity, and its ownership and trade as fundamental corporate rights. The culture of commodification is at war with diverse cultures of sharing, of receiving and giving water as a free gift' (Shiva, 2002, p. x).

Figure 12.1 The Indian environmental activist and author Vandana Shiva campaigns for local communities to have access to local resources, such as water, forests and farmland

In a discussion of these complex and controversial issues, Bakker (2007) explains that a human right to water does not imply that water should be accessed free. She says 'many citizens of capitalist democracies accept that commodities are not inconsistent with human rights ... but that some sort of public, collective "safety net" must exist if these rights are to be met for *all* citizens' (Bakker, 2007, p. 439). In other words, commodification of water can be consistent with human rights if it is coupled with constraints, such as laws prohibiting disconnections of residential consumers, and a strong regulatory framework for price controls and quality standards.

This raises the question of the price of water and how, in a regulated market, it should be set. Accurate pricing of water is considered to be a key mechanism for reducing consumption and achieving sustainable use of water across all sectors (EEA, 2009). The argument that if people pay for water they will value it more and therefore use it less can be supported with evidence. For example, in England and Wales, the Environment Agency reports that people in households that pay by meter, on average, use 13 per cent less water than those who pay a fixed charge regardless of the volume they use (EA, 2008). From this it can be concluded that price signals are necessary to encourage consumers to conserve water (Bakker, 2005). Note that the price, the amount consumers pay, is distinct from cost and value, as described in Table 12.1.

Table 12.1   Three important concepts from water economics

| | |
|---|---|
| Cost | Operation and maintenance (O&M) costs, capital costs, opportunity costs, costs of economic and environmental externalities |
| Value | Benefits to users, benefits of returned flows, indirect benefits and intrinsic values |
| Price | Amount set by the political and social system to ensure cost recovery, equity and sustainability. The price may or may not include subsidies |

Source: Rogers et al., 2002, p. 3, Table 2

A principle from economics is that the price of a service should be at least as high as the cost of providing it, otherwise there would be no profit from selling the service and hence no incentive to supply it (Rogers et al., 2002). So, if cost recovery is the aim, what costs should be included? The full costs of water provision include not only the capital costs and maintenance of the supply system (treatment,

pipework, etc.) but also the opportunity costs and externalities.
Figure 12.2 summarises how these different elements make up the full
supply cost, full economic cost and full cost of water.

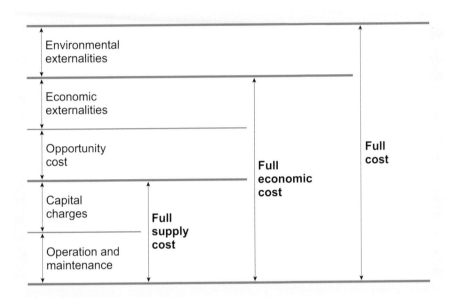

Figure 12.2  General principles of full cost of water (Source: based on
Agarwal et al., 2000, p. 20, Figure 2b)

Proponents of full cost pricing argue that it should lead to both water
conservation and environmentally sustainable solutions (Bakker, 2005).
However, putting the concept into practice raises many difficulties and
opportunities for controversy. Karen Bakker, in a discussion of the
issues in England and Wales (2005, p. 556), summarises the problems
thus:

- Costing of externalities is difficult to measure and the methodologies
  used are disputed.

- Water supply infrastructure has high capital costs which creates a
  'lumpy' profile to water resource investment, implying sudden and
  large increases in water bills during periods of capital investment if
  the full costs are passed on to consumers.

- Costs of supply vary over time (due to peaks at certain times of day
  or year), and over space (due to distance from the source and the
  topography of the landscape).

Under a full cost recovery system, this last point would mean that each
consumer would have to pay a price related to the costs they imposed

on the system, leading to variable prices in different locations and at different times. For example, to meet the additional costs of extended water pipes, consumers in remote rural locations would have to pay more than people living in urban areas with a compact distribution network. In practice, therefore, water pricing is usually based on modified systems; for example, setting prices according to costs that have been averaged for a particular location or time period. This requires some sort of price regulation system to smooth out the variations and maintain prices at affordable levels without discriminating against particular locations or types of consumer.

However, this system assumes that everyone is able to pay for the water they use. For some people, even the lowest of prices can be too much. Is it fair that all users should pay the same price, regardless of their ability to pay? Water is essential for life and has no substitute, therefore should people living in poverty be expected to pay the same price as the better off? The supporters of full cost pricing argue that it is misleading to say that higher prices will limit access to water. They say that higher prices will increase revenue to water providers, thereby enabling them to invest in improving supplies, and the poor, therefore, will benefit from the higher prices (Morriss, 2006; Rogers et al., 2002). The opposing view is that full cost recovery risks pricing the poor out of the market, 'seriously aggravating water deprivation and poverty' (Mollinga et al., 2007, p. 703) (Figure 12.3). This could result, they say, in farmers being forced out of farming if they have to pay high prices for irrigation water, and poor households being cut off from domestic supplies.

The case of Cochabamba in Bolivia provides an example of the injustice and conflict that can arise from the lack of an appropriate price regulation system (Box 12.1). Davis (2007, p. 436) recognises both positions and points out that water is 'simultaneously an input to economic activities and a nonmarket good'. But other authors remain convinced that the economic arguments can never overcome the fundamental problems. To repeat the quotation used in Chapter 9, Dellapenna returns to the connectivity of the water cycle as the essential issue: 'The basic reason that markets do not work comes back to the most basic aspect of water as a resource – it moves' (Dellapenna, 2007, p. 401).

Figure 12.3   A girl collecting water near Mwamanongu village in Tanzania. People who do not have access to safe water or cannot afford to pay may be forced to use free, but unsafe, sources

---

## Box 12.1   The case of Cochabamba, Bolivia

In the middle of the 1990s, the World Bank offered Bolivia a loan of $14 million to expand its water services. It was much-needed money in one of the poorest countries in Latin America. However, as a condition of this loan, the World Bank demanded that the publicly owned water system of Cochabamba, Bolivia's third largest city, be privatised. The Bolivian government complied and a company largely owned by Bechtel, a major US corporation, took over not only the urban water system but also the surrounding rural irrigation system and local wells. Bills for water were raised, other charges instituted and a local resistance took form. The resistance group was called La Coordinadora, and for months it organised protests, blockades, strikes and refusals to pay bills. Negotiations were instituted and reneged on. There was violence and serious confrontation with heavily armed police forces (Figure 12.4). A state of emergency was declared. Through email despatches, news went round the world, and some sympathetic actions were initiated. Eventually, the water system contract was cancelled. One of the leaders of the protests, Evo Morales, was later elected president of Bolivia in 2005.

Figure 12.4    Stand-off during the water wars, Cochabamba, Bolivia

# 3 Whose water is it anyway?

In economic terms, water may be seen as a commodity that can be bought and sold. But how then should ownership of water be allocated? Disputes over rights to water resources have long been a cause of conflict. In English, the word 'rival' comes from the Latin *rivalis* meaning a person using the same stream as another; the word 'river' is derived from the same source. Different systems of water rights have developed that attempt to reduce the likelihood of conflict and impose some regulation on water allocation (Box 12.2). Note that having water rights means a legal right to abstract and use a quantity of water from a natural source such as a river, stream or aquifer (Hodgson, 2006). This is very different from the human right to water that was declared by the United Nations in 2010.

## Box 12.2  Traditional approaches to water rights

Historically, the development of water rights was strongly influenced by two main European legal traditions: common law and civil law. Common law is developed from precedents made by judgements and decisions in the courtroom whereas civil law is based on statutes. Common law originated in England and, as a consequence, this approach is found in the UK and in many former British colonial countries. The civil law tradition, derived in part from Roman law, is found in most of Europe, Latin America, large parts of Africa, Indonesia and Japan and the former Soviet Union. These two traditions have led to three main systems of water rights:

- *Riparian rights* (Latin: *riparius* = bank). Riparian owners own the river banks (i.e. the land through which a river flows). Part of the common law tradition, riparian rights denote that ownership of river water is linked to ownership of the adjacent lands, or overlying lands in the case of an aquifer. In essence, the riparian owner has the right to use the water in a river flowing through their land, although this is frequently limited by regulation or licence.

- *Public allocation*. Found in civil law countries, this system also confers a privileged position on landowners but is more codified than riparian rights, with allocation of water rights administered by legal process.

- *Prior appropriation rights*. This system, developed from riparian rights, originated in the nineteenth century in the arid western part of the USA. It separates water rights from land ownership. Prior appropriation rights are based on the doctrine that the right to water is acquired by actual use over time. In other words, if you have made use of the water supply in the past, then that gives you the right to continue to use it. The separation between land ownership and water rights means that the water rights could be transferred and, therefore, traded.

Source: based on Hodgson, 2006, and Savenije and van der Zaag, 2000

These traditional approaches to rights are gradually being replaced by what Hodgson (2006) calls 'modern water rights'. These are described as 'formal and explicit water rights that specify the volume of water subject to each right together with the associated institutional arrangements for their allocation, registration, monitoring and enforcement' (Hodgson, 2006, p. 1). The drivers for this change to modernise and increase the levels of control are principally the pressures on water resources from a growing population, increasing levels of consumption, and climate change. The notion of modern water rights may be seen as an attempt to avoid controversy. It recognises that if conflict is to be avoided and cooperation encouraged, then more realistic and fairer systems of water allocation are needed. Several major international summits and meetings have contributed to this change in attitude.

The International Conference on Water and the Environment, held in Dublin, Ireland in 1992, attempted to address a complex set of problems including 'alleviation of poverty and disease, protection against natural disasters, water conservation and reuse, sustainable urban development, agricultural production and rural water supply, protecting aquatic ecosystems, and resolving water conflicts' (Conca, 2006, p. 141). The outcomes from the conference included the four 'Dublin Principles' which underpin current international water governance. The original Dublin Principles were:

1   Fresh water is a finite and vulnerable resource, essential to sustaining life, development and the environment.

2   Water development and management should be based on a participatory approach, involving users, planners and policy makers at all levels.

3   Women play a central part in the provision, management and safeguarding of water.

4   Water has an economic value in all its competing uses and should be recognised as an economic good.

---

## Activity 12.2   The Dublin principles

Think about these four principles and consider whether they are internally consistent.

This is a subjective question so your response will probably differ from mine; there is no right or wrong answer.

### Comment

These appear to be sound and admirable principles but there are potential inconsistencies, and much depends on how they might be interpreted and applied. For example, a participatory approach (in 2) is desirable but I wonder how many of the 'planners and policy makers' are likely to be women, so is women's 'central part' (in 3) always likely to be taken into account? Do women and other users have an equal say in development and management with planners and policy makers? Or would their relative power positions come into play?

The emphasis on economic value and water as an economic good (in 4) raises the question of ownership, but this is not mentioned explicitly. This leads me to wonder if the users of the water (in 2) are assumed to be the owners, in which case, what is the status of the many users who are not owners? The competition between uses is recognised (in 4), as is the fact that water is a finite resource (in 1), but attributing economic value to water (in 4) does not appear to provide a means to resolve the potential conflict between competing users. Nothing is said on how possible conflicts could be resolved.

---

The Dublin agreement laid down some important principles for water management, but they remain controversial and have been criticised for a number of reasons. Some authors have argued that attempting a set of global principles, applicable to all countries, is a questionable approach. Each country faces its own water issues depending on water resource supply and uses. Hodgson (2006, p. 4) comments that 'what is normal and reasonable in one country as regards both the use and regulation of water may appear quite strange or even irrational elsewhere'. However, the main controversy arising from the Dublin principles is the decisive statement that water is an economic good. Although this is widely recognised as a necessity if water is to be efficiently managed (e.g. Bakker, 2005; Meinzen-Dick and Rosegrant, 1997; Perry et al., 1997), it is strongly opposed by those who, like Vandana Shiva, see water as a social and a cultural, rather than an economic, good.

# 4 International rivers

Issues of water ownership and governance become all the more controversial when the catchment area crosses international borders. More than 260 rivers flow through more than one country, with over 50 shared by more than three nations (Draper, 2007). The Danube, Congo, Niger, Nile, Rhine and Zambezi are all shared by more than eight countries (Table 12.2). Aquifers present an added difficulty because the geographical extent of the underground reservoir may be uncertain.

Table 12.2   International river basins shared by nine or more countries

| River basin | No. of states | States sharing the basin |
| --- | --- | --- |
| Danube | 19 | Romania, Hungary, Serbia, Austria, Germany, Bulgaria, Slovakia, Bosnia-Herzegovina, Croatia, Ukraine, Czech Republic, Slovenia, Moldova, Switzerland, Italy, Poland, Albania, Montenegro, Macedonia |
| Congo | 11 | Democratic Republic of Congo, Central African Republic, Angola, Republic of the Congo, Zambia, Tanzania, Cameroon, Burundi, Rwanda, Gabon, Malawi |
| Niger | 11 | Nigeria, Mali, Niger, Algeria, Guinea, Cameroon, Burkina Faso, Benin, Côte d'Ivoire, Chad, Sierra Leone |
| Nile | 11 | Egypt, Sudan, South Sudan, Ethiopia, Eritrea, Uganda, Tanzania, Kenya, Burundi, Rwanda, Democratic Republic of Congo |
| Rhine | 9 | Germany, Switzerland, France, Netherlands, Belgium, Luxembourg, Austria, Liechtenstein, Italy |
| Zambezi | 9 | Zambia, Angola, Zimbabwe, Mozambique, Malawi, Tanzania, Botswana, Namibia, Democratic Republic of Congo |

Source: adapted from Gleick, 2000, p. 34, Table 2.6

The likelihood of controversy and conflict over water between nations sharing a river basin depends on a range of geographical and geopolitical circumstances. The degree of water scarcity that already exists in the region and the availability of alternative sources are bound to be central to the issue; disputes are unlikely where water is plentiful. However, drought is not a sufficient condition for conflict. The risks of conflict are increased when there is lack of equitable sharing between countries and user groups. Water quality, as well as quantity, may be the source of disagreement, so the degree of water pollution in a shared river is also relevant. In theory, the upstream riparians have the advantage over the downstream countries in that they get the water first. In practice, the power relationships and the cultural, political and economic links between water-sharing states are critical. In Gleick's water conflict chronology, referred to at the start of this chapter, the significance of these other factors is apparent. Nearly all of the recent entries that involve more than one country are examples of neighbouring states that already have an uneasy relationship, such as China and India, North and South Korea, and Israel and Palestine (Gleick and Heberger, 2012).

If conflict is to be avoided in situations where water, or any other resource, is shared, the countries concerned must reach agreement on the principles by which they will share. In the historical context of water use, two extremes have emerged. The first, which actually involves no sharing at all, is the principle of *total sovereignty*. This assumes that each state has complete sovereignty over the drainage basin, or part of the basin, located within its territory and does not allow any other claims on the resource. This is also known as the Harmon Doctrine, after Judson Harmon, the US Attorney General in 1895, who said, in a dispute with Mexico over water rights on the Rio Grande, that there was no reason why the USA should take Mexico's needs into consideration (Figure 12.5). Harmon argued that a state could use the water in its territory without concern for the impact this might have on other riparian states (Cooley et al., 2012). This argument has tended to be favoured by upstream countries because they can make whatever use of the water they choose without consideration of downstream users. In the USA–Mexico example, it also reflects the relative power positions of the two countries. At the opposite end of the spectrum to the Harmon Doctrine is the concept of *community of interest*. This principle holds that within a shared river basin, no single riparian can block the action of any other; in other words, any use of the water resource must be agreed by all other riparian states.

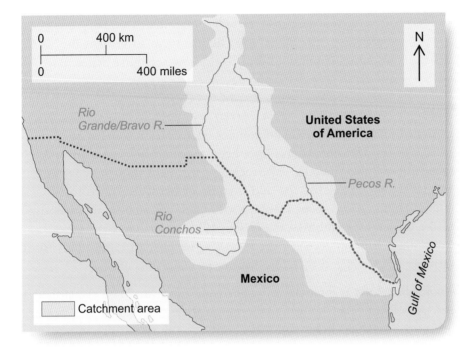

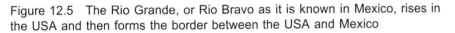

Figure 12.5  The Rio Grande, or Rio Bravo as it is known in Mexico, rises in the USA and then forms the border between the USA and Mexico

The injustice of one extreme and the impracticality of the other led to a middle ground between the two, which is the principle of *limited sovereignty*. This can be summarised as 'use what is yours so as not to cause harm to another' (Waterbury, 1993, p. 47). This is also known as equitable utilisation theory because it requires that international rivers should be used by different states on an equitable basis (Shiva, 2002).

Several attempts have been made to codify these principles in international agreements. The Helsinki Rules on the Uses of the Waters of International Rivers, drawn up in 1966, specified 11 principles to guide water use between two or more countries. Principles based on the Helsinki Rules have since been developed further and were adopted by the United Nations in 1997 in the Convention on the Law of the Non-Navigational Uses of International Watercourses. The two central principles of the convention are:

- Watercourse states shall utilise an international watercourse in an equitable and reasonable manner. Watercourse states have both the right to utilise the watercourse and the duty to cooperate in the protection and development thereof.

- Watercourse states shall, in utilising an international watercourse, take all appropriate measures to prevent the causing of significant harm to other watercourse states.

(Adapted from United Nations, 2000)

Designed to reduce the risks of conflict over water resources, the articles of the UN convention have been criticised because of their imprecise wording. Judging and reaching agreement on what constitutes 'equitable and reasonable' use and 'significant harm' are open to interpretation by the states involved. Although adopted by the majority of the General Assembly of the UN in 1997, as of July 2012 the Convention had not received the necessary number of ratifications from member countries and therefore has yet to enter into effect.

Another attempt at international agreement, made in 2004, established a new set of principles known as the Berlin Rules. These follow a similar line to the Helsinki Rules and UN Convention but they also incorporate more recent issues such as 'ecological integrity, sustainability, public participation, and minimization of environmental harm' (Cooley et al., 2012, p. 5). Whether the inclusion of these environmental and social issues will encourage greater acceptance of the Berlin Rules as opposed to the UN convention is as yet unknown.

As in any other conflict situation, solutions lie in negotiation, cooperation and mutual consideration of the needs of others. In the field of transboundary river catchments, this requires international treaties and agreements. Despite the lack of internationally endorsed guidelines, many such treaties exist and have operated with varying degrees of success for many years. The first transboundary water agreements date from the nineteenth century in Europe, and include agreement between the countries that share the Rhine. Other examples of the approximately 300 agreements on record are the Nile Basin Treaty, the Indus River Treaty and the Mekong River Commission. Some treaties also set up associated shared institutions with responsibility for scientific services for monitoring water quantity and quality. International river basin organisations should have a moderating effect that enables differences between riparian countries to be reconciled (Tir and Stinnett, 2012). By monitoring water quantity and quality, developing action programmes, exchanging information and identifying mutually acceptable agreements for sharing, these organisations should mitigate the risks of conflict between basin partners (Conca, 2006). There are, however, inherent difficulties in managing internationally shared rivers in a cooperative manner. The relative power positions of riparian states are likely to be unequal in terms of, for example, economic strength, military capability or geographical size (Jägerskog and Phillips, 2006). These power inequalities frequently determine the outcome in water management disputes. The success of possible solutions will always depend on there being sufficient political will in the countries involved in the negotiations and agreements.

# 5   Catchment management

International river basin organisations are necessary because so many rivers cross national borders. Indeed, many borders are defined by the path taken by a watercourse, raising inevitable sharing issues. Transboundary treaties recognise that the catchment area or river basin is a more natural geographical and hydrological unit for water management than one defined by national borders. The streams and rivers within a catchment are part of one connected system, and any upstream activities such as abstraction or pollution will affect the downstream stretches of the river. Equally, the land use within the catchment area will affect the surface water and groundwater. These interconnections make the river basin the logical unit to use for water management organisation and resolution of any controversies that arise over management.

The principle of the catchment and its watershed as the boundary for water management and governance lies at the centre of the European Union's Water Framework Directive (WFD) (Chapter 11, Section 4, Box 11.1). Adopted in 2000, the WFD brought several policy areas together into one piece of legislation covering three areas: ecology, economy and governance (Gleick, 2012). The ecological requirement is for all water bodies to achieve 'good' ecological status. On economy, the WFD specifies that water pricing policies of member states should aim for full cost recovery as an incentive for sustainable water use and thus to achieve the environmental objectives in the Directive. However, in practice this requirement has been weakened and member states are now only required to ensure that prices charged to consumers 'take into account' the full environmental costs (Klawitter, 2009, quoted in Brooks et al., 2009). Governance, under the terms of the WFD, is structured, with River Basin Districts (RBDs) as its organisational unit. Figure 12.6 shows a map of Europe and the RBDs within European states.

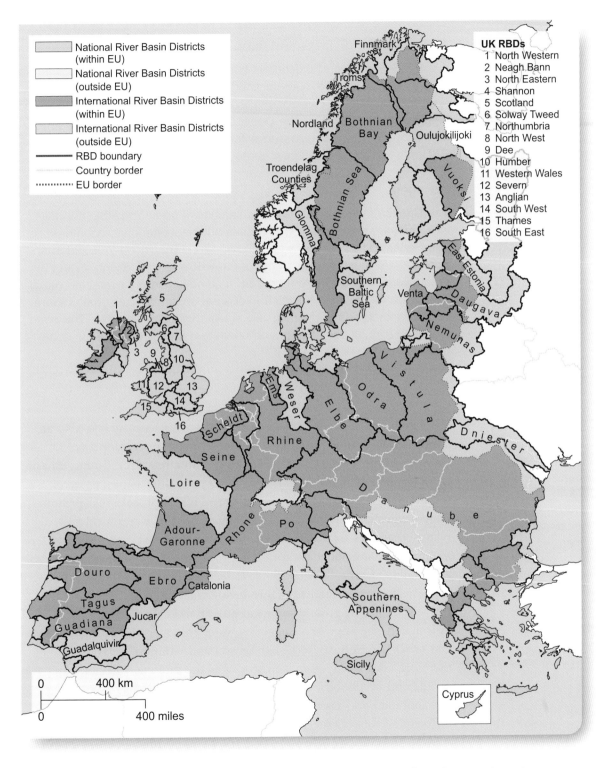

Figure 12.6 Map of European River Basin Districts (note that only selected names have been included)

## Activity 12.3   European Union River Basin Districts

Putting the principle of catchment-based management into practice in the EU has required some different approaches to defining RBD boundaries to accommodate the variations in size of river catchment areas. Look at Figure 12.6 and compare the Danube RBD with the RBDs in England and Scotland. They are classed differently as international and national RBDs, but what other differences do you notice?

### Comment

The Danube river has a very large catchment area. The RBD not only includes parts of several EU countries but also extends to countries outside the EU as well (see also Table 12.2). The RBDs in England and Scotland are much smaller. Most of the RBDs (e.g. Scotland, South West, Northumbria) are formed from a combination of several individual river catchments. If each British river were separately designated there would be hundreds of impractically small administrative units. The need to combine small catchments into one larger unit also applies in some other EU countries (e.g. Italy).

**Integrated water resource management (IWRM)**
A process that promotes the coordinated development and management of water, land and related resources.

Understanding the natural boundary of the river basin unit is also an important element of an approach that is increasingly adopted throughout the world called **integrated water resource management** (IWRM). IWRM is an approach to developing and managing water resources that 'integrates' in several ways. It is a process that promotes the coordinated development and management of water, land and related resources to maximise the resultant economic and social welfare in an equitable manner without compromising the sustainability of vital ecosystems (Agarwal et al., 2000). It recognises the connections inherent in the water system and therefore includes all water resources (i.e. surface water, groundwater, oceans). Rather than considering water in isolation, the approach integrates water management with land use and other natural resources such as soil and natural vegetation. It therefore acknowledges and incorporates the multiple roles of water for people and livelihoods, for agriculture and for healthy ecosystems. Collaboration and coordination between agencies responsible for these different sectors is crucial. Historically, it has been more usual for separate agencies to be responsible for different functions; for example, drinking water managed by one agency, agricultural use by another and environmental protection by a third (Cap-Net, n.d.). IWRM principles also include a commitment to participation by all user groups and brings in the full range of stakeholders from decision makers to users. A case study from Japan of a lake catchment where IWRM principles have been applied is described in Box 12.3. The changes made at Lake Biwa started before the concept of IWRM was coherently formulated, but they illustrate some of the important elements of an IWRM approach.

## Box 12.3   Lake Biwa, Japan

Lake Biwa is the largest lake in Japan with an area of 670 square kilometres (Figure 12.7). It lies in one of the most industrialised and urbanised regions of the world and provides the water supply for the cities of Osaka and Kobe. The lake had a history of flooding and, in dry seasons, the supply was unreliable. During the 1960s, rapidly increasing population and industrial development led to wide-scale pollution and the destruction of lakeside habitats. By the 1970s, the pollution from untreated sewage and industrial effluents including heavy metals and other chemicals had become a threat to human and ecosystem health. In addition, eutrophication from fertiliser run-off and other wastes caused massive algal blooms.

Figure 12.7   Lake Biwa, Japan

Since the 1970s, a series of interventions and processes with IWRM characteristics have transformed the lake. Mostly initiated by the Lake Biwa Comprehensive Development Project (LBCDP), these processes included:

- Flood protection works and infrastructure development to improve water supply in times of drought.

- Citizens' action groups, led by a local women's group, who campaigned against pollution caused by domestic detergents.

- Improved knowledge base through research and collection of physical, environmental and social data. The Lake Biwa Environmental Research Institute was established in 1993.

- Involvement of the private sector. An association of 400 local companies adopted codes of practice to reduce pollution and improve water quality.

- New sewerage and sewage treatment systems.

- Development of financial mechanisms that mobilised contributions from national government.

- Changing structures in local government from a narrow focus on anti-pollution measures in 1970 to a broader, integrated environment department with responsibility for water policy, environment policy, waste management, nature conservation, forest conservation and ecological lifestyle.

Source: adapted from Lenton and Muller, 2009

Using the natural watershed boundaries of a catchment may make sense from a hydrological and ecological point of view, but what other boundaries are relevant? First, some water issues extend beyond the catchment boundary. For example, conservation policies to protect the habitat of migratory birds or finding markets for new, drought-resistant crops would both require liaison with agencies outside the river basin. Second, and of wider significance, there are boundaries that the catchment management approach places around the issue which confine it to being an issue that is only about water. In practice, this is highly unlikely because many other factors come into play. In the context of conflict and cooperation in transboundary catchments, the effectiveness of water management depends on the history, relationships and behaviours of the constituent members. Any underlying political differences, for whatever reason, are likely to remain in evidence. So although river basins are seen as the natural and holistic basis for water management, in practice the benefits this approach ought to bring are not necessarily realised. For example, Vogel (2012) studied the management of the Columbia River in North America, which is shared by seven US states and one Canadian province. She found that the fragmentation and conflicts of conventional government and politics still persisted, even after 75 years of collaborative basin-based management.

# 6   Summary

This chapter's discussion on conflict and cooperation concerning water has highlighted a number of key senses in which environmental issues may be controversial. One important consideration is the ownership of the resource. Water may be defined as a common resource, but it is also a commodity that can be privately owned, and thus traded. Who owns a resource – whether it is a community, the state or a business corporation – will help to determine who has rights of access to the resource and how much, if anything, they should pay. The question of rights is an important one in determining access, although the idea of rights can itself be controversial. As you have seen, a legal right is very different from a human right.

Environmental issues may also be controversial when a resource is shared by different countries. Conflicts may be resolved in different ways. In the case of transboundary water conflicts, for example, where a river spans two or more countries, conflict may be resolved through the exercise of power. In theory, upstream users have more power than downstream users. The upstream user can make decisions on resource use that impact on the downstream user, such as volume of water to be abstracted, dam construction and pollution. But similar decisions by the downstream user do not affect those upstream. However, this does not mean that the upstream user can always do what they want. The downstream user may have other sources of power – such as economic strength, military capability or geographical size – that they can bring to bear on a resource conflict. Either way, reducing conflict-solving to a matter of power is far from desirable.

A fairer way of determining how resources should be shared internationally is negotiation and the agreement of principles that reflect the interests of all countries. However, principles may conceal political divisions and fail to resolve the underlying conflicts of interest. So, for example, while governments have agreed the Convention on the Law of the Non-Navigational Uses of International Watercourses, the wording of the convention (for example, on 'equitable and reasonable' use) is often ambiguous and open to competing interpretations. Such ambiguity in international negotiations usually indicates the absence of a hard political agreement, which helps explain why this instrument has yet to enter into legal effect. Similarly, the Dublin Principles, it can be argued, contain some internal inconsistencies which make their practical application difficult. So, while attempting to resolve controversies through international dialogue is more desirable than the exercise of power, attempts to do so may lead to further controversies.

# References

Adler, J. H. (2008) 'Warming up to water markets', *Regulation*, vol. 31, no. 4, Property and Environment Research Center [online], http://www.perc.org/files/water_markts_jadler.pdf (Accessed 17 August 2012).

Agarwal, A., delos Angeles, M. S., Bhatia, R., Chéret, I., Davila-Poblete, S., Falkenmark, M., Gonzalez-Villarreal, F., Jønch-Clausen, T., Aït Kadi, M., Kindler, J., Rees, J., Roberts, P., Rogers, P., Solanes, M. and Wright, A. (2000) *Integrated Water Resources Management*, Global Water Partnership Technical Advisory Committee, Background Papers, no. 4. Global Water Partnership, Stockholm [online], http://waterwiki.net/images/a/a5/GWPIWRM.pdf (Accessed 17 August 2012).

Anderson, T. L., Scarborough, B. and Watson, L. R. (2012) *Tapping Water Markets*, New York, Routledge.

Bakker, K. (2005) 'Neoliberalizing Nature? Market environmentalism in water supply in England and Wales', *Annals of the Association of American Geographers*, vol. 95, no. 3, pp. 542–65 [online], DOI: 10.1111/j.1467-8306.2005.00474.x (Accessed 16 August 2012).

Bakker, K. (2007) 'The "Commons" versus the "Commodity": alter-globalization, anti-privatisation and the human right to water in the global south', *Antipode* [online], http://aguabolivia.org/wp-content/uploads/2010/07/1er_04_documento_-Bakker2007.pdf (Accessed 17 August 2012).

Barlow, M. (2009) *Our Water Commons: Towards a New Freshwater Narrative*, The Council of Canadians [online], http://www.canadians.org/water/publications/water%20commons/index.html (Accessed 17 August 2012).

Brooks, D. B., Brandes, O. M. and Gurman, S. (eds) (2009) *Making the Most of the Water We Have: The Soft Path Approach to Water Management*, London/Washington, DC, Earthscan.

Cap-Net (n.d.) *Integrated Water Resources Management* [online], http://www.archive.cap-net.org/iwrm_tutorial/mainmenu.htm (Accessed 17 August 2012).

Conca, K. (2006) *Governing Water: Contentious Transnational Politics and Global InstitutionBuilding*, Cambridge, MA, MIT Press.

Cooley, H., Christian-Smith, J., Gleick, P. H., Allen, L. and Cohen, M. J. (2012) 'Climate change and transboundary waters', in Gleick (2012).

Davis, M. D. (2007) 'Integrated water resource management and water sharing', *Journal of Water Resources Planning and Management*, vol. 133, no. 5, Sep/Oct, pp. 427–45.

Dellapenna, J. W. (2007) 'Transboundary water sharing and the need for public management', *Journal of Water Resources Planning and Management*, vol. 133, no. 5, Sep/Oct, pp. 397–404.

Draper, S. E. (2007) 'Introduction to transboundary water sharing', *Journal of Water Resources Planning and Management*, vol. 133, no. 5, Sep/Oct, pp. 377–81.

Environment Agency (EA) (2008) *Water Resources in England and Wales – Current State and Future Pressures*, Bristol, Environment Agency [online], http://publications.environment-agency.gov.uk/PDF/GEHO1208BPAS-E-E.pdf (Accessed 17 August 2012).

European Environment Agency (EEA) (2009) *Water Resources Across Europe – Confronting Water Scarcity and Drought*, Copenhagen, EEA [online], http://www.eea.europa.eu/publications/water-resources-across-europe (Accessed 17 August 2012).

Gleick, P. H. (2000) *The World's Water 2000–2001*, Washington, DC, Island Press.

Gleick, P. H. (2012) *The World's Water: Volume 7: The Biennial Report on Freshwater Resources*, Washington, DC, Island Press.

Gleick, P. H. and Heberger, M. (2012) 'Water conflict chronology', in Gleick (2012).

Hodgson, S. (2006) *Modern Water Rights: Theory and Practice*, FAO Legislative Study 92, Rome, FAO [online], ftp://ftp.fao.org/docrep/fao/010/a0864e/a0864e00.pdf (Accessed 17 August 2012).

Jägerskog, A. and Phillips, D. (2006) *Managing Trans-Boundary Waters for Human Development*, Human Development Report Office [online], http://78.136.31.142/en/reports/global/hdr2006/papers/jagerskog%20anders.pdf (Accessed 17 August 2012).

Kay, M., Franks, T. and Smith, L. (eds) (1997) *Water: Economics, Management and Demand*, London, E & FN Spon.

Klawitter, S. (2009) 'Water soft path thinking in other developed economies: B The European Union: economic elements of the European Water Framework Directive: soft path instruments to enhance sustainable water use?', in Brooks et al. (2009).

Lenton, R. and Muller, M. (2009) *Integrated Water Resources Management in Practice: Better Water Management for Development*, London/Washington, DC, Earthscan.

Meinzen-Dick, R. and Rosegrant, M. W. (1997) 'Water as an economic good: incentives, institutions and infrastructure', in Kay et al. (1997).

Mollinga, P. P., Meinzen-Dick, R. S. and Merry, D. J. (2007) 'Politics, plurality and problemsheds: a strategic approach for reform of agricultural water resources management', *Development Policy Review*, vol. 25, no. 6, pp. 699–719.

Morriss, A. P. (2006) 'Real people, real resources, and real choices: the case for market valuation of water', *Texas Tech Law Review*, vol. 38, pp. 973–1010.

Perry, C. J., Rock, M. and Seckler, D. (1997) 'Water as an economic good: a solution, or a problem?', in Kay et al. (1997).

Robson, A. (2007) 'A "public good" is not just something which is "good for the public"', *Institute of Public Affairs Review*, July [online], http://ipa.org.au/library/59_2_ROBSON.pdf (Accessed 16 August 2012).

Rogers, P., de Silva, R. and Bhatia, R. (2002) 'Water is an economic good: how to use prices to promote equity, efficiency and sustainability', *Water Policy*, vol. 4, no. 1, pp. 1–17.

Savenije, H. and van der Zaag, P. (2000) 'Conceptual framework for the management of shared river basins; with special reference to SADC and EU', *Water Policy*, vol. 2, nos 1–2, pp. 9–45.

Shiva, V. (2002) *Water Wars: Privatisation, Pollution and Profit*, London, Pluto Press.

Tir, J. and Stinnett, D. M. (2012) 'Weathering climate change: can institutions mitigate international water conflict?', *Journal of Peace Research*, vol. 49, no. 1, pp. 211–25.

United Nations (2000) *A/RES/51/229: Convention on the Law of the Non-navigational Uses of International Watercourses* [online], http://www.un.org/documents/ga/res/51/ares51-229.htm (Accessed 17 August 2012).

United Nations (2010) *A/RES/64/292: The Human Right to Water and Sanitation* [online], http://www.un.org/ga/search/view_doc.asp?symbol=A/RES/64/292 (Accessed 17 August 2012).

Vogel, E. (2012) 'Parcelling out the watershed: the recurring consequences of organising Columbia River management within a basin-based territory', *Water Alternatives*, vol. 5, no. 1, pp. 161–90 [online], http://www.water-alternatives.org/index.php?option=com_content&task=view&id=188&Itemid=1 (Accessed 17 August 2012).

Waterbury, J. (1993) 'Transboundary water and the challenge of international cooperation in the Middle East', in Rogers, P. and Lydon, P. (eds) *Water in the Arab World*, Cambridge, MA, Harvard University Press.

# Acknowledgements

Grateful acknowledgement is made to the following sources:

## Book cover

*Cover Image*: Copyright © M R Hasan/Getty Images

## Chapter 1

### Figures

*Figure 1.1(a) and 1.1(b)*: NASA; *Figure 1.4*: Copyright © Darren Shaun Mann. This file is licensed under the Creative Commons Attribution-Share Alike Licence; *Figure 1.6*: Copyright © Andrew Dunn. This file is licensed under the Creative Commons Attribution-Share Alike Licence; *Figure 1.7*: Photo courtesy of Texas Southern University; *Figure 1.8*; Frank J. (Frank John) Aleksandrowicz, 1921, Photographer (NARA record: 8452210). This media is available in the holdings of the National Archives and Records Administration, cataloged under the ARC Identifier (National Archives Identifier) 550183; *Figure 1.9*: Copyright © Eastern Daily Press; *Figure 1.12*: Copyright © John Sibbick Limited; *Figure 1.16(a), 1.16(b) and 1.17(b)*: Copyright © Bob Glover.

## Chapter 2

### Figures

*Figure 2.1*: Copyright © Bob Glover; *Figure 2.4*: Cynthia Goldsmith/US Government-HHS-CDC; *Figure 2.5* : Copyright © Stephen Harris/Alamy; *Figure 2.7*: Copyright © Dennis Price; *Figure 2.8*: Copyright © Manu25. This file is licensed under the GNU Creative Commons Attribution Licence; *Figure 2.9(a), 2.9(b), 2.9(c) and 2.9(d)*: Copyright © RSPB; *Figure 2.10(a)*: Copyright © Adriadne Van Zandbergen/Alamy.

## Chapter 3

### Figures

*Figure 3.1*: Copyright © Heritage Images/Corbis; *Figure 3.2 top*: Federal Government of USA; *Figure 3.2 bottom left*: Copyright © World Economic Forum. This file is licensed under the Creative Commons Attribution-Share Alike Licence; *Figure 3.2 bottom right*: Copyright ©

Peter Zoon. This file is licensed under the Creative Commons Attribution-Share Alike Licence; *Figure 3.3(a) and 3.3(b)*: Copyright © RSPB; *Figure 3.3(c )*: Copyright © nigel pye/Alamy; *Figure 3.3(d)*: Copyright © Organica/Alamy; *Figure 3.4:* Copyright © Nbminor. This file is licensed under the Creative Commons Attribution-Share Alike Licence; *Figure 3.6(a)*: Copyright © Pam Furniss; *Figure 3.6(b), 3.7 and 3.8*: Copyright © Julie Major and Bruno Glaser  source www.biochar-international.org; *Figure 3.9(a)*: Copyright © Shell. This file is licensed under the Creative Commons Attribution-Noncommercial Licence; *Figure 3.9(b)*: Copyright © Mario Roberto Duran Ortiz. This file is licensed under the Creative Commons Attribution 3.0 licence.

## Chapter 4

### Figures

*Figure 4.2(a)*: Copyright © North Wind Picture Archives/Alamy; *Figure 4.4*: Copyright © Olivier Epron. This file is licensed under the Creative Commons Attribution 3.0 licence; *Figure 4.9*: Copyright © Olaf1541. This file is licensed under the Creative Commons Attribution-Share Alike Licence 3.0; *Figure 4.10*: Copyright © Atlantide Phototravel/Corbis.

## Chapter 5

### Figures

*Figure 5.1*: US Coast Guard; *Figure 5.2*: Copyright © UN Photos; *Figure 5.3(b)*: US Geological Survey; *Figure 5.3(c)*: NOAA; *Figure 5.4*: Copyright © Bettmann/Corbis; *Figure 5.5(a) and 5.5(b)*: Copyright © Joe Raedle/Getty Images; *Figure 5.8*: Copyright © Thomson Reuters.

## Chapter 6

### Figures

*Figure 6.5(a)*: Copyright © David Hoffman Photo Library/Alamy; *Figure 6.5(b)*: Copyright © James Allan/geograph.org.uk. This file is licensed under a Creative Commons Attribution Licence; *Figure 6.5(c)*: Copyright © James Davies/Alamy; *Figure 6.6 and 6.7*: LA Bird Response Working Group (2010). A Citizen Scientist's Protocol for Monitoring Oiled Birds in Louisiana, Louisiana State University School of Renewable Natural Resources, LSU AgCenter and Baton Rouge

Audubon Society; *Figure 6.9(a)*: Copyright © Brian Harris/Alamy; *Figure 6.9(b)*: Copyright © Peter Macdiarmid/Getty Images; *Figure 6.10*: taken from www.aljazeera.com.

## Chapter 7

### Figures

*Figure 7.1*: Andrew Dobson; *Figure 7.4*: Copyright © Michael Freeman/ Alamy; *Figure 7.6*: Copyright © Sabena Jane Blackbird/Alamy; *Figure 7.7*: Copyright © Peter Brogden/Alamy; *Figure 7.10 and 7.11*: US Fish and Wildlife Service; *Figure 7.12(a)*: Copyright © Chris Howes/Wild Places/ Alamy; *Figure 7.12(b)*: Copyright © The Art Archive/Alamy.

## Chapter 8

### Figures

*Figure 8.1(a)*: taken from http://hereandnow.wbur.org/2011/03/28/ moby-duck-ocean/0328_ocean-trash5; *Figure 8.2*: Copyright © Projeto Tamar Image Bank; *Figure 8.3*: 'The Fish Market', 1618-21 (oil on canvas), Snyders or Snijders, Frans (1579–1657)/Hermitage, St. Petersburg, Russia/The Bridgeman Art Library; *Figure 8.4*: Copyright © Hulton Archive/Getty Images; *Figure 8.6*: Copyright © David Lavigne; *Figure 8.12*: Copyright © Teemu Rajala. This file is licensed under the Creative Commons Attribution-Share Alike Licence 3.0; *Figure 8.13*: Copyright © Bruno Comby. This file is licensed under the Creative Commons Attribution-Share Alike Licence 1.0 Generic License; *Figure 8.15*: Copyright © Justin Watt.

## Chapter 9

### Figures

*Figure 9.1, 9.8(b) and 9.8(d)*: Copyright © Pam Furniss; *Figure 9.7*: Copyright © Paul Springett 06/Alamy; *Figure 9.8(a)*: Copyright © Superstock/Alamy; *Figure 9.8(c )*: Copyright © Science Photo Library/ Alamy.

## Chapter 10

### Figures

*Figure 10.1*: Copyright © Jon Arnold Images Ltd/Alamy; *Figure 10.4*: Copyright © Ian Britton/FreeFoto.com; *Figure 10.1*: by permission of Llyfrgell Genedlaethol Cymru/National Library of Wales.

## Chapter 11

### Figures

*Figure 11.1(a)*: Copyright © Surfers Against Sewage Ltd; *Figure 11.1(b)*: Green Family Youth Association of Environment Protection, China; *Figure 11.2(a), 11.2(b), 11.4 top right, 11.4 bottom right and 11.8*: Copyright © Pam Furniss; *Figure 11.7*: Copyright © Professors P M Motta and F M Magliocca/Science Photo Library; *Figure 11.9(a) and 11.9(e)*: Copyright © Blickwinkel/Alamy; *Figure 11.9(b)*: Copyright © Nigel Cattlin/Alamy; *Figure 11.9(c )*: Copyright © Chris Grady/Alamy; *Figure 11.9(d)*: Coyright © Arterra Picture Library/Alamy; *Figure 11.9(f)*: Copyright © Arco Images GmbH/Alamy; *Figure 11.10*: Agricultural Research Services, US Department of Agriculture; *Figure 11.11*: Copyright © Rolf Nussbaumer Photography/Alamy; *Figure 11.13(a)*: Copyright © James King-Holmes/Science Photo Library; *Figure 11.13(b)*: courtesy of WaterAid in Ethiopia.

## Chapter 12

### Figures

*Figure 12.1*: Copyright © Stefanie D'Alessandro/Getty Images; *Figure 12.3*: Copyright © Bob Metcalf; *Figure 12.4*: Copyright © Tom Kruse; *Figure 12.7*: Copyright © Toshitaka Morita/Seburn Photo/Getty Images.

# Index